Violence Against Women

RCOG Press

VIOLENCE

AGAINST

WOMEN

Edited by
Susan Bewley
John Friend and
Gillian Mezey

RCOG Press

It was not possible to refer all the material back to the authors or discussants but it is hoped that the proceedings have been reported fairly and accurately.

S. Bewley MB BS MD MA MRCOG
Director of Obstetrics, Department of Obstetrics and Gynaecology, St Thomas' and Guy's Hospitals Trust, St Thomas' Hospital, Lambeth Palace Road, London SE1 7EH

J. R. Friend, MA, BM, BCh, DM, FRCOG
Vice President, Royal College of Obstetricians and Gynaecologists, 27 Sussex Place, London NW1 4RG. Consultant Obstetrician and Gynaecologist, Derriford Hospital, Derriford Road, Plymouth, Devon PL6 8DH

G. C. Mezey, MB BS MRCPsych
Senior Lecturer and Consultant, Section of Forensic Psychiatry, Department of General Psychiatry, St. George's Hospital Medical School, Jenner Wing, Cranmer Terrace, London, SW17 0RE.

First published 1997
© Royal College of Obstetricians and Gynaecologists 1997

Chapter 5: 'Analysis of cohort' and Chapter 12: 'Police practice' by Stephanie Yearnshire © Stephanie Yearnshire 1997
Chapter 7: 'Understanding women's experience of abuse' and Chapter 15: 'The role of Women's Aid and refuge support services for women and children' by Nicola Harwin © Nicola Harwin 1997
Chapter 10: 'The law and domestic violence' by Susan S.M. Edwards © Susan S.M. Edwards 1997

ISBN 1 900364 03 4

Published by the **RCOG Press** at the
Royal College of Obstetricians and Gynaecologists
27 Sussex Place, Regent's Park
London NW1 4RG

Registered Charity No. 213280

Cover designed by Geoffrey Wadsley
Printed by Latimer Trend & Co. Ltd, Estover Close, Plymouth PL6 7PL

Contents

Top row (from left to right): Ms Helene Langley, Dr Gwyneth H. Lewis, Mr Richard H. J. Kerr-Wilson, Mr Patrick G. Walker, Dr Patricia A. Crowley, Ms Anne Viney, Dr K. Lindsey H. Stevens, Ms Chris Bewley, Mrs Siobhan Lloyd, Ms Anne Spence, Detective Superintendent Stephanie Yearnshire, Dr Helen M. Cameron, Ms Nicola Harwin

Bottom row (from left to right): Dr Jo Richardson, Ms Debbie Crisp, Dr Elizabeth A. Stanko, Dr Richard F. Jones III, Dr Susan Bewley, Mr John R. Friend, Ms Gillian C. Mezey, Professor P. M. Shaughn O'Brien, Dr Susan S. M. Edwards, Dr Petra Wilson, Dr Mary Hepburn

Participants

Ms Chris Bewley
Senior Lecturer, School of Midwifery and Family Health, Faculty of Health Studies, Middlesex University, 10 Highgate Hill, London N19 5ND

Dr Susan Bewley
Director of Obstetrics, Guys and St Thomas' Hospital Trust, Department of Obstetrics and Gynaecology, St Thomas' Hospital, Lambeth Palace Road, London SE1 7EH

Dr Helen M. Cameron
Consultant Obstetrician and Gynaecologist, Sunderland District General Hospital, Kayll Road, Sunderland SR4 7TP

Dr Patricia A. Crowley
Senior Lecturer, Consultant Obstetrician and Gynaecologist, Trinity College Dublin, Coombe Women's Hospital, Dublin 8, Ireland

Dr Susan S. M. Edwards
Senior Lecturer in Socio-Legal Studies, Law School, University of Buckingham, Buckingham MK18 1EG

Ms Nicola Harwin
National Co-ordinator, Women's Aid Federation, PO Box 391, Bristol BS99 7WS

Dr Mary Hepburn
Senior Lecturer in Women's Reproductive Health, University of Glasgow, Glasgow Royal Maternity Hospital, Rotten Row, Glasgow G4 0NA

Dr Richard F. Jones III
Chief of Staff, Hartford Hospital, 80 Seymour Street, Hartford, Connecticut 06102–5037, United States of America

Ms Helene Langley
Project Manager, Rising Sun Women's Refuge, 265 Sturry Road, Canterbury, Kent CT1 1DS

Dr Gwyneth H. Lewis
Principal Medical Officer/Director Maternity Services, Department of Health, Room 729, Wellington House, 133–155 Waterloo Road, London SE1 8UG

Mrs Siobhan Lloyd
Lecturer in Sociology/Head of Counselling Service, Department of Sociology, University of Aberdeen, Aberdeen AB24 3QY

Ms Gillian C. Mezey
Senior Lecturer and Consultant, Section of Forensic Psychiatry, Department of General Psychiatry, St. George's Hospital Medical School, Jenner Wing, Cranmer Terrace, London, SW17 0RE

Dr Jo Richardson
General Practitioner and Research Fellow, Island Health, 145 East Ferry Road, London E14 3BQ

Ms Anne Spence
Lead Administrator-Maternity Services Team, Department of Health, Room 422, Wellington House, 133–155 Waterloo Road, London SE1 8UG

Dr Elizabeth A. Stanko
Reader in Criminology, Department of Law, Brunel University, Uxbridge, UB8 3PH

Dr K. Lindsey H. Stevens
Clinical Director, Accident and Emergency, St Helier Trust, Wrythe Lane, Carshalton, Surrey SM5 1AA

Ms Anne Viney
Assistant Director, Victims Support, National Office, Cranmer House, 39 Brixton Road, London

Dr Petra Wilson
Lecturer in Law, Expert to European Commission, European Commission, DG13, Avenue de Beaulieu 29 3/27, 1160 Brussels, Belgium

Detective Superintendent Stephanie Yearnshire
Head of Community Safety Strategy Crime Prevention and Research for Northumbria Police, Northumbria Police Headquarters, North Road, Ponteland, Newcastle-upon-Tyne NE20 0BL

Discussants and Observers

Ms Debbie Crisp
Research Fellow, Brunel University, Uxbridge, UB8 3PH

Mr John R. Friend
Vice President, Royal College of Obstetricians and Gynaecologists, 27 Sussex Place, London NW1 4RG. Consultant Obstetrician and Gynaecologist, Derriford Hospital, Derriford Road, Plymouth, Devon PL6 8DH

Mr Richard H. J. Kerr-Wilson
Chairman – RCOG Ethics Committee. Consultant Obstetrician and Gynaecologist, Cheltenham General Hospital, Sandford Road, Cheltenham, Gloucestershire GL53 7AN.

Professor P. M. Shaughn O'Brien
RCOG Convener of Study Groups. Department of Obstetrics and Gynaecology, School of Postgraduate Medicine, North Staffordshire Hospital, Thornburrow Drive, Hartshill, Stoke-on-Trent, Staffordshire ST4 7QB

Mr Patrick G. Walker
Consultant Obstetrician and Gynaecologist, Royal Free Hospital, Pond Street, London, NW3 2QG

Additional contributors

Ms Siobhan McCartney
Researcher, Department of Public Health, (Women's Health), Greater Glasgow Health Board, 225 Bath Street, Glasgow, G2 4JT

Dr Gene Feder
Senior Lecturer, Department of General Practice and Primary Care, St Bartholomew's and the Royal London School of Medicine and Dentistry, Mile End Road, London E1 4NS

Mr Andy Gibbs
Head of Department, Maternal and Child Health, Mental Health and Handicap, Napier University, Comely Bank Campus, 13 Crewe Road South, Edinburgh EH4 2LD

Preface

The special Study Group has for the first time at the RCOG addressed a problem which is widespread but often hidden, intimately related to the practice of medicine but usually ignored.

Violence affects women in all walks of life and can take many different forms, both physical and psychological. Increasing awareness of the extent of domestic violence has led to practical co-operation between organisations within the community e.g. the police, social services, and voluntary bodies, in order to integrate an appropriate response.

However, many working in health care are still oblivious to the manifestations and sequelae of violence. The incidence of violence against pregnant women, for example, is higher and produces more morbidity than many other conditions for which we routinely screen. Exceptionally, strategies have been devised in General Practice, Accident and Emergency and amongst community midwives but compared with North America, obstetricians and gynaecologists have been slow to acknowledge the issue.

One purpose of this Study Group was to raise awareness of the size and nature of the problem and to counter disbelief and myths, particularly amongst doctors. Practitioners and academics from around the world were brought together to look at the current situation and available evidence, to discuss the role of health workers and to devise strategies to identify and reduce the damage inflicted.

We are immensely grateful to all those who were prepared to give so much of their time and energy towards producing the manuscripts and participating in the discussions. The deliberations are documented in this volume together with a comprehensive list of recommendations for clinical practice, education and training, and research. The organisation of the Study Group and publication of the book was only possible through the unfailing expertise and persistence of Beryl Stevens, Deputy College Secretary, Sandra Wegerif and Susan Bull, Publications Editors. We wish to thank them and their staff for their hard work and courtesy.

The extent of violence against women is clearly demonstrated. If we can grasp this opportunity and progress the recommendations outlined, then a significant impact may be made in making relevant interventions and reducing suffering amongst our patients. Health professionals who work with women cannot afford to disregard women's experiences of violence, abuse and discrimination.

John R. Friend, Senior Vice-President,
Royal College of Obstetricians and Gynaecologists
Susan Bewley
Gillian C. Mezey

SECTION 1

SETTING THE SCENE

Chapter 1

Defining violence against women

Siobhan Lloyd

INTRODUCTION

We know that the family is the environment for many different forms of violence – physical, sexual, economic and emotional – and that violence is perpetrated on young and old alike in child abuse and elder abuse (Kingston and Penhale 1995). We also know that violence against women and children knows no boundaries of culture, age, sexual preference, body ability, class, ethnicity or creed. In 1995 the United Nations published a report on world-wide violence against women and children which makes grim reading (United Nations 1995). It confirms that it is predominantly women and children who are abused in their homes by the men with whom they live. The report opens with the statement that, throughout their adult lives, millions of women become victims and survivors of battering, marital rape, dowry violence, domestic murder, forced pregnancy, abortion and sterilisation. It asks why, despite the universality of such experiences, a conspiracy of silence conceals the extent of such violence against women. It documents that, in the United States, an estimated two million women are beaten by their male partners each year; approximately half of them seek medical treatment. In one survey of 800 Japanese women, 77 per cent reported some form of domestic abuse and about 11,000 each year file for divorce because of domestic abuse. A study of Zambian women cited in the United Nations report showed that 17 per cent believe that violence in marriage is normal. A random sample of women in Guatemala found that half were physically, sexually or emotionally abused by their partners.

The report documents how forced prostitution by male partners is widespread in third-world countries. Native women from Nepalese villages are sold or tricked by their husbands into being trafficked to India for prostitution. They are detained as sexual slaves and are systematically raped and repeatedly subjected to other forms of sexual torture. In India many such women are forcibly sterilised and, denied medical care, are returned to their villages where they are ostracised by their communities if they have caught sexually transmitted diseases.

A recent survey from China, quoted in the report, indicated that 12 per cent of all female fetuses were aborted following screening to determine the sex of the unborn baby. In 1994 in China there were 117 boys born to every 100 girls, compared with a world-wide figure of 106 to 100. The United Nations research estimates that the forced abortion of female fetuses and the murder of girl babies means that there are 100 million fewer women world-wide than expected according to demographic trends.

We could extend this litany by looking at the documentary evidence on the sexual abuse of children, the practice of suttee (burying women alive with their deceased husbands), clitorectomy and the exploitation of women and children in snuff movies, pornographic videos and reading matter (Russell 1993). We could consider, if we are not already too shocked at the implications of all of this, the ultimate form of sexual violence against women – femicide – the misogynist killing of women (Russell and Radford 1992). These global violations against women illustrate, if illustration were needed, that the abuse of women is widespread, that it is often culturally acceptable and that it is frequently condoned by the state.

DEFINING AND NAMING VIOLENCE AGAINST WOMEN

Even within all of this, violence is not an easy concept to define. Popular usage gives the term many different meanings and there is often less agreement than might be expected on what kinds of behaviour and what circumstances constitute violence in interpersonal relationships and social interactions. Behaviour, whether expected or unexpected, feelings and language are often conflated in our definition and understanding of violence. Our language does not clearly separate violence as a feeling from violence as an act, though some of the words we use put the accent on feelings (fury, rage, anger) whilst others convey action (push, hit, assault, rape). There is a further conflation with concepts such as road rage, which we know to have both a strong feeling component and a physical action/reaction which may be unanticipated and extreme. Where feelings appear to be absent, as in premeditated murder, we use the term 'cold blooded' in a censorious way. The separation of feeling does not, however, automatically lead to moral condemnation for violent acts. A violent act committed 'in the heat of the moment' may be excused by the lack of rational thought which went into the assault. Until recently the law on provocation would have supported that view for men but not for women accused of killing their partners (Kennedy 1992).

Examining all forms of physical violence and aggression as a single abstraction is clearly limited since it may include such diverse behaviour as a slap, a shove, a punch in the face, a kick in the stomach or a wound from a knife or a bullet. The context in which the violence takes place is also significant and the violent act has a different meaning if it takes place in the home, in an intimate relationship, on the street between strangers or on a battlefield between nation states. At the interpersonal level, the nature of the relationship between the individuals involved is significant, the motivation behind the use of force, the material or personal gain to be had from it and the degree of intimidation involved in the act. Socially, these acts vary in terms of the degree of legitimacy accorded to them, the institutional and moral support for them and their meaning in the wider society (Dobash and Dobash 1979, 1992).

There is also the idea that violation is crucial to a definition of violence as unacceptable behaviour and the question of where power lies between the perpetrator of violence and the person who experiences it. There is also the question of those who are 'deserving' or 'undeserving' of violence and factors which appear to minimise or excuse violence can have the effect of shifting responsibility for the violence from the perpetrator to the victim. The degree to which violence is taken seriously by the criminal justice system may reflect some of these variables. It may also limit the responsibility assigned to the aggressor for his or her violent behaviour. In this sense we can say that violence is socially defined. It is not just the behaviour itself or how it is represented which determines its categorisation as violent, but the interpretation put on that behaviour by each of the parties involved – the assailant, the person against whom the violence is perpetrated, witnesses, the police, criminal justice system and helping agencies.

Taking time to define terms and to 'name' issues is not simply an academic exercise. In the field of violence against women, clarity is essential, since for many years the nature, extent and social implications of the abuse of women were obscured or trivialised by the use of inappropriate language. Although common sense might lead us to believe that what comprises violence against women is self-evident, it has been a contentious area. Three significant kinds of definition can be identified: the legal view, professional/expert views and definitions based on the experiences of women themselves.

Legal definitions

Legal definitions of violence are usually the most narrow and they tend to carry most authority since they determine whether agencies such as the police, social services or the courts of law can intervene or prosecute. The law plays a central role in constructing what counts as crime and, in the case of violence against women, focuses almost entirely on extremes, thereby discounting the experiences of many women (Stanko 1990). Thus, only a proportion of women's complaints are seen as legitimate according to the law – with legitimacy here determined by the actions, behaviour and relationship of the male assailant to the female he victimises.

Laws, too, are socially and historically constructed and we need look no further than the history of some of our laws in Britain to see a clear idea of women as the property of men. In the late 18th and early 19th centuries, women were unable to enter into contracts, had few legal rights to property or claims to their children and they were barred from certain professions and trades. It was not until 1829 that a husband's legal right to chastise his wife, provided he used a stick 'no thicker than a man's thumb' was removed. In 1853 the Act for Better Prevention and Punishment of Aggravated Assaults on Animals and Children was passed and extended to women some of the same protection that was already afforded to animals. In 1857 the Matrimonial Causes Act accepted violence by a partner as grounds for divorce on grounds of cruelty but it was not until 1891 that the legal right of the English husband to restrain his wife's liberty by physical means could be said to have been completely abolished. The Married Women's Property Act of 1895 added to this and made conviction for an assault sufficient grounds for divorce (Dobash and Dobash 1979). The removal of legal rights to control and punish wives was not attained without difficulty since the use of the courts was restricted to women with money and the required standard of proof was high. Nonetheless, the Married Women's Property Acts of 1870 and 1882 were historic pieces of legislation, ending previous laws which gave men full ownership of their wives' property (Sachs 1978).

Walby (1990) notes that legal definitions omit acts which many women would regard as violent. It was not until 1989 in Scotland and 1991 in England and Wales, for example, that the law was changed to recognise that a woman could be raped by her husband: until then she was deemed to have consented to sexual intercourse subsequent to her marriage. Interestingly, this law extends to cases where the partners are no longer living together but there has yet to be a conviction where they are still living in a shared home. Furthermore, the legal definition of rape in Scotland is unlawful sexual intercourse, which means that the penis must penetrate the vagina. In England and Wales the law changed in 1994 to include penetration of the anus by the penis, so allowing cases of 'male rape' to be prosecuted. Yet there is still no provision in the law for the forced penetration by other objects to constitute a form of rape.

These kinds of legalistic problems have led researchers to document how the law's definition of violence against women routinely takes precedence over definitions of their experience by women themselves. Researchers have examined the mechanisms through which the law defines the 'truth' in rape, domestic violence and child abuse, for example, in the face of evidence and experience which contradicts this understanding (Russell 1982, 1984, 1985; Kelly and Radford 1987; Stanko 1987; Kelly 1988; Hanmer et al. 1989; Mama 1989; Russell and Radford 1992; Smart 1995). The ability of the law to define what is or is not a violent act gives it great power and often this power works against the interests of women in favour of men when they are the perpetrators of violent acts against women and children. The law is neither defined nor experienced as gender neutral.

Professional/expert definitions

Another way of defining violence is the codification of its application. Consider, for example, definitions of domestic violence. Finding the most accurate description of the violence which is inflicted on one partner by another entails considering the variables involved in the acts of violence. The couple may be heterosexual, bisexual or gay, so 'battered woman' may not always apply; 'domestic dispute' is unsatisfactory because it can minimise the degree of violence and it implies mutuality. The term 'domestic violence' itself implies that the abuse takes place inside the home and this is not always the case – it can occur outside the home, in the home where one party has been rehoused or it can happen before they have set up home together. The word 'domestic' can also be said to trivialise the abuse, to keep it in the private sphere and, by implication, to imply that it is not a matter for public concern. The term 'domestic abuse' is increasingly replacing 'domestic violence' because it includes not only physical violence but the emotional, sexual and economic abuse of one individual by another.

One definition of domestic violence is 'the intentional physical abuse of a woman by the male partner with whom she lives or has lived' (Montgomery and Bell 1986). As a working definition this focuses on three key aspects:

(1) It is most frequently directed against women by men;

(2) It is intentional;

(3) It involves physical aggression.

There is, in this definition, no recognition of other forms of violent behaviour and abuse – emotional, sexual or economic. The definition by McKay and MacGregor (1994) – 'the physical, emotional or sexual abuse of an adult woman by a male with whom she has or has had an intimate relationship, whether or not the couple are living together' – gives a clearer sense of the three main categories of abuse. However, there are inevitably variations within each category and the definition gives little indication of the way in which they are interlinked. Many of the research studies of domestic violence have not spared the reader detailed descriptions of domestic abuse (Women's Aid Federation 1991).

The different forms of domestic violence are closely linked in two main ways:

(1) Repeated physical, sexual and emotional abuse has emotional and psychological as well as physical consequences, which may be cumulative.

(2) It is unusual for any one form of violence to occur singly. The terror for women who experience it is therefore considerable and silence can be

easily assured by threats to the woman or to her children (Mullender and Morley 1994).

Finally, the word 'victim' to describe the person on whom the abuse has been perpetrated is not always accurate or helpful. It may be temporarily exact but is not a label which any person should have to carry throughout his or her life and fails to recognise the dangers of acting.

Domestic abuse is widespread, it is not confined to particular social classes, ethnic groups or geographical locations; it is experienced by young people and older women, able-bodied people and women with disabilities. Kelly (1996) has discussed violence in lesbian couples and she notes that an understanding of this violence 'requires taking account of the context in which lesbian relationships exist . . . one of marginalisation at best and secrecy and fear at worst'. There is also the question of 'which woman' has her voice heard. The complexity of violence against women, its variable meaning and its impact in terms of race, ethnicity, culture, class, sexuality, body ability and age have emerged as important differences. Whilst domestic violence and sexual abuse make the home a dangerous place for many women and children, homeless women are among the most vulnerable (Hendessi 1992). Class can shape the experience of women making complaints of violence to the police. Middle-class women may be taken more seriously, yet this may be a negative factor in dealing with police and other agencies who may believe that middle-class men are not violent to their partners. Poor, working-class women and minority ethnic women often encounter other obstacles in seeking support and encounter stereotyped responses which draw on assumptions about the commonness or acceptability of abuse in certain social groups (Mama 1989).

Additionally, there is the violent event itself. Dobash and Dobash (1984) have analysed violent incidents and demonstrate how they occur in the context of an ongoing relationship. They show that the cessation of one cycle of violence may constitute the beginning of another, even though the next attack may not occur until considerably later. They conclude that: 'taking the beginning of the violent event as that period immediately preceding it is in some ways artificial and misleading because the events are never-ending'.

Definitions of violence by women themselves

A third approach to the definition of violence is to adopt the accounts of women themselves (Hanmer and Saunders 1984; Hall 1985; Stanko 1985; Hanmer and Maynard 1985; Kelly 1988; Hanmer et al. 1989). The argument here is that, in order to understand the extent of the impact of violence on women, it is important not to pre-determine the meaning of the term. The starting point is to hear from women themselves and the meaning they attach to their experiences. Kelly (1988) has developed the concept of a continuum of violence as a way of showing how the abuse that women experience as children and adults is not reflected in legal codes or in the conventional formulations of social scientists. She describes a range of male behaviour which women perceive to be threatening, violent or sexually harassing which is much wider than any legal or scientific definitions. She suggests that our common-sense definitions of violence are, in fact, male definitions so the limitations imposed on those forms of behaviour are restricted to the most extreme, gross and public forms.

This explains why women find themselves caught between their own experiences of intrusive or unacceptable male behaviour and external interpretations of that behaviour as normal or insignificant. Two examples from either end of Kelly's continuum serve to illustrate the point. At one end are acts such as the threat of violence in public, flashing and obscene phone calls, all of which rely in part for their impact on the explicit or implicit threat of further assault. They are unwanted intrusions into women's lives and personal space which can transform an everyday or pleasurable experience such as a walk in the park or a train journey into an upsetting and often threatening experience.

Incidents recorded in the sexual assault category of Kelly's work reflect a continuum of experience, ranging from being touched by strangers in the street, which some women define as harassment, to attempted rape. One end of the continuum shades into sexual harassment, the other into rape. What categorises sexual assault for women is physical assault and the intentions of the man. Pressurised sex includes altruistic sex (women feeling guilty about saying no or feeling sorry for the man), compliant sex (where the consequences for women of not doing it are worse than the consequences of doing it) and coercive sex which she suggests is being 'like rape'.

An additional issue is the inclusion of the threat or fear of force as well as its actual use. Hanmer and Saunders (1984) argue that the fear of violence both compels and constrains women to behave or not to behave in certain ways. It affects what they can do, where they go and with whom they associate. Both the reality and the threat of violence act as a form of social control on women. Radford and Stanko (1996) argue that safety itself becomes problematic for women. Rather than take it for granted, they argue, women build strategies of precaution into their lives and speak of situations as being 'less unsafe' rather than safe. The gendered nature of public danger to women is often ignored (Cameron 1988).

Kelly and Radford (1990) also suggest that women play down incidents of violence. They argue that when women preface an account of a violent incident with 'nothing really happened', they are minimising or denying their experiences: 'very real things happen when we are followed or chased on the street, when male partners insist on sex or engage in systematic emotional abuse – we do not feel safe, our trust is abused'. When women say 'nothing really happened', they are making a statement about how much worse things could have been. On the other hand, when the law says 'nothing really happened', it implies that a woman has not been violated or abused.

THE ROLE OF PUBLIC AWARENESS CAMPAIGNS IN DEFINING VIOLENCE AGAINST WOMEN

Recent public awareness campaigns have played an important part in re-defining violence against women. Two campaigns in Scotland have taken very different approaches. The first example originated in Edinburgh where, since 1992/3, a series of conferences, public debates and a highly visible poster campaign was instigated by the local authority in conjunction with local women's organisations, community groups and academics. The combined campaign is called 'Zero Tolerance' and, drawing on experience from Canada, has taken as its main theme the simple idea that violence against women and children should not be tolerated in a civilised society. The campaign was the first major advertising campaign in Britain with the aim of attempting to challenge societal attitudes towards the physical and sexual assault of women and children by men. It also carries a strong message about the need for men to change their behaviour (Lloyd 1995). Conferences and public meetings debated a wide range of issues relating to violence against women and at the same time a poster campaign, which used simple and direct images, was erected on key sites in many Scottish cities. Domestic violence was the explicit subject of one of these posters which carry the message that a continuum of male violence is an abuse of power.

The second phase of the campaign focused on educational programmes – in schools, colleges, youth groups and community groups. Early indications suggest that the campaign has been effective. It has been successful in raising public awareness about violence against women. It has also, however, been followed by an increase in referrals to Women's Aid, health agencies and social work departments. Women's Aid is ill equipped to deal with this increase and women and their children may have been put in the position of having expectations raised about help which is simply not available (Scottish Women's Aid 1995, 1996).

The third phase of the campaign started in October 1996 and its main theme relates to the way in which the criminal justice system fails to protect women and children who experience crimes of violence by men. Standards of evidence and the questioning of women as witnesses in rape and sexual assault cases have been given prominence. In London the campaign was reworked to focus on domestic violence alone and the images it used were of male perpetrators rather than the women they abuse.

There is also a substantive difference in the slogans used in the two locations. Scottish posters have the line: '*Male abuse of power is a crime*' on every display, whilst the London posters have adopted the softer tag-line: '*It's not just a fact of life, it's a crime.*' Another point is that the Scottish campaign deliberately opened with child abuse – and it gradually worked towards domestic abuse in a way that was desensitising and challenging. As Riddoch (1994) notes: 'Violence against women has happened for centuries. It takes a persuasive approach, not a prescriptive one, to get real change happening.' An evaluation of the first part of the Scottish campaign has concluded that it has been successful in attracting attention and generating debate about the issue of violence against women. It has also caused people to reflect on the power which they have as adults and as men and it has also challenged some misconceptions about the nature of domestic violence and child abuse (Kitzinger and Hunt 1994).

At the time the first phase of Zero Tolerance was coming to a close, the Scottish Office introduced its own public awareness campaign on domestic violence. Again using billboards, it took a rather different approach, asking the question: '*Which one will you give her tonight?*' Here the image of a tattooed male fist was explicitly working class and a wedding ring implied marriage. The message was also explicitly sexualised. An accompanying television advertisement showed a woman in a pub becoming transformed into a brutalised person as she was singled out by her violent male partner.

These public awareness campaigns demonstrate clearly how far we have come and the possibility that we have not come very far at all in defining violence against women. One campaign challenges the idea of male violence being confined to specific social classes, geographical locations, age or ethnic groups. The other manages to reinforce old myths in an explicitly sensationalised way. Which of these campaigns is a more accurate reflection of the current state of our knowledge about defining violence against women and which will be more effective in changing societal attitudes is hardly open to question.

REFERENCES

Cameron, D. (1988) *Lust to Kill*. Oxford: Polity Press

Dobash, R.E. and Dobash, R.P. (1979) *Violence against Wives. A Case against the Patriarchy.* New York: The Free Press

Dobash, R.E. and Dobash, R.P. (1984) The nature and antecedents of violent events. *British Journal of Criminology* **24**, 269–88

Dobash, R.E. and Dobash, R.P. (1992) *Women, Violence and Social Change*. London: Routledge

Hall, R. (1985) *Ask Any Woman. A London Inquiry into Rape and Sexual Assault*. London: Falling Wall Press

Hanmer, J. and Maynard, M. (Eds) (1985) *Women, Violence and Social Control*. London: Macmillan

Hanmer, J. and Saunders, S. (1984) *Well-Founded Fear.* London: Hutchinson

Hanmer, J., Radford, J. and Stanko, E.A. (1989) *Women, Policing and Male Violence.* London: Routledge

Hendessi, N. (1992) *4 in 10. Report on Young Women who Become Homeless as a Result of Sexual Abuse.* London: CHAR

Kelly, L. (1988) *Surviving Sexual Violence*. London: Polity Press

Kelly, L. (1996) 'When does the speaking profit us?: reflections on the challenges of developing feminist perspectives on abuse and violence by women' in M. Hester, L. Kelly, and J. Radford (Eds) *Women, Violence and Male Power*, p.39. Buckingham: Open University Press

Kelly, L. and Radford, J. (1987) 'The problem of men' in P. Scraton (Ed.) *Law, Order and the State*. Milton Keynes: Open University Press

Kelly, L. and Radford, J. (1990) 'Nothing really happened': the invalidation of women's experiences of sexual violence. *Critical Social Policy* **30**, 39–53

Kennedy, H. (1992) *Eve Was Framed. Women and British Justice*. London: Chatto and Windus

Kingston, P. and Penhale, B. (1995) *Family Violence and the Caring Professions*. London: Macmillan

Kitzinger, J. and Hunt, K. (1994) *Evaluation of Edinburgh District Council's Zero Tolerance Campaign: The Full Report*. Edinburgh: Edinburgh District Council Women's Committee

Lloyd, S. (1995) 'Social work and domestic violence' in P. Kingston and B. Penhale (Eds) *Family Violence and the Caring Professions*. London: Macmillan

Mama, A. (1989) *The Hidden Struggle. Statutory and Voluntary Sector Responses to Violence Against Black Women in the Home*. London: Runnymede Trust

McKay, A. and MacGregor, L. (1994) *Hit or Miss*. Dundee: Tayside Regional Council

Montgomery, P. and Bell, V. (1986) *Police Response to Wife Assault: A Northern Ireland Study*. Belfast: Women's Aid Federation

Mullender, A. and Morley, R. (1994) *Children Living with Domestic Violence. Putting Men's Abuse of Children on the Childcare Agenda*. London: Whiting and Birch

Pahl, J. (1995) 'Health professionals and violence against women' in P. Kingston and B. Penhale (Eds) *Family Violence and the Caring Professions*. London: Macmillan

Radford, J. and Stanko, E.A. (1996) 'Violence against women and children: the contradictions of crime control under patriarchy' in M. Hester, L. Kelly and J. Radford (Eds) *Women, Violence and Male Power*. Buckingham: Open University Press

Riddoch, L. (1994) Zero Tolerance: the second wave. *Harpies and Quines* **12**, 8–11

Russell, D. (1982) *Rape in Marriage*. New York: Macmillan

Russell, D. (1984) *Sexual Exploitation*. Beverley Hills, CA: Sage

Russell, D. (1985) *Incest. The Secret Trauma*. New York: Basic Books

Russell, D. (1993) *Making Violence Sexy. Feminist Views on Pornography*. Buckingham: Open University Press

Russell, D. and Radford, J. (1992) *Femicide. The Politics of Women Killing*. Buckingham: Open University Press

Sachs, A. (1978) 'The myth of male protectiveness and the subordination of women: an historical analysis' in C. Smart and B. Smart (Eds) *Women, Sexuality and Social Control*. London: Routledge

Scottish Women's Aid (1995) *Annual Report*. Edinburgh

Scottish Women's Aid (1996) *Annual Report*. Edinburgh

Smart, C. (1995) *Law, Crime and Sexuality. Essays in Feminism*. London: Sage

Stanko, E. (1985) *Intimate Intrusions*. London: Unwin Hyman

Stanko, E. (1987) 'Typical violence, normal precautions: men, women and interpersonal violence in England and Wales, Scotland and the United States' in J. Hanmer and M. Maynard (Eds) *Women, Violence and Social Control*. London: Macmillan

Stanko, E. (1990) *Everyday Violence*. London: Pandora

United Nations (1995) *Violence Against Women: A World-wide Report*. New York: United Nations

Walby, S. (1990) *Theorising Patriarchy*. London: Blackwell

Women's Aid Federation (1991) Information Pack. Bristol: Women's Aid Federation

Chapter 2

Models of understanding violence against women

Elizabeth A. Stanko

Violence and the threat of violence is an acute reality for many women. All the research concurs: women's fear of sexual violence has resulted in restrictions to our lifestyles and mobility. Despite all the evidence that women encounter more danger at home, women take more precautions outside the home than do men (Stanko 1990; Gordon and Riger 1988). Clearly, domestic violence and sexual assault are interwoven within women's heterosexual relationships with men. Women are also targets for sexual harassment and pestering on the street (Gardner 1980, 1988, 1990, 1995) and may also be subjected to attack because they are or are perceived to be lesbian (Kitzinger 1994); because they are women of colour or of minority groups (Crenshaw 1994); or because they are not able-bodied (Gardner 1995; Stanko 1990).

Feminist work on violence against women has forced recognition of the difference between what we now define as violence and how little of it was and is recognised as crime. Such violence does not offend against the state, it is not injurious to property nor is it a threat to public order (see Cretney *et al.* 1994). This holds true whether we are discussing partner–woman abuse, child abuse, elder abuse or abuse in residential care settings. Broadly speaking, violence involves inflicting emotional, psychological, sexual, physical and/or material damage. I include emotional and psychological harm because threat and intimidation have consequences on how safe women, children and men feel. Panic about criminal violence is often fuelled by fear, focused on the diffuse threat people feel from its potential. Curiously, this threat is typically associated with *strangers*, not those known (Pain 1993). Whether physical or psychological, the harm felt by the recipient of violence varies, as does the long-term impact on his or her everyday life (Glass 1995; Stanko 1990). A recent experience of violence, or its threat, may have significant effects, altering an individual's routines and personal lifestyle or it may have little noticeable influence on daily life. Living within 'climates of unsafety' (Stanko 1990), such as in a violent household – where typically women and children feel specially vulnerable to verbal, sexual and/or physical aggression – also takes its toll. Those experiencing repeated, serious and life-threatening violence are likely to experience long-term trauma (Herman 1994).

For too long, violence was unspeakable, and when women and children attempted to speak out, they were often silenced, told that such behaviour was 'private' and could not be mediated by state agencies. And yet, as Gordon (1988) found in the US study of welfare provision to children, Allen (1990) in her Australian work and Clark (1987) in her English study, abuse against girls is embedded within the histories of the courts, social welfare debates, and actions of the nineteenth- and early twentieth-century feminists. It is as if the strength of the ideology of the family could not sustain its darkest secrets. Then, as now, women's typical assailants were their intimate and former partners and other men known to them, such as male friends, acquaintances, employers, co-workers, teachers, fellow students, neighbours and clients. So the legacies of the unspeakable horrors of family life became the stuff of quiet resistance and survival, until the second wave of feminism, in the 1960s.

The foundation work of many authors cannot be retold in great detail here.[1] Suffice it to say that when women began to talk about their lives, not only with their current partners but during their childhood, a catalogue of violence was told. Sexual assault research on children and adult women suggests the common danger to sexual integrity is from those who have authority over, access to, and intimacy with their victims. Moreover, as research by Kelly and colleagues (1991) in England tells us, children's peers can abuse: approximately one quarter of reported sexual abuse was committed by neighbouring and school-attending peers. When we think about violence against women, we must also think about women in context. Somehow, when we think about promoting safe environments within which children can grow and thrive, we fail to remember that the contexts of women's lives are also crucial. Campbell's *Goliath* (1993) describes some high-crime estates in England and Wales and the impact of these environments on women's lives in particular. Women were intimidated by their sons, their sons' friends and other men who lived on these estates.

Being female – in spite of our many differences – has profound implications for our lives. But we are not just female: we are equally affected by our age, class, race, religion, ethnicity, sexuality and whether we are mothers. Many women seeking the protection of state-provided resources are 'burdened by poverty, child-care responsibilities, and the lack of job skills' (Crenshaw 1994) and it is therefore important to confront many multi-layered and routine forms of abuse at the hands of men, to which many of us are

---

[1] What is interesting is how much of the work exists in some countries, such as the US, Canada, UK, Australia, and how other countries are beginning to build up profiles of abuse of women and children. Useful starting points include: Dobash and Dobash 1979 (UK); Dobash and Dobash 1992 (USA/UK); Russell 1982, 1984 (USA); Gordon 1988 (USA); Stanko 1985, 1990 (UK/USA); Statistics Canada 1994; McWilliams and McKiernan 1993 (UK); Kelly 1988 (UK); Hague and Malos 1993 (UK); Glass 1995 (UK); Koss *et al.* 1994 (USA); Fineman and Mykitiuk 1994 (USA).

subjected. For the purposes of this chapter, I will concentrate primarily on the kinds of violence which most affect women: violence from those familiar and familial.

LOCATING VIOLENCE AGAINST WOMEN

Domestic violence has become a catch-all referent for a variety of behaviours. It generally refers to emotional, physical and sexual violence which occurs among those who live or have lived within a family-like arrangement, however constituted. As such, it would include violence between siblings, husband and wife, former husband and wife, boyfriend and girlfriend, same-sex partners (or former partners), parent (or caretaker) and child, child and parent (or caretaker), or adult child and elderly parent. By far most attention has focused on the male assailant (either as husband, former husband or boyfriend) and female survivor. The physical and sexual abuse of women in heterosexual partnerships will be my focal point.

Because domestic violence by definition takes place within a complex web of familial and friendship ties, it is often understood by its recipients, its perpetrators and their support networks as behaviour which is embedded within intimacy and familiarity. This understanding clashes with common-sense thinking about criminal violence: that criminal violence only occurs between strangers (Stanko 1990).

Perhaps most important in understanding domestic violence is that assailants use forms of brutality, sometimes to assert control, sometimes to punish the target of violence for a perceived (usually imagined or illusory) transgression and sometimes to impose cruelty. Perpetrators often justify their use of force, intimidation, threat and violence as deserved. While some assailants are diagnosed as suffering from a personality disorder, head injury or mental illness (Coleman 1994; Dutton 1994; O'Leary 1993; Warnken *et al.* 1994), perpetrators are usually considered to be ordinary members of the public, with some leading law-abiding lives, except for terrorising their relations, and some who may have frequent encounters with the law (Sherman 1992).

WHAT IS THE EXTENT OF THE PROBLEM?

Estimates of the extent of domestic violence are 'guesstimates': informed calculations of the existence of domestic violence among the general population. The 1993 Home Affairs Select Committee Report on Domestic Violence concludes that 'domestic violence is common' (p.vii). Police reports gravely underestimate the extent of the problem, because most victims refuse to involve the authorities in their 'personal matter' (Dobash and Dobash 1979; Smith 1989; Mooney 1994). ACPO's (Association of Chief Police Officers) evidence to the Home Affairs Select Committee characterised police reports of domestic violence as not 'based on either reliable or accurate data'

(Parliamentary Select Committee on Violence in the Family 1975, p.vii). In 1975, the Select Committee on Violence in Marriage estimated that just under 1 per cent of married women experienced violence from partners. No improvements to the collection and analysis of national data occurred between the 1975 Select Committee and that held in 1992.

Crime surveys attempt to capture the prevalence of crime involving physical threats and assaults, whether or not the police are informed. Crime survey respondents were asked about incidents which involved some degree of physical force against the victim and included common assaults and situations resulting in more serious injury. The 1992 British Crime Survey (Mayhew et al. 1993) recorded the following information on domestic violence:

(1) One in 10 women (11 per cent) reported some degree of physical violence in their relationships;

(2) Those most at risk of domestic violence were divorced and separated women.

The 1996 British Crime Survey (Mirrlees-Black et al. 1996) found that:

(1) Nearly one in two (46 per cent) of all violence incidents against women were domestic;

(2) Sixty per cent of domestic violence incidents involved current partners;

(3) Twenty-one per cent involved former partners;

(4) Four out of five incidents of domestic violence against women took place at home.

Half of the reported victims suffered more than one attack (with a third who had been attacked three times or more (Mayhew et al. 1993; Mirrlees-Black 1995; Mirrlees-Black et al. 1996). The 1996 British Crime Survey also reported that victims were more likely to be injured in domestic assaults (19 per cent of victims). Injuries were usually bruises and/or scratches, but 13 per cent of incidents resulted in cuts. Nearly a third of incidents resulted in the victims receiving medical help, with 3 per cent seeking hospital attention.

Other surveys suggest that the British Crime Survey figures undercount the prevalence of domestic violence, especially in some local areas. Mooney's 1993 crime survey in Islington, London found one in four women reported experiencing domestic violence during their lifetimes (Mooney 1994). One in ten reported that they had experienced such violence within the past twelve months. In a survey exploring the extent of rape in marriage, Painter (1991) found that, of the 1000 women interviewed, one in eight had been raped by a partner or former partner. McGibbon and colleagues' 1989 study of women's experiences of domestic violence in Hammersmith, London showed that for the 281 respondents:

(1) One-hundred and nine (39 per cent) had experienced verbal or physical threats from a male partner;

(2) Seventy-five (27 per cent) experienced such abuse repeatedly;

(3) Forty-seven (18 per cent) reported they had been beaten up by their partners;

(4) Twenty-four (10 per cent) reported being attacked with a weapon.

Whilst many women may experience threats or assaults from partners during their relationships, a small number of women (2–5 per cent) reported serious, frequent attacks. Dominy and Radford's 1996 report included a survey of 484 women. Thirty-one per cent of this sample reported that they had at some time in their lives experienced what they termed 'domestic violence'; another 15 per cent reported forms of abuse similar to what other women labelled as 'domestic violence'. Similar studies around Britain support the above findings. In Northern Ireland, for instance, estimates are that one in four women are affected by domestic violence (see McWilliams and McKiernan 1993). Previous research suggests that when women feel their lives or the lives of their children are threatened, they are most likely to seek help (Binney *et al.* 1981).

It is also useful to take a brief look at the 1993 Canadian survey on violence against women (Statistics Canada 1994). This is the most comprehensive survey conducted to date world-wide and provides some additional insight into a broader picture of domestic violence involving women as its targets. The Canadian results help make sense of domestic violence as it affects a general population of adult women. According to this national survey (12,300 women over 18 years of age interviewed):

(1) Three in ten women currently or previously married have experienced at least one incident of physical or sexual violence at the hands of a marital partner;

(2) The highest rates of assault were found among young women, and among marital partnerships of less than two years;

(3) Women whose partners had witnessed violence by their fathers endured more severe and repeated violence than women whose partners' fathers were not violent;

(4) Children witnessed violence against their mothers in almost 40 per cent of marriages with violence.

Summary observations on domestic violence

Overall, there are a number of findings which suggest that we should take the impact of domestic violence seriously, despite its persistence as a hidden problem (Stanko 1988). Its impact goes beyond the individual suffering of the woman; it also involves the suffering of her children, her social and friendship support and the wider networks of her (and her assailant's) families. Some of these observations are:

(1) Violent conflict, including physical and sexual assault, is common;

(2) Many women leave violent partners, and violence escalates and is most acute during this leaving stage. Campbell *et al.* (1994) found that after two-and-a-half years, 43 per cent of battered women they interviewed had left their abusers, and two-thirds of them were living in non-violent situations;

(3) Some women experience life-threatening, repeated violence and currently live in fear of their lives from the men they live, or did live, with;

(4) Many children are exposed to violence within their own homes. Approximately 28,000 such children who flee violence with their mothers to UK Women's Aid refuges are profoundly affected by this experience (Saunders 1994, 1995; see also Mullender and Morley 1994);

(5) Kelly (1994) suggests that 'woman protection is frequently the most effective form of child protection' (p.53);

(6) Child maltreatment (which includes domestic violence) has a long-term impact on youth development (Smith and Thornberry 1995).

It is essential that we begin to explore the impact on children of living within an abusive household. O'Hara's (1994) essay exploring child deaths and other serious harm to children, of which the Department of Health receives approximately 120 notifications annually, observes:

> Of these, a large proportion of the parents responsible for the child's death are fathers or stepfathers who have a history of violence towards their female partners as well as towards the child concerned. . . . In many cases, the professionals involved have been aware of the context of domestic violence in which the abuse or neglect of the child was taking place, but generally seem to have failed to take this context into account in their assessment of the danger or in their strategies for protecting the child. (p.57)

The most contentious debate in the literature is the continued speculation about the extent to which both parties participate in domestic violence. This debate is at its most heated in the discussions of violence within heterosexual couples' relationships. Straus (1993) argues that, according to his US national surveys, wives hit husbands slightly more often than husbands hit wives. He suggests that if women stopped initiating violence then they would be less likely to suffer severe retaliatory violence themselves. He persistently argues that promoting less violence from wives will reduce the more serious consequences of husbands' retaliation. Straus also concludes: 'Although women may assault their partners at approximately the same rate as men assault theirs, because of the greater physical, financial and emotional injury suffered, women are the predominant victims' (p.80).

The most dangerous time for a woman is from the time she decides to leave to 18 months to two years after she does so. The Canadian survey found that one-fifth of the women who experienced violence by a previous partner reported that the violence occurred following or during separation and in one-third of these cases, the violence *increased* in severity at the time of separation. Johnson (1995) argues that we should make distinctions between what he terms 'common couple violence' and 'patriarchal terrorism'. He criticises Straus for using 'common couple violence' as a representation of domestic terrorism, and thus distorting the view of domestic violence as a mutual dual. He wisely suggests that: 'As in most areas of intervention, family practitioners will be most effective if they work with a set of alternative interpretative frameworks rather than with a single-minded assumption that every case of violence fits the same pattern' (p.292).

Assuming that all domestic violence is mutual combat misses the many cases of terrorism; and assuming that all violence is terrorism equally distorts. The debate continues about whether women and men are victims/offenders or both. Whilst it is important to recognise that some men may experience violence from their intimate partners (who may be male or female), it is essential not to adopt a 'gender-neutral' approach to intimate violence. No doubt, for that small proportion of men, the experience is demeaning, confusing and frightening. But all the evidence suggests that, by and large, men do not live in constant terror after they have separated, are rarely killed by women pursuing them, nor do men live within a climate of sexual terrorism that women report living in.[2] Unpicking the extent of domestic violence will necessarily entail unpicking the forms of violence used by women and men and the outcomes of violence for women and men (for a careful analysis, see Dobash and Dobash 1992; Stanko 1995). This careful unravelling has implications for the gnawing debate about who the offender is; what kind of treatment she or he should receive; and, should the violence be defined as crime and enter the criminal justice system for adjudication, how it should be prosecuted and what type of criminal justice sanction should be imposed.

EXPLANATIONS OF DOMESTIC VIOLENCE

We still live within societies which often excuse violence and many social, cultural, religious and political institutions support aggression (Dobash and Dobash 1992). As women and children tell us, men's violence is not confined to one category of men, usually said to be poor men; some wealthy and

---

[2] All the information we have about men and their experiences of sub-lethal (Stanko and Hobdell 1993) and lethal assault tells us that *men are attacked typically by men, even in domestic situations*. It is men's relationships to other men that gets men killed (Polk 1994a, b). There is, in general, **little evidence that women pose the same *danger* to men in the home as men do to women**.

working men also abuse their wives, rape their daughters or sexually harass their employees. The contribution of women to violent crime is still very low and, when women are violent, the targets of their actions are often their already violent spouses, the children in their care, other women, and/or themselves.

The amount of research about violence against women is now voluminous. There are many differences in perspectives (see Dixon 1995). Some still view violence as an aberration, a symptom of individual, psychological disturbance. Others may only see discrete problems associated with physical and mental torment: wounds call solely for medical treatment; displaced and homeless families pose housing dilemmas; crisis calls may come just to police attention; depression and nervousness are soothed with pills. These fragmented responses, taken in isolation, prevent many from seeing domestic violence in any holistic way. More importantly, this fragmentation has real consequences: for policy, for practice and, ultimately, for the kinds of support available to survivors and their friends and family.

Individual pathology

The problem is the victim

A common explanation for domestic violence is that it is a reflection of individual pathology or sickness. Typically the individual victim is analysed for (usually her) provocation to what is assumed to be expressive violence arising from inevitable conflict in close living situations. For instance, Kenny (1995) asked why modern women 'freely' choose to stay with their torturers. But blaming individual women (and some men) for being recipients of violence is little help in conceptualising domestic violence in the first place. Speculation about women being attracted to men who abuse begs the questions: Why do men abuse? Why do men stay with women they abuse?

A number of psychological truisms abound here: the myth of female masochism; the assumption that some women are addicted to violence (Pizzey and Shapiro 1982); the generalisation that all battered women suffer from learned helplessness and thus exhibit what is now commonly called 'battered women's syndrome' (a term coined by Walker 1984). These various justifications for women's responses to domestic violence blame 'the victim' for the violence, or for failing to escape its tentacles.

Focusing solely on the individual victim of domestic violence ignores its collective features. While clearly enduring violence has serious consequences for individuals (see Dobash and Dobash 1979; Stanko 1985; Smith 1989; Herman 1994; Koss *et al.* 1994), individual treatment of each recipient will not halt domestic violence. As Dobash and Dobash (1992) suggest:

> The more women are seen as clients in need of therapy rather than people in need of alternatives and choices, the less the movement [for battered women] challenges prevailing conceptions of the problem. ... One of the most significant limitations of

this approach is that it deflects our attention away from the roots of the problem, violent men, and from the social and political structures which support male violence. (pp.234–5)

The problem is the perpetrator

The assailant too is scrutinised for individual defects, caused by mental illness; factors such as stress due to unemployment, over-employment, personal irritability, or excessive drinking and/or the use of drugs are mentioned as explanations for violence. Even when serious mental illness is diagnosed, however, it is often the families and/or partners who are responsible for the primary care of the mentally ill. No doubt some serious violence is linked with serious mental illness. Limited assistance and/or adequate intervention by social and medical services allow safety nets for families caring for those suffering from mental-health problems.

The use of drugs or drinking is sensibly often linked with domestic violence (Smith 1989). Yet research shows there is no simple cause and effect relationship. While it is often observed that individuals who use drugs or drink excessively come to the attention of some services (medical, legal and social), there is no evidence that the drinking or drug use *per se* causes violence. There is evidence that men with drug and/or drink problems often abuse when sober. As an interesting aside, the 1996 British Crime Survey's figures indicate that the offender is under the influence of alcohol and/or drugs in 38 per cent of the reported domestic violence situations (Mirrlees-Black *et al.* 1996). The proportions of offenders 'under the influence' for stranger and acquaintance violence are 57 and 53 per cent respectively. Only offenders reported to have 'mugged' had the lowest reported 'under the influence': 25 per cent (p.31).

Inter-generational cycle of violence is another alleged explanation for domestic violence. The Canadian study (Statistics Canada 1994), for instance, illustrates that women reported experiencing more abuse from men whose mothers had been beaten by their fathers (or other partners). Research also suggests that there are many more people who experience abuse as children who do not perpetuate it in their own adulthood. What we do know is that those who abuse, and especially those who sexually abuse, are more likely to have themselves experienced abuse as children. Thus abuse in childhood may provide the foundation for being abusive in adulthood, but it is by no means a determinant. Morley and Mullender (1994) summarise the arguments about the inter-generational cycle of violence, and note:

> To argue against the certainty that 'violence breeds violence' is not, however, to argue that children enjoy or thrive on violence, or that childhood experiences do not bear on the kinds of adults we become. But there is a great deal of evidence that many children survive violent childhoods and grow into loving and socially productive adults. Certainly some men with violent childhoods are violent to women and children; for

others, that childhood experience precludes a repetition. Moreover, it may also be that the damage caused by living in violent families is internalised as depression, withdrawal or *self*-destructive behaviours. (p.38; see also Widom 1989)

A cautionary word about the prevailing wisdom about 'the cycle of abuse', the notion that being abused in childhood leads to abusive patterns in adult life. Those who suffer abuse do not automatically grow up and commit crime or pose any other social problems. Nor do they necessarily grow up to be attracted to those who abuse. Thus, I do not imply that there is any simplistic 'cycle of abuse' present. Glass (1995), for instance, speculates that:

> . . . those who endured child abuse or who witnessed domestic violence actively avoid potential abusers and seek out jobs that allow them to make up for the pain of their childhoods: social work, nursing, teaching, home help. Maybe people who like finding behaviour patterns should consider examining the possibility that there is actually a 'cycle of healing'. (p.105)

Social pathology as triggers of violence

Unemployment, over-employment, stress at work or stress from not working, and pregnancy are also linked with triggering domestic violence. While these factors may provide a background to some domestic violence, they do not explain why violence is seen as the solution to alleged frustration and tension. Sport, fitness, parenting classes (or shopping) could be alternate choices to release tension.

Explanations which explore cultural values are also put forward as another way of accounting for the existence of violence in families. Cultural explanations may emphasise features of groups (based on social class, ethnicity, race or geography), thereby suggesting that these differ from other supposedly normal ones. Wolfgang (1958) proposed, in his early study of homicide, that there 'may be a sub-culture of violence which does not define personal assaults as wrong or antisocial' (p.329). But the question must be asked: Why are so many assaults within families targeted on those most vulnerable, either because of age, gender and so forth? Cultural, religious or other factors may explain why women remain silent, but do not explain why vulnerable members of a household become legitimated as targets for violence.

Feminists' analyses

Feminist analysis has emphasised the impact of serial, intentional and directed violence by men on women (Dobash and Dobash 1979; Hoff 1990). Much of the evidence in studies of violence between intimates (or former intimates) (Dobash and Dobash 1992) suggests that:

... the sources of conflict leading to violent events reveal a great deal about the nature of relations between men and women, demands and expectations of wives, the prerogatives and power of husbands and cultural beliefs that support individuals' attitudes of marital inequality. (p.4)

In other words, the meaning of violence for each party lies within the individual, collective and cultural understandings of being male or female. The men who use violence against women in domestic situations, as most notably Dobash and Dobash (1992) and Daly and Wilson (1988) observe, do so as:

(1) A result of men's possessiveness and jealousy;

(2) An expectation concerning women's domestic work;

(3) A punishment for women for perceived wrongdoing;

(4) A prop to men's authority.

The lessons learnt from exploring partner–woman abuse are relevant to the study of other forms of domestic violence. There is overwhelming evidence that intimate violence *is* gendered, as are individual and institutional responses to that violence (Renzetti 1994). Questions should be raised about why those most vulnerable, because of age, physical stature, or finances, are the targets for lethal and sub-lethal violence within settings assumed to be 'havens from a harsh world'. Intimate violence within lesbian (Renzetti 1992; Kelly 1994) or gay relationships (Island and Letellier 1992) have not been explored fully due to the emphasis on partner–woman abuse. Such explorations occur today because of the strength of the lesbian and gay movements, whose proponents are asking questions not only about homophobic violence but about violence within same-sex relationships. This also means that we must find ways to explore help-seeking by many different kinds of people in many different situations involving domestic violence.

Research suggests that women's ties to heterosexual partnerships are reflected in patterns of domestic abuse, in women's escape plans and in the widespread, continued denial of the existence of such violence within presumably happy marriages. The significant contribution of feminist scholarship is that we finally see the ordinariness of violence within the home and within the ritual of courting.

REFERENCES

Allen, J. (1990) *Sex and Secrets*. Melbourne: Oxford University Press

Binney, V., Harkell, G. and Nixon, J. (1981) *Leaving Violent Men: A Study of Refuges and Housing for Battered Women*. Leeds: Women's Aid Federation

Campbell, B. (1993) *Goliath*. London: Methuen

Campbell, J., Miller, P. and Cardwell, M.M. (1994) Relationship status of battered women over time. *Journal of Family Violence* 9, 99–111

Clark, A. (1987) *Women's Silence, Men's Violence: Sexual Assault in England 1770–1845.* London: Pandora

Coleman, V. (1994) Lesbian battering: the relationship between personality and the perpetration of violence. *Violence and Victims* **9**, 139–52

Crenshaw, K.W. (1994) 'Mapping the margins: intersectionality, identity politics, and violence against women of color' in M.A. Fineman and R. Mykitiuk (Eds) *The Public Nature of Private Violence*, pp.93–114. London: Routledge

Cretney, A., Davis, G., Clarkson, C. and Shepherd, J. (1994) Criminalising assault: the failure of the 'offence against society' model. *British Journal of Criminology* **34**, 15–30

Daly, M. and Wilson, M. (1988) *Homicide.* New York: Aldine de Gruyter

Dixon, J. (1995) The nexus of sex, spousal violence and the state. *Law & Society Review* **29**, 359–76

Dobash, R.E. and Dobash, R.P. (1979) *Violence Against Wives.* New York: Free Press

Dobash, R.E. and Dobash, R.P. (1992) *Women, Violence and Social Change.* London: Routledge

Dominy, N. and Radford, L. (1996) *Domestic Violence in Surrey: Developing an Effective Inter-agency Response.* Surrey County Council/London: Roehampton Institute

Dutton, D. (1994) Patriarchy and wife assault: the ecological fallacy. *Violence and Victims* **9**, 167–82

Fineman, M. and Mykitiuk, R. (1994) *The Public Face of Private Violence.* London: Routledge

Gardner, C.B. (1980) Passing-by: street re female. *Sociological Inquiry* **50**, 328–56

Gardner, C.B. (1988) Access information: public lies and private peril. *Social Problems* **35**, 384–97

Gardner, C.B. (1990) Safe conduct: women, crime and self in public places. *Social Problems* **37**, 311–28

Gardner, C.B. (1995) *Passing By: Gender and Public Harassment.* Berkeley, CA: University of California Press

Glass, D.D. (1995) *All my Fault.* London: Virago

Gordon, L. (1988) *Heroes of their own Lives: The Politics and History of Family Violence.* New York: Viking

Gordon, M. and Riger, S. (1988) *The Female Fear.* New York: Free Press

Hague, G. and Malos, E. (1993) *Domestic Violence: Action for Change.* Cheltenham: New Clarion Press

Herman, J.L. (1994) *Trauma and Recovery.* London: Pandora

Hoff, L.A. (1990) *Battered Women as Survivors.* London: Routledge

Home Affairs Select Committee (1993) *Domestic Violence* (2 vols). London: HMSO

Island, D. and Letellier, P. (1992) *Men who Beat the Men who Love Them.* New York: Harrington Park Press

Kelly, L. (1988) *Surviving Sexual Violence.* Oxford: Polity Press

Kelly, L. (1994) 'The interconnectedness of domestic violence and child abuse: challenges or research, policy and practice' in A. Mullender and R. Morley (Eds) *Children Living with Domestic Violence*, pp.43–56. London: Whiting and Birch

Kelly, L., Regan, L. and Burton, S. (1991) An exploratory study of the prevalence of sexual abuse in a sample of 1200 16 to 21 year olds. Final report to the ESRC. London: Child Abuse Studies Unit, University of North London

Kenny, M. (1995) Why do women marry beastly men? *Sunday Telegraph*, 10 December, Review, p.2

Kitzinger, C. (1994) 'Sexual harassment of lesbians' in C. Brand and Y. Lee Too (Eds) *Rethinking Sexual Harassment.* London: Pluto

Koss, M., Goodman, L., Browne, A., Fitzgerald, L., Keita, G. and Russo, N. (1994) *No Safe Haven: Male Violence Against Women at Home, at Work, and in the Community.* Washington, DC: American Psychological Association

Mayhew, P., Maung, N.A. and Mirrlees-Black, C. (1993) *The 1992 British Crime Survey.* London: HMSO

McGibbon, A., Cooper, L. and Kelly, L. (1989) *What Support?* London: Hammersmith and Fulham Council, Community Safety Committee

McWilliams, M. and McKiernan, J. (1993) *Bringing it Out in the Open: Domestic Violence in Northern Ireland.* Belfast: HMSO

Mirrlees-Black, C. (1995) Estimating the extent of domestic violence: Findings from the 1992 BCS. *Research Bulletin* **37**, 1–10

Mirrlees-Black, C., Mayhew, P. and Percy, A. (1996) *The 1996 British Crime Survey: England and Wales.* London: The Stationery Office

Mooney, J. (1994) *The Hidden Figure: Domestic Violence in North London.* London: Islington Council

Morley, R. and Mullender, A. (1994) 'Domestic violence and children: what do we know from research?' in A. Mullender and R. Morley (Eds) *Children Living with Domestic Violence,* pp.24–42. London: Whiting and Birch

Mullender, A. and Morley, R. (1994) (Eds) *Children Living with Domestic Violence.* London: Whiting and Birch

O'Hara, M. (1994) 'Child deaths in contexts of domestic violence: implications for professional practice' in A. Mullender and R. Morley (Eds) *Children Living with Domestic Violence,* pp.57–66. London: Whiting and Birch

O'Leary, K. (1993) 'Through a psychological lens: personality traits, personality disorders and levels of violence' in R. Gelles and D. Loseke (Eds) *Current Controversies on Family Violence.* London: Sage

Pain, R. (1993) Crime, social control and spatial constraint: a study of women's fear of sexual violence (unpublished PhD thesis, University of Edinburgh)

Painter, K. (1991) *Wife Rape, Marriage, and the Law.* Manchester: University of Manchester, Department of Social Policy and Social Work

Parliamentary Select Committee on Violence in the Family (1975) *Vol. I. (Report with Proceedings of the Committee).* London: HMSO

Polk, K. (1994a) 'Masculinity, honour and confrontational homicide' in T. Newburn and E. Stanko (Eds) *Just Boys Doing Business?,* pp.166–88. London: Routledge

Polk, K. (1994b) *When Men Kill.* Cambridge: Cambridge University Press

Renzetti, C. (1992) *Violent Betrayal.* London: Sage

Renzetti, C. (1994) On dancing with a bear: reflections on some of the current debates among domestic violence theorists. *Violence and Victims* **9**, 195–200

Russell, D.E.H. (1982) *Rape in Marriage.* New York: Free Press

Russell, D.E.H. (1984) *Sexual Exploitation.* Beverly Hills, CA: Sage

Saunders, A. (1994) 'Children in women's refuges: a retrospective study' in A. Mullender and R. Morley (Eds) *Children Living with Domestic Violence.* London: Whiting and Birch

Saunders, A. (1995) Children speak about violence. *NISW Noticeboard,* Spring, 1

Sherman, L. (1992) *Policing Domestic Violence.* New York: Free Press

Smith, L. (1989) *Domestic Violence.* London: HMSO

Smith, C. and Thornberry, T. (1995) The relationship between childhood maltreatment and adolescent involvement in delinquency. *Criminology* **33**, 451–79

Stanko, E. (1985) *Intimate Intrusions.* London: Routledge

Stanko, E. (1988) 'Hidden violence against women' in M. Maguire and J. Pointing (Eds) *Victims of Crime: A New Deal?* Milton Keynes: Open University Press

Stanko, E. (1990) *Everyday Violence.* New York: Pandora

Stanko, E. (1995) Policing domestic violence: contradictions and dilemmas. *Australian and New Zealand Journal of Criminology* Special Issue: 31–44

Stanko, E. and Hobdell, K. (1993) Assault on men. *British Journal of Criminology* **33**, 400–15

Statistics Canada (1994) Wife assault: the findings of a national survey. *Juristat Service Bulletin* **14**, March

Straus, M. (1993) 'Physical assaults by wives: a major social problem' in R. Gelles and D. Loseke (Eds) *Current Controversies on Family Violence.* London: Sage

Walker, L. (1984) *The Battered Women's Syndrome*. New York: Springer

Warnken, W.J., Rosenbaum, A., Fletcher, K.E., Hoge, S.K. and Adleman, S.A. (1994) Head-injured males: a population at risk for relationship aggression. *Violence and Victims* **9**, 153–66

Widom, C. (1989) Does violence beget violence? A critical examination of the literature. *Psychol Bull* **106**, 3–28

Wolfgang, M. (1958) *Patterns in Criminal Homicide*. New York: John Wiley

Chapter 3

Setting the scene

Discussion

Mezey: For people from ethnic minority groups, there are issues about the definition of violence and about acknowledging oneself as a victim of abuse or violence to the white community.

I wondered whether, through her work in Hackney, Elizabeth Stanko had any thoughts about cultural influences in the recognition and identification of domestic violence and how we can enable women from ethnic minority groups to talk about this as an issue and receive help.

Stanko: We did not use any different definitions for any particular groups. The most important thing is that when you work in a place like Hackney, you have to represent the community. Second, the access to public services in Hackney is dominated by those who are poor. The strongest lesson I have learned is that the context of the community is very important, but the context of the use of public services is also extremely important. Looking at housing, for example, Hackney is 70 per cent council housing; this influences the way in which those who have no resources may call on public services. People are asking for help and this is despite the difficulties.

Crisp: The other point which came across is that what individuals think is asking for help is often not necessarily recognised by the agencies as that. It will just be seen as a visit and not registered as anything relating to domestic violence. Thus, the extent of the problem and the demand on services is grossly underestimated.

Jones: The comment about poverty contributing to domestic violence is intriguing but the question is, why? It seems to me that poor people often lack self-esteem. They have been forced into a situation which they feel bad about and, indeed, they feel bad about life in general. My observation is that there is potential for abuse in all of us and it does not matter whether you are poor or rich. In the United States, in the medical community, we have seen that physicians who are being sued for malpractice very commonly become abusive. Again very commonly, they feel very badly about themselves; they are often told they are 'poor doctors', etc.

My point is that how people feel about themselves has a lot to do with abusive behaviour, and abuse is more common in poor people, more common in our clinics than in our private practices. However, I am astonished in our private practices at the number of professional people who are abusive. I would suggest that it is self-esteem rather than poverty that is the significant factor.

Stanko: I am not saying poverty is the most significant factor. What I am saying is that when we overlook additional factors, we are overlooking the ways in which silence is maintained. I am not somebody who advocates that violence does not exist across the continuum but, as a criminologist, what is astounding to me is that if you look particularly at homicides, there are some recurrent themes which we are not addressing. I am not putting it as issue number one but in the UK, so much debate centres around what kind of public services should be adequate for all citizens. In the USA, there is a real difference between Medicare and other forms of healthcare. In the UK, the National Health Service should and does provide medical care for all and the fact that it recognises that care should be available to all citizens regardless of income is very important.

Mezey: I am concerned about losing the ethnic issue. There is evidence from survivor groups that where black women disclose abuse, they talk about terrible obstacles in terms of their inability to speak out about the violence. When they do speak out about violence, they are silenced or their experiences are minimised, because 'this is what is expected' in black families. They feel terribly betrayed by the system. Similar dynamics probably operate in the area of violence towards women generally, so we need to think about how we, as agencies, organisations and professionals, can be more responsive and sensitive to the barriers that prevent women in ethnic minority groups from getting the kind of help they need and deserve.

Kerr-Wilson: Could I ask Siobhan Lloyd why there is a difference of emphasis in 'zero tolerance' advertising campaigns in England and Scotland? It smacks slightly of a political agenda, especially when what Elizabeth Stanko was saying was that the advertising in England seems to be more criminally aligned and may not be appropriate. The subtle advertising seems to be north of the border, and the progressive, up-front advertising seems to be in the south!

Lloyd: I suppose this relates to Elizabeth Stanko's point about how violence is defined and conceptualised. The way it was conceptualised in Scotland was around the unequal power relationships between women and men, between adults and children. It presented a clear and unambiguous statement about power relationships. In London, the campaign adopted a more straight-forward criminological paradigm.

The impact of the campaign in Scotland has been quite astounding. There has been an amazing alliance of people right across the spectrum. It is not unusual, for example, to see buses going around towns with big banner headlines declaring: 'Male abuse of power is a crime.' It is not unusual to see billboards, T-shirts, hats and badges carrying these slogans. Many local authorities are now employing educationists who are specifically asked to educate children in primary schools and in secondary schools about domestic violence, bringing it out into the open. That is the kind of paradigm which is operating in Scotland, and it has been very successful.

Hepburn: To emphasise what Siobhan Lloyd said, the zero tolerance campaign in Scotland has been successful because it addresses the whole of society – service providers, educational organisations and the general public. It has generated a huge amount of discussion and been very successful, largely due to its multi-agency approach.

Lewis: Because the campaign in Scotland is more visible and consciousness has been raised more, is that the definition of success?

Hepburn: The campaign was designed as a campaign to inform people. By success, I mean that it has informed people and raised the issue on many agendas. This has made it possible for people to discuss it as a service issue, as a training issue and as an issue among the public, particularly among the women who are affected by violence.

Lloyd: If I could add to that, another way of reviewing the success of the campaign has been the huge increase in referrals and contact with or-ganisations such as Women's Aid, social services and the health service. Of course, the downside is that Women's Aid does not have the resources to respond to the huge and, in some areas, overwhelming increase in contact from women and their children. However, nor do social services and the health service but what has happened is that in many areas multi-agency working groups have been set up to look at the issue across all the different services and to bring Women's Aid in from the cold.

Harwin: I wanted to pick up on the issue of public awareness and zero tolerance and seeing domestic violence as a crime. The comparison between the zero tolerance campaigns carried out in Edinburgh and that carried out by the London authorities is that, although the Scottish campaign was more successful, the one in London tried to take up issues of difference, for example, having a range of figures about the effect of ethnic origin. The other point was locating the responsibility with men, which was a shift. Both campaigns have value.

Where the Scottish version of zero tolerance has been imported to England, there have been problems. In some areas, local authorities have thought, 'Right, we have £10,000 to spend; we want to show we are doing something about domestic violence. Let's have a quick zero tolerance campaign.' They have not done what was done in Scotland, which was to look at the impact of the campaign; how every agency needs to develop its policies and think about how they are going to respond, looking at the consequences for organisations like WAFE which has very few resources. That is a problem throughout England. Referrals are increasing as every agency improves their practice, and the knock-on effect is quite serious.

The immediate response to domestic violence is to throw some money at public awareness, to get more information out. Sometimes, women do not know how to get help or the information is not there, but often it is the case that when they do seek help, the response is unhelpful and discouraging.

Lastly, in relation to the crime paradigm, there is a problem in treating domestic violence simply as a crime, because much of what women experience does not fit into it. The new government has made a commitment to reviewing the civil and criminal law, but unless we start to redefine 'crime' publicly in the media as talking about violence against women and women's safety, then things will not shift.

Langley: Another problem with the crime paradigm is that women themselves find it difficult to define their experience in those terms and, however much one might try to extend the definition in research or academic discourse, women's own definition does not reflect this.

Friend: We were talking about the campaign in Scotland being much more sensitive and subtle than it is south of the border. Has this campaign alerted obstetricians and gynaecologists to any extent up there, and have they changed their practice in any way?

Hepburn: No, I don't believe that the zero tolerance campaign has affected the behaviour of obstetricians. You need these campaigns to raise awareness as a background against which we look at people's behaviour and services, and how we are going to devise service provision. Many of my colleagues feel that they should not ask about domestic violence unless women volunteer the information because they don't want to cause offence. Having finished the information campaign, we now need to look at how we educate and train people who are working in fields like obstetrics and gynaecology and that is a big issue that we need to discuss during this meeting. We cannot achieve that with the zero tolerance campaign alone; we need many other initiatives before we get that far.

Jones: I would say that obstetricians and gynaecologists should ask every patient on every visit. You say that many doctors do not ask because they are afraid of a 'no' answer and that it might be offensive. I have asked every patient for the last four years, amounting to thousands of women and I have never had a patient be offended. Patients often say that I am the first doctor who has ever asked them and it can make a huge difference to a woman's life, particularly coming from a male gynaecologist.

Hepburn: In the service I lead, we routinely ask every woman about violence but, because it is not done in the rest of the hospital, it is perceived as somewhat stigmatising for our patients, rather than an act of omission by colleagues who do not ask.

Stanko: I agree that all women should be asked about domestic violence. It is not the most sensitive question they will ever be asked, but certainly in the work around sexual abuse of children, one of the lessons we have learned is that if you do not ask a direct question, you do not have even the possibility of getting a direct answer.

Stevens: Going back to the ethnicity issue, in the Islington study it was quite interesting that they found the Afro-Caribbean rate was theoretically less than either Asian or white (Mooney 1994). Whether that was to do with the nature of the study, I do not know. However, there are a couple of studies in the States which appeared to show that if you were black you were more likely to be battered, but if you adjust for housing, which one could take as a measure of poverty and population density, violence figures were on a par with the other groups (Centerwall 1995). Immigration status also has a huge influence. We have had a number of eastern European cases where this has been a very real problem.

REFERENCES

Mooney, J. (1994) *The Hidden Figure: Domestic Violence in North London*. London: Islington Council
Centerwall, B.S. (1995) Race, socio-economic status and domestic homicide. *JAMA* **273**, 1755–8

SECTION 2

PERPETRATORS OF DOMESTIC VIOLENCE

Chapter 4

Perpetrators of domestic violence

Gillian C. Mezey

INTRODUCTION

Although there is a growing literature on the wife-beater's wife, the characteristics of the wife-beater are more elusive. Traditionally, the state has upheld the sanctity of family life as a rationalisation for non-intervention. Whilst condemning the brutality of certain behaviours, there is at the same time within society an implicit acceptance that violence is a legitimate means of resolving conflict between man and wife and that some women not only invite such a response, but deserve it. Prevailing attitudes seek to neutralise the event by using terms that equalise the power status between victim and perpetrator, such as 'mutual combat', implying an equal attribution of blame. Domestic violence is often attributed to a dysfunctional family rather than seen as the product of a disturbed and violent individual. Domestic violence, however, is a problem not only for the direct victims, but for the wider community. Given the prevalence of domestic violence and its damaging consequences, unequivocal condemnation and effective intervention is essential so that women can feel safe in their own homes.

CHARACTERISTICS OF PERPETRATORS OF DOMESTIC VIOLENCE

Domestic violence is the use of physical force or restraint carried out with the intent of causing physical pain or injury to another person, within an intimate relationship (Hotaling and Sugarman 1986). Psychological abuse, isolation, capricious enforcement of punishments and rewards, the interruption of sleep or eating, critical and abusive comments alternating with praise and reconciliation, jealousy and isolation, as well as sexual abuse are also commonly reported. It has been argued that domestic violence is an extension and expression of patriarchal norms (Yllö and Straus 1984; Smith 1990). Women are vulnerable to abuse by their spouses because of their relative lack of power within the home and society in general. The lower the status of women in society and the more prevalent the gender inequality within that society, the higher the rates of documented and reported domestic violence against women (Smith 1990). Domestic violence occurs across the whole social spectrum, ethnic groupings and ages, although social deprivation, unemployment, poor education and financial difficulties are cited as precipitating and perpetuating factors (Straus *et al.* 1980; Kennedy and Dutton 1989; Smith 1990).

Mental illness is rarely a significant factor in domestic violence although violence may be precipitated and justified by extreme and pathological jealousy (Shepherd 1961; Brisson 1981). Other personality disorders, including borderline personality disorder, antisocial personality disorder and sadistic personality disorder (Gondolf 1990; Else *et al.* 1993; Hart *et al.* 1993; Dutton 1994) are also associated, although there is no pathognomonic psychological abnormality that has been linked to the batterer.

Perpetrators of domestic violence rarely see themselves as disturbed or their behaviour as unreasonable. They have a vested interest in their violence remaining a private issue and do not normally seek out medical help. Batterers commonly employ a variety of mechanisms to avoid talking about their violent behaviour: denial, forgetting, blanking out or not knowing, minimisation, removal of intent, excuses and justification (Ptacek 1988). They express high levels of hostility towards women, and yet are highly dependent on their partners (Maiuro *et al.* 1988). They tend to polarise women as 'Madonnas' or 'whores'. They have rigid sex role expectations and low self-esteem (Maiuro *et al.* 1986) and are socially and sexually inadequate. Whilst they need to control their partner, they lack the verbal resources to do so and resort to violence as a means of conflict resolution (Dutton and Strachan 1987; Else *et al.* 1993). Pagelow (1981) described men who batter as having low self-esteem, being traditionalists, emotionally inexpressive and lacking in assertiveness. Men who have witnessed parental violence in their childhood or who have been physically abused themselves appear to be at greater risk of behaving violently within adult intimate relationships, the so-called cycle of violence (Brisson 1981; Rosenbaum and O'Leary 1981; Fagan *et al.* 1983; Hotaling and Sugarman 1986; Kaufman and Zigler 1987), although a history of abuse is not universal. Brisson (1981) reported on a self-report survey of 122 violent men in treatment. About two-thirds of the group had been exposed to physical violence in their immediate family as children, either as direct victims or as witnesses.

One must be cautious about developing explanations of violent men which serve to remove their responsibility for, and excuse, their behaviour. There is some justifiable anxiety about the medicalisation of domestic violence which depicts the perpetrator as 'sick' and their behaviour as outside their control. A number of typologies have been developed for men who batter their partners, although the subjects are often highly selective and therefore not necessarily representative of the population as a whole. Faulk (1974) examined 23 men in custody, following violence against their spouses. He described five groups:

(1) Dependent and passive;

(2) Dependent and suspicious;

(3) Violent and bullying;

(4) Dominating;

(5) Stable and affectionate.

Langley and Levy (1977) identified four categories of batterers:

(1) Alcoholics;

(2) Psychotics;

(3) Psychopaths;

(4) Bullies.

Simpson-Subotnik (1983) described the 'over-controlled' and 'under-controlled' batterer. The over-controlled batterer's violence represents an uncharacteristic explosion of anger, followed by considerable guilt and remorse. This contrasts with the under-controlled batterer, who is unable to tolerate frustration and whose violence is repetitive and compulsive.

Some perpetrators of domestic violence confine their violence to the home and can appear relatively well socialised to outsiders. Their problems arise in the context of intimate interpersonal relationships which may well have its genesis in early insecure attachments (Mayseless 1991). Other men are more sociopathic in their behaviour, being liable to commit acts of violence outside as well as inside the home, exhibiting high rates of drug and alcohol consumption, reckless and impulsive acts. Kandel-Englander (1992) found a degree of specialisation in 2291 violent men surveyed, with only 10 per cent reporting violent assaults towards wives and non-family members, referred to as pan-violent. Brisson (1981), described 48 per cent of his subjects as generally violent, i.e. inside and outside of relationships. Self-report surveys, however, must be considered unreliable because of the tendency of subjects to minimise and deny aspects of their behaviour.

CHARACTERISTICS OF THE VIOLENCE

Some victims of domestic violence describe a cyclical pattern, which consists of a gradual build-up of tension, followed by an explosion of violence and then a period of relative calm in which the man may express some remorse and contrition (Walker 1979). Not all domestic violence, however, reflects this pattern and as the violence progresses the periods of calm become fewer and contrition is less in evidence. Battering episodes are likely to be precipitated by real or perceived provocation by the woman and threats to the man's competence or power (Sonkin *et al.* 1985; Holtzworth-Munroe and Hutchinson 1993), jealousy (Dobash and Dobash 1984) or arguments over money (Brisson 1981). Male power, or lack of power, is a central underlying theme in domestic violence (Babcock *et al.* 1993; Petrik *et al.* 1994), as well as the lack of verbal means to resolve conflict (Dobash and Dobash 1977). Thus, increased rates and severity of violence have been associated with the wife having more education than the man (Hotaling and Sugarman 1986), or having a higher work status (Hornung *et al.* 1981). Violence commonly results from real or perceived challenges to the man's position, authority or control over the woman (Dobash and Dobash 1977). Women are most at risk when they try to break away from their violent partners, which often precipitates an escalation in the severity and frequency of violence, or is followed up by stalking behaviours (Geberth 1992). The nature of the batterer's attachment is, by nature, fragile and insecure (Dutton 1994) and the violence represents a dysfunctional attempt to regain control, preserve the relationship, or defend against intimacy (Kobak and Sceery 1988). Many men who batter find the threat of abandonment or rejection by their partner almost unbearable and it may be their extreme neediness that psychologically ties the women to them. Many instances in which men kill their partners are preceded by a history of violence; about 50 per cent of killings occur in the period around separation and, in some cases, are justified by the man in terms of: 'if I can't have her, no one will' (Browne 1987).

The role of alcohol is important as a background factor as well as being cited by men and their partners as a causal or precipitating factor in the violence (Gayford 1975; Brisson 1981; Rosenbaum and Maiuro 1990; Bergman and Brismar 1992). Alcohol is often used to excuse behaviour and deny responsibility. The mechanism linking alcohol consumption with violence is unclear and is likely to be psychologically and socio-culturally bound, rather than physiologically driven (Chritchlow 1986).

INTERVENTIONS

There are few sanctions against men who batter and these are often incompletely enforced (Edwards 1989). The failure of law-enforcing agencies to properly impose sanctions against men who attack and degrade their partners, may be seen to condone the violence and perpetuate the problem.

Over the years there have been a number of community and institution-based intervention programmes set up for men who are violent towards their partners (Jennings 1987), largely as a result of widespread disaffection with existing sentencing options, which fail to protect women and children. The general philosophy of such groups is to encourage the man to take responsibility for his behaviour, to gain awareness of the internal and external precipitants of violence and to appreciate the consequences of his actions. It is assumed that violence occurs as a result of faulty socialisation, which can be undone through a process of re-education and appreciation of alternative non-aggressive ways of resolving conflict. Treatment approaches include:

(1) Dealing with anger;

(2) Relaxation and arousal reduction techniques;

(3) 'Time out' training (teaching the man to walk away from potential conflict and remove himself physically from his partner);

(4) Challenging and changing distorted cognitions, which the man uses to excuse and justify his behaviour;

(5) Enhancing communication skills and appropriate assertion.

Couple work should probably only be carried out with skilled therapists after an initial period of work with the man alone. The continuing risk to the woman and children must not be underestimated and should be monitored, by reference to both parties, throughout any treatment programme. It is important that the fact that the man is in treatment does not lead to complacency and a false sense of security, at a time when the woman remains as vulnerable as ever.

Problems with alcohol and drug dependence must be addressed within any treatment programme for batterers. In addition, coexisting psychiatric problems, particularly depression, must be assessed and treated.

Treatment can be done on an individual basis but group work is probably more effective in that it encourages mutual challenging and confrontation whilst enabling men to feel accepted within the group as a whole. Given the extent of denial and avoidance of responsibility amongst these men, treatment is likely to be more effective if mandated through the courts.

Evaluation of the effectiveness of treatment cannot reliably be done without accountability to the victim, or to groups representing the victim. Most treatment programmes operate 'zero tolerance' of violence as an outcome measure. Reduction in the use of psychological abuse is both more difficult to measure and to achieve. It may be that, as the man learns to reduce the incidence of physical aggression, he will expand his repertoire of psychological abuse, as a means of retaining power and control within the relationship.

In Britain, the CHANGE project, a criminal justice based programme for batterers, was set up at Stirling University in 1989, based on the Duluth model developed in Minnesota for perpetrators of domestic violence (Figures 4.1 and 4.2). The movement also recognises the need to address social and institutional tolerance of male violence to women and to embark on a wider social re-education programme involving the police, social services and the courts. The treatment programme involves groups of 4–8 men, who attend two-hourly groups over 22 weeks as part of a probation order. The programme encourages men to take responsibility for their violent behaviour, by increasing

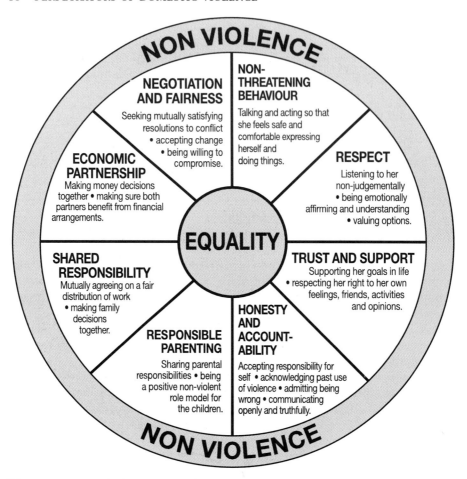

Figure 4.1.   Duluth model of non-violent behaviour

their awareness of the dynamics in its use; it challenges attitudes and beliefs about violence and male/female relationships and aims to develop skills for relating non-violently to others (Wilson 1996). Voluntary sector organisations, such as the Everyman Centre, adopt similar approaches.

EVALUATION OF THERAPEUTIC APPROACHES

The effect of treatment is, as yet, inconclusive. Variability in the selection of subjects, the length of follow-up, the unreliability of self-report measures compared with reports from the women, differing criteria used to define success, etc., make interpretation of results quite difficult. Most authors report high drop-out rates (Harris *et al.* 1988; Edleson and Syers 1991; Rosenfeld 1992) and difficulty in engaging men in treatment. A further confounding factor in interpreting treatment success is the fact that some men spontaneously stop their violence, regardless of any intervention (Gon-

Figure 4.2. Duluth model of violent behaviour

dolf 1990; Saunders and Azar 1989). Although completion of a treatment programme is associated with decreased recidivism, men who are arrested, but not referred to treatment, are no more likely to be violent than men who are arrested and treated. The deterrent effect of arrest, particularly the first arrest and legal sanctions (Sherman and Berk 1984; Berk and Newton 1985; Jaffe *et al.* 1986; Fagan 1989; Syers and Edleson 1992) is well recognised. However, it appears that legal system involvement may not be sufficient to motivate men who would otherwise be disinclined to change their behaviour (Rosenfeld 1992). The evidence as to whether court-mandated treatment actually affects outcome is inconclusive (Dutton 1986; Waldo 1988; Edleson and Syers 1990).

Edleson and Syers (1991) compared 283 batterers who were randomly assigned to one of six treatment conditions:

(1) Self-help (12 or 32 sessions);

(1) Self-help (12 or 32 sessions);

(2) Education (12 or 32 sessions);

(3) Combined (12 or 32 sessions).

The duration of each group was 12 sessions or 32 sessions. Subjects were followed up over an 18-month period. This study found that the duration of treatment had no effect on outcome, i.e. prolonged treatment was no more likely to be effective than treatment over a shorter time frame. The structured groups were more effective in reducing recidivism (although not significantly) than the self-help groups: almost two-thirds of men who completed the 'education' and 'combined' group were reported non-violent at 18 months' follow-up. Harris (1988) randomly assigned 81 couples into individual/couple counselling, group counselling or a 10-week waiting list and found no significant difference between the three in abuse recidivism.

CONCLUSIONS

Men who batter their partners are not, in general, mentally ill, but have a range of personality deficits, particularly apparent within intimate re-lationships, which centre around insecurity, inadequacy and dependency. Identifying batterers, applying legal sanctions in an effective way, offering re-education programmes and condemning the use of violence within any relationship may ultimately offer some protection and hope for victims.

REFERENCES

Babcock, J.C., Waltz, J., Jacobsen, N.S. and Gottman, J.M. (1993) Power and violence: the relation between communication patterns, power discrepancies and domestic violence. *J Consult Clin Psychol* **61**, 40–50

Bergman, B. and Brismar, B. (1992) Chemical dependency and psychiatric disorder in imprisoned wife beaters. *Journal of Forensic Psychiatry* **3**, 487–95

Berk, R.A. and Newton, P.J. (1985) Does arrest really deter wife battery? An effort to replicate the findings of the Minneapolis Spouse Abuse experiment. *American Sociological Review* **50**, 253–62

Brisson, N.J. (1981) Battering husbands: a survey of abusive men. *Victimology* **6**, 338–44

Browne, A. (1987) *When Battered Women Kill*. London: Collier Macmillan

Chritchlow, B. (1986) The powers of John Barleycorn: beliefs about the effects of alcohol on social behaviour. *Am Psychologist* **41**, 751–64

Dobash, R.E. and Dobash, R.P. (1977) Wives: the 'appropriate' victims of marital violence. *Victimology* **2**, 426–42

Dobash, R.E. and Dobash, R.P. (1984) The nature and antecedents of violent events. *British Journal of Criminology* **24**, 269

Dutton, D.G. (1986) The outcome of court mandated treatment for wife assault: a quasi experimental evaluation. *Violence and Victims* **1**, 163–75

Dutton, D.G. and Strachan, C.E. (1987) Motivational needs for power and spouse-specific assertiveness in assaultive and non-assaultive men. *Violence and Victims* **2**, 145–56

Dutton, D.G. (1994) Behavioral and affective correlates of borderline personality or-
    ganisation in wife assaulters. *Int J Law Psychiatry* **17**, 265–77
Edleson, J.L. and Syers, M. (1990) Relative effectiveness of group treatments for men
    who batter. *Social Work Research and Abstracts* **26**, 10–17
Edleson, J.L. and Syers, M. (1991) The effects of group treatment for men who batter:
    an 18 month follow up study. *Research on Social Work Practice* **1**, 227–243
Edwards, S. (1989) *Policing Domestic Violence*. London: Sage
Else, L., Wonderlich, S.A., Beatty, W.W., Christie, D.W. and Saton, R.D. (1993)
    Personality characteristics of men who physically abuse women. *Hospital and Community
    Psychiatry* **44**, 54–8
Fagan, J. (1989) 'Cessation of family violence: deterrents and dissuasion' in L. Ohlin
    and M. Tonry (Eds) *Family Violence*, pp. 377–425. Chicago: University of Chicago
    Press
Fagan, J.A., Stewart, D.K. and Hansen, K.B. (1983) 'Violent men or violent husbands:
    background factors and situational correlates' in D. Finkelhor (Ed.) *The Dark Side of
    Families: Current Family Violence Research*. Beverly Hills, CA: Sage
Faulk, M. (1974) Men who assault their wives. *Med Sci Law* **14**, 180–3
Gayford, J.J. (1975) Wife battering: A preliminary survey of 100 cases. *BMJ* **1**, 194–7
Geberth, V.J. (1992) Stalkers. *Law and Order* October, 138–43
Gondolf, E.W. (1990) 'How some men stop their abuse: an exploratory programme
    evaluation' in G.T. Hotaling, D. Finkelhor, J.T. Kirkpatrick and E.W. Gondolf (Eds)
    Psychiatric Response to Family Violence: Identifying and Confronting Neglected Danger, pp.
    39–43. Boston, MA: Lexington Books
Harris, R., Savage, S., Jones, T. and Brook, W. (1988) A comparison of treatments for
    abusive men and their partners within the Family Service Agency. *Canadian Journal
    of Community Mental Health* **7**, 147–55
Hart, S.D., Dutton, D.G. and Newlove, T. (1993) The prevalence of personality disorder
    among wife assaulters. *Journal of Personality Disorders* **7**, 329–41
Holtzworth-Munroe, A. and Hutchinson, G. (1993) Attributing negative intent to wife
    behaviour: the attributions of maritally violent versus non-violent men. *J Abnorm
    Psychol* **102**, 206–11
Hornung, C.A., McCullough, B.C. and Sugimoto, T. (1981) Status relationships in
    marriage: risk factors and spouse abuse. *Journal of Marriage and the Family* **43**, 675–92
Hotaling, G.T. and Sugarman, D.B. (1986) An analysis of risk markers in husband to
    wife violence: the current state of knowledge. *Violence and Victims* **1**, 101–24
Jaffe, P. D., Telford, A. and Autin, G. (1986) The impact of police laying charges in
    cases of wife assault. *Journal of Family Violence* **1**, 37–50
Jennings, J.L. (1987) History and issues in the treatment of battering men: a case for
    unstructured group therapy. *Journal of Family Violence* **2**, 193–213
Kandel-Englander, E. (1992) Wife battering and violence outside the family. *Journal of
    Interpersonal Violence* **7**, 462–470
Kaufman, J. and Zigler, E. (1987) Do abused children become abusive parents? *Am J
    Orthopsychiatry* **57**, 186–92
Kennedy, L.W. and Dutton, D.G. (1989) The incidence of wife assault in Alberta.
    Canadian Journal of Behavioural Sciences **21**, 40–54
Kobak, R.R. and Sceery, A. (1988) Attachment in late adolescence: working models
    affect regulation and perception of self and others. *Child Development* **59**, 135–46
Langley, R. and Levy, R.C. (1977) *Wife Beating: the Silent Crisis*. New York: E.P. Dutton
Maiuro, R.D., Cahn, T.S. and Vitaliano, P.P. (1986) Assertiveness, deficits and hostility
    in domestically violent men. *Violence and Victims* **1**, 279–89
Maiuro, R.D., Cahn, T.S., Vitaliano, P.P., Wagner, B.C. and Zegree, J.B. (1988) Anger,
    hostility and depression in domestically violent versus generally assaultative men and
    non-violent control subjects. *J Consult Clin Psychol* **56**, 17–23
Mayseless, O. (1991) Adult attachment patterns and courtship violence. *Family Relations*
    40, 21–8

Pagelow, M.D. (1981) 'Abused wives and their abusers' in M.D. Pagelow (Ed.) *Woman Battering: Victims and their Experiences*. Beverley Hills, CA: Sage

Petrik, N.D., Petrik-Olsen, R.E. and Subotnik, L.S. (1994) Powerlessness and the need to control: the male abuser's dilemma. *Journal of Interpersonal Violence* **9**, 278–85

Ptacek, J. (1988) 'Why do men batter their wives?' in K. Ylló and M. Bograd (Eds) *Feminist Perspectives on Wife Abuse*. London: Sage

Rosenbaum, A. and O'Leary, K.D. (1981) Marital violence: characteristics of abusive couples. *J Consult Clin Psychol* **49**, 63–71

Rosenbaum, A. and Maiuro, R.D. (1990) 'Perpetrators of spouse abuse' in R.T. Ammerman and M. Hersen (Eds) *Treatment of Family Violence – a Source Book*, pp. 280–309. Chichester: John Wiley

Rosenfeld, B.D. (1992) Court ordered treatment of spouse abuse. *Clinical Psychology Review* **12**, 205–26

Saunders, D.G. and Azar, S.T. (1989) 'Treatment programmes for family violence' in L. Ohlin and M. Tonry (Eds) *Family Violence: Crime and Justice: A Review of Research*, pp. 481–545. Chicago: University of Chicago Press

Shepherd, M.M. (1961) Morbid jealousy: some clinical and social aspects of a psychiatric symptom. *Journal of Mental Science* **107**, 687–753

Sherman, L.W. and Berk, R.A. (1984) The specific deterrent effects of arrest for domestic assault. *American Sociological Review*, **49**, 261–72

Simpson-Subotnik, L. (1983) Overcontrolled and undercontrolled types of men who batter women. Paper presented at the North American meeting at the International Society for Research on Aggression. Victoria, B.C.

Smith, M.D. (1990) Patriarchal ideology and wife beating: a test of a feminist hypothesis. *Violence and Victims* **5**, 257–73

Sonkin, D.J., Martin, D. and Walker, L.E.A. (1985) *The Male Batterer: a Treatment Approach*. New York: Springer

Straus, M.A., Gelles, R.J. and Steinmetz, S.F. (1980) *Behind Closed Doors: Violence and the American Family*. New York: Anchor

Syers, M. and Edleson, J.L. (1992) The combined effects of co-ordinated criminal justice intervention in woman abuse. *Journal of Interpersonal Violence* **7**, 419–502

Waldo, M. (1988) Relationship enhancement counselling groups for wife abusers. *J Mental Health Counselling* **10**, 37–45

Walker, L.E. (1979) *The Battered Woman*. New York: Harper and Row

Wilson, M. (1996) 'Working with the CHANGE men programme' in K. Cavanagh and V. Cree (Eds) *Working with Men – Feminism and Social Work*, pp. 28–44. London: Routledge

Ylló, K. and Straus, M. A. (1984) Patriarchy and violence against wives. *J Family Issues* **5**, 307–20

Chapter 5

Analysis of cohort

Stephanie Yearnshire

INTRODUCTION

Domestic violence is by no means a 'new' crime, nor is it a new social problem. Furthermore, the crimes of domestic violence which are reported represent only a tiny fraction of the total offences committed. On average, a woman will be assaulted by her partner or ex-partner 35 times before actually reporting it to the police. On many occasions she will repeatedly return to the batterer, in spite of knowing the batterer's propensity for violence.

Repeat victimisation often escalates in severity as time passes, leading in some cases to severe injuries and even death. Home Office data indicate that in the period 1986–1995 between 38 and 49 per cent of all female homicide victims were killed by current or former partners; by contrast, only 7–11 per cent of male victims suffered the same fate (Home Office 1996).

Statistics like these give some representation of the extent of the problem faced by the police and other agencies and in recent years domestic violence has been given a higher profile and greater recognition. This is illustrated by a plethora of research and media coverage resulting in numerous published studies in this field. The majority of this work has, understandably, focused on the victim's perspective in coping with the violence. Comparatively little research has focused on the male perspective. It is suggested that without this viewpoint being explored there is little hope of achieving a full understanding of domestic violence.

The research presented in this chapter was commenced with the intention of exploring the experience of being a perpetrator of domestic violence. This report highlights some of the findings of the research and considers the significance of the findings.

The research centred on interviews with men in police custody charged with assaulting their wives or partners and was conducted in the North East of England. No attempt was made to locate or interview wives and partners, as the key focus of the research was the man's perspective to establish why men batter. As a consequence, it is recognised that there may be some bias in the accounts given.

THE STUDY FINDINGS

Description of cohort

All 23 interviewees were white Europeans, a sample which is representative of the local population. The men were aged between 19 and 51 years, with half falling into the 20–30 years of age category. These figures are in line with Home Office statistics for arrests for violence and are supported by the British Crime Survey. All but one of the men classed themselves as being in either full-time, part-time or contractual employment. Employment was wide ranging – from labourer to scaffolder, rig worker to taxi driver. The non-manual categories were represented by an estate officer and a supermarket manager. Thus, although unemployment has been cited as a factor in the incidence of violent acts, this was not found in this study.

There were no professional men amongst those arrested, but this is unsurprising. While research shows that domestic violence permeates through all social classes, it is usually the less affluent who rely on the police as their only source of protection. The middle and upper classes are more likely to have the means to deal with problems privately and, moreover, have a cultural imperative to keep their business private.

Three-quarters of the sample had fathered children, a fact which highlights that the abuse of partners has ramifications for the children involved.

Before highlighting the main findings of the study, three of the interviewees' background cases will be outlined, in order to a give a flavour of the characteristics which are typical of the domestic violence cases in this study.

Case studies

Alan

Alan was arrested after his wife called the police. His explanation of her reasons were no more than 'she felt threatened I suppose'. He had been married for five years, with the violence erupting approximately every three months over the previous two-year period. He could not recall any particular cause and the violence could erupt at any time although he considered that every incident was 'drink' related. He described the worst injuries as involving bruising and scratching to both his wife and himself. At the end of a typical violent episode, he would walk out of the house and return to a lecture regarding his drinking habits. Parents, friends, other family members and the doctor were all well aware of the problem, and they recommended treatment or talking about the problem. He thought the violence would continue unless he actually stopped drinking. He felt his wife had an unreasonable attitude towards his drinking and going out. This would lead her to yell at him, and he would 'have a little go now and then'.

Alan had been arrested at 7 pm, after a full weekend absent from home drinking with friends and leaving little money left from his wages to pay the family bills. He did not consider this behaviour unreasonable, especially in his own home and thought that his wife should not complain.

Alan appeared to view himself as a 'married single', in that marriage and family were a separate entity and completely distinct from his right to have the social life of his choice.

The arrest and detention appeared to have had a sobering effect on him, which supports theories that suggest that arrest is an effective measure, but he still couldn't understand why the police had interfered.

Brian

Brian had lived with his partner for three years and they had a nine-month-old son. He had been arrested six weeks previously for violence to his partner and again at the time of this research. He believed the police were called by his partner because 'she feels protected by the police at Farringdon,' adding, 'she has been diagnosed as having postnatal depression'. This, in his view, was the root cause of the problem.

He acknowledged regular, fortnightly, physical violence, where slapping was a regular feature. He further stated that the worst assaults he inflicted on his partner included head butts, scratches, bites and punches. He added that the violence enhanced sex, stating that, '. . . sex often follows the violence, where we sometimes have kinky sex and sometimes we argue during sex'.

Brian felt that the arguments were sometimes orchestrated because his partner wanted to go out with someone else and therefore started an argument to get him out of the house for a few days. He cited jealousy as a frequent trigger for his violence. Having split up with his partner about 50 times, Brian found it difficult to think of what might help his situation. Brian reported 'hating himself' over the violence, feeling both remorse and guilt, especially where the violence would flare up for no particular reason. In fact, minor considerations would often cause shouting and abuse. They had been together for three years in what can only be described as a turbulent relationship, yet both partners would clearly be reunited.

Clive

Clive's partner had a 'past reputation', which preoccupied him whenever she went nightclubbing. The night before the arrest, his partner had been nightclubbing, as a result of which Clive accused her of 'going with other lads'. This resulted in an argument, during which he punched his partner, causing bruising to her head and ear, while he received cuts to his forehead and lip in return. He was surprised to be arrested on this occasion, stating that, 'the police have been called about ten times, they've suggested I stay with my parents but I've never been arrested before'. Clive had been inflicting violence for two-and-a-half of their five years together.

Although brief, these case studies highlight the complexity of feelings which cumulate in situations of domestic violence. The factors mentioned in the case studies, for example, patterns of violence triggers and causes, action taken to ease the violence, and response to the police, will now be explored in the main results of the study.

Frequency and duration

In the sample examined, patterns of violence revealed an equal spread of incidents on weekdays with a noticeable increase on Saturday and Sunday. Grouping the incidents into time of day, the majority were between the period of 10 pm to 2 am. The police were often not called at the time of the incident itself, therefore the time of arrest was later, mostly the next morning.

In terms of when the violence started, six of the sample stated that the incidents had begun in the last 1–2 years. The range for the rest of the interviewees was split into two periods: one grouping identified 1–3 months, while the second spoke of troubles spanning 10–15 years.

Four of the men acknowledged weekly violence, while 30 per cent acknowledged intermittent violence over the previous six months. This is in agreement with other research (Dobash and Dobash 1984) which implies that violent eruptions tend to occur intermittently rather than being persistent, regular bouts.

Patterns of violence

The findings in the study support a wide range of research, showing that violence can begin fairly early on in relationships and progress by stages to more severe acts.

During the latest violent incident, while most of the men spoke of one or more injuries being inflicted on their partner, 39 per cent alleged that the female had no injuries at all. In 60 per cent of cases the men agreed there had been previous violence. All of those who denied previous physical violence acknowledged previous verbal abuse. A history of violence is an important factor in documenting any partner violence. Twenty-six per cent of the men had been involved in violence with their partner during the previous four weeks, though in the main this was not reported to the police. Ossie's comments highlight the escalation of violence, stating: '... I think I broke her arm last night, but I'm not injured. We got together 11 months ago and five months after that it started. Before, we would slap each other, and I would walk out.'

Triggers and causes

The most cited reasons given by the interviewees for the violence being triggered were jealousy (52 per cent of the cases), drink (43 per cent), with general arguments following closely behind (35 per cent). In many cases there was more than one reason mentioned.   Replies related to jealousy are typically illustrated by the following remark by George: '. . . I'd be paranoid if she was in late, after seeing her sister. I'd say she was seeing someone else.'

As mentioned above, where either partner had been drinking, alcohol played a significant part in exacerbating feelings of jealousy and possessiveness. This is highlighted by Ian's response: '. . . I knew she had had an affair, it ended in April, but it eats me up inside. It's worse when I have a drink.'

Many writers have cited excessive consumption of alcohol as a contributory factor to domestic violence. For example, Roy's (1982) study of 4000 US couples over a four-year period showed that just over a third of abusive partners had alcohol problems. Also, in Pahl's (1985) research, over half of the women said their husbands drank alcohol excessively and a third named alcohol as the cause of the most recent violence inflicted on them. The consumption of alcohol is by no means a pre-requisite for domestic violence, but alcohol abuse and domestic violence are frequently associated. Perhaps the most interesting view put forward was that suggested by Pahl (1985), when she asserted that excessive alcohol consumption often serves as an excuse for violence rather than a trigger. Perhaps most alarmingly, several interviewees could not explain what triggered the violence. As Tony says: '. . . I don't like violence but sometimes my temper goes and that's it. I can't hold it back. I just crack.'

Many theories have been put forward to explain the causes of the violence, involving social explanations and individual pathology. One theory often cited is a transmission of violent behaviour through generations which establishes a 'cycle of violence'. This means that if an individual has observed violence between his or her parents or has been a victim of violence as a child, there is an increased likelihood that they in turn will abuse. This is because these children are socialised to see violence as a way of life and as a legitimate solution to any disagreement.

Questions were therefore asked regarding the interviewees' previous experience of abuse as children or whether they had observed violent acts between their parents while growing up.

Eighty-three per cent of the interviewees claimed not to have been subjected to parental violence. Only 17 per cent agreed that they had been abused and these acts were mostly isolated incidents. Only one man said he had been subjected to regular physical violence by his father. Furthermore, when asked whether the interviewees observed violence when they were children, only 21 per cent of the men recalled their parents fighting, and again these were isolated events.   The findings of this study do not support the view that being abused or observing abuse as a child is a very significant factor in determining whether that child will become an abuser himself.

Each interviewee was asked what he saw as the main cause of his violence. Here, rather than accepting that they had violent tendencies which they found difficult to control, the majority apportioned the blame to the partner, arguing that if the partner had not goaded them, the incident would never have happened. Even if this is true, it does not explain why the interviewee should actually strike his partner.

Sexual violence

Although the majority of interviewees were in custody for physical violence, two of the men were charged with sexual offences, one for rape of his live-in girlfriend and the other for kidnap and rape of a recent ex-girlfriend. Both were surprised that they had been arrested for rape. As George stated: '. . . I thought rape was when you attacked a lass, pulling off her clothes and had sex. Last night she started screaming and I slapped her to make her quiet, then I had sex. I didn't think that what I did was rape.'

This highlights a lack of awareness in some sections of society as to what constitutes rape. Recently the law has changed to incorporate marital rape but many people do not class sexual violence between partners as amounting to an offence. Because of this, the under-reporting of sexual violence is even more acute when it occurs within relationships.

The interviewees were asked if sex took place while fighting and arguing. Most of the men said no, but said that sex took place after making up.

Attempts to stop the violence

Questions on whether the men or their partners had taken steps to put the relationship on a less violent footing revealed that some had talked together, others had split up but had later resumed the relationship and the rest said they had done nothing to stop the violence. About a third of the sample had said that they had spoken to friends, family or social workers. Only one man had said he had tried to change. However, when these results are related to replies regarding the frequency and pattern of violence, it is clear that remedial steps had been largely unsuccessful.

Surprisingly, in many cases third parties knew of the violent incidents. In half of the cases, the parents of the couple were aware of the violence in the relationship and friends of the couple were aware in about a third of the sample. Only one case had been referred to a doctor for advice on drinking. This highlights the difficulties of this type of crime: people may be well aware of the situation but feel powerless because the violence is taking place in what they see as the 'private domain'. They may be able to offer advice, but feel ill equipped to take action. Equally, even if help is offered, the perpetrator or the victim may reject it, either feeling that it is no one else's business or that the situation is too complex to solve.

Where help had been offered, none of the interviewees had found it particularly helpful and five of the men admitted that the violence would probably continue.

The interviewees' personal views on ending the violence were wide ranging. Some thought of ending the relationship while others did not know what action to take. Two of the interviewees thought that abstinence from alcohol might work and three thought their partners should not go out to nightclubs. Three of the men thought that if they argued less over the children, the violence might lessen or that talking together more might help. Only two thought professional help might be beneficial. Brian summed up the feelings of remorse and frustration at his behaviour, which many of the men highlighted, by commenting: 'We've talked with friends and our parents but it is difficult to know what would stop it. I feel it is always aimed at throwing me out of the house. It can flare up over nothing, too strong tea, her untidiness, or nagging. I hate myself afterwards and feel remorseful and guilty.'

As mentioned earlier, much of the blame was attributed to the partner. When asked 'How would you stop the violence?', some answers reflected that if the partner changed her behaviour, then the violence would stop. As Hugh commented, 'It will continue unless she now leaves me alone to get on with my life.'

Some feel frustration over the sexual relationship, illustrated by George's comments 'My Dad has advised me to walk around the block if I lose my temper. If I wasn't frustrated over sex I wouldn't lose my temper.'

Calls to the police and responding to arrest

Finally, the interviewees were asked about their reactions at being arrested for the violence. In 14 of the cases the wife or partner called the police. In only two cases, the neighbours called the police, while one call was made by a child. When asked who called the police and why he thought they were called, most of the interviewees sought to minimise the incident and indicated that their behaviour was not worthy of arrest. Typical of the minimising comments was Tony's version of when the police were called: 'The step-daughter phoned the police when a little bit of an argument got out of hand.'

In terms of the arrest itself, 82 per cent of the men were surprised that they had been arrested for the violent incident.

Examining the reasons why the man thought police help had been requested, produced a broad range of answers: because the partner had felt threatened, because they were fighting in public or at home, or out of spite. Only two men accepted that their behaviour had caused the incident.   These results highlight the fact that domestic violence is not viewed as a crime by the majority of the men interviewed, thus identifying a significant obstacle in interviewing with this kind of abuse. It is only when domestic violence is more fully recognised by society as criminal behaviour, that meaningful steps will be taken to reduce it. These attitudes will be discussed in Chapter 12 which deals with the police practice.

CONCLUSION

The findings of this study highlight several areas worthy of further discussion, including insights as to how perpetrators of domestic violence view the causes of their violence and how they think it could be reduced. Perhaps the most stark result is the interviewees' lack of awareness that their domestic violence constituted criminal conduct. This is reflected in their apparent surprise at being arrested. This lack of awareness may have one or more causes in each case. It may be because the victim has, in the past, endured the violence, thereby legitimising it, or simply because society has, in the main and until very recently, condoned domestic violence.

Whatever the reasons, the awareness of domestic violence must be raised in our society in order for it to be recognised as a problem. Until then, the police and other agencies in the criminal justice system will have little impact in reducing the incidence of this serious offence.

REFERENCES

Dobash, R.E. and Dobash, R.P. (1984) The nature and antecedents of violent events. *British Journal of Criminology* **24**, 269–88

Home Office (1996) *Criminal Statistics for England and Wales*. London: HMSO

Pahl, J. (1985) *Private Violence and Public Policy*. London: Routledge

Roy, M. (1982) 'Four thousand partners in violence: a trend analysis' in M. Roy (Ed.) *The Abusive Partner*. New York: Van Nostrand Reinhold

Chapter 6

Perpetrators of domestic violence

Discussion

Edwards: In my research on homicide cases, pathological jealousy was used as an indication of diminished responsibility in a significant number of cases, when in fact the problem seems to be that pathological jealousy is no more than a social construct which enables and excuses violent men. Part of my work has been to look at how precisely these stereotypes have been replicated and reinforced in medical literature to inform the law and provide excuses and justifications. I wanted to add to what you have already said that this is a problem which is recognised by some of us and yet it continues to inform cases where men kill wives and provides a defence. It is quite abhorrent and disturbing that this is the case.

I have an unrelated second point in connection with the whole area of treatment for perpetrators. I am very concerned that, although you say this is about education and not treatment, I do not want to go back to pathologising male violence whereby offering probation orders with a condition of education (treatment) will be seen as a quick fix.

Moving on to the CHANGE programme, one of the problems is that if you are on the programme as a perpetrator, you will probably try and control your violence, otherwise you will be in breach of the probation order and may find yourself either in prison or being punished for that breach. We have to be very wary of how we go forward with this, although it is important to recognise that we have to do something in terms of re-educating batterers.

Finally, a point on the Duluth model which is inspiring us all here in terms of multi-agency approach to domestic violence. It is important to stress that intervention must be multi-agency and any treatment for perpetrators must be part of an holistic approach by the criminal justice system with involvement from women's aid organisations.

Walker: When Gill Mezey described the characteristics of men proven to be violent, some of those characteristics almost certainly exist in men who have not been proven to be violent, or who are not violent. When you are putting together the profile of the perpetrator, how do you get your matched controls?

Mezey: We are not talking about good methodologically rigorous research here. These are descriptive studies. In this area you get what you can, you grab the men as they come your way and you describe them. Good research is lacking in this area, particularly the use of comparison groups, which allow us to describe norms within society. For example, Susan Edwards referred to jealousy. Jealousy is a very common emotion, but it gets to a point where it becomes extreme and by definition it is then termed pathological; it becomes a mental illness and is then used as an excuse or justification for certain kinds of behaviours. The classification of battering men is derived from a number of descriptive studies, essentially of men who have been assessed following arrest or conviction at that stage. We do not know how they compare with men who do not beat their wives, or with men who do engage in these behaviours but are too clever, or for other reasons manage to avoid any kind of detection.

Harwin: We have to treat these findings with caution because one of the problems is, who comes to public attention? Very often middle-class men do not come to public attention, in the same way that they do not in child abuse cases. Perpetrators of domestic violence can be very charming, they may have a lot of authority and influence. There is no single profile of a perpetrator.

The second point I want to make relates to the term 'cycle of violence', which has been mentioned in two different contexts in the past session. The first was in terms of the description of the process. There used to be a view that in a violent relationship, the violence went up and down like a wave and there would be good and bad times. Whilst that may describe some relationships, the model of Duluth which was mentioned was based on work with women in small groups. This showed how physical and sexual violence and the fear permeated all those other experiences. Second, the term 'cycle of violence' is talked about a great deal in the media in connection with domestic violence but there is not much reliable evidence for the theory of inter-generational violence.

Finally, one of the problems with some of the re-education models if they do not focus centrally on beliefs and rights to control and dominate women, not just about rights to use violence, is that you can get a situation where perpetrators will stop being physically violent, but they will carry on using other forms of dominance. This is exactly what the Duluth programme showed, where about 40 per cent of men had stopped being physically abusive. In a survey of women whose partners had been in the programme and had stopped being physically violent, many of them stated that they wished they had left during the violence because later on they found it was difficult to get anybody to take them seriously and believe that they did not want to be in that relationship.

Stanko: One thing which would be interesting for this College to do would be to find a way of conducting research into how violent men, regardless of who and where they are, impact on obstetric and gynaecological examinations, e.g. when men insist on being present, how they are present, what women themselves say about their choices to be examined and whether those choices are undermined and subverted by their male partners. It seems to me that in standard procedures, you may be able to collect data which will be able to answer in a very systematic way the kinds of questions that have been raised over the years about the way abuse works, particularly around women's health issues.

O'Brien: Obstetricians generally have encouraged husbands to take part in the whole process of birth, from the clinic to the labour ward, even coming into the operating theatre. That has probably had two effects: one is that the presence of the husband during any examination may have an important impact which has not been measured but also, a point which I am sure is recognised by this group, it prevents the woman from being able to report and communicate her anxieties of violence to a health carer.

Jones: This would be an important and exciting area to research. We are certainly able, in my practice, to identify the controlling man in a second: if in an obstetric examination, you ask the woman how the baby is doing, and the husband says, 'the baby is fine,' and, 'how are you feeling, Mrs Smith?' he answers, 'she's fine'.

My experience with batterers is that they are the ultimate con-artists. It is as difficult to pick out the batterers as it is to try and pick out the battered women and that is why it is important for health providers to consider that everybody is potentially a batterer.

To profile a batterer or one who is battered is to miss some, just as it is dangerous in the health profession to decide, on the basis of somebody's job, whether they might be gay or HIV-positive.

Kerr-Wilson: Can I ask a question about the characteristics of perpetrators? Does this cross all boundaries of society, religion and race?

Mezey: Again, the quality of research is very poor in this area and the fact is that, both in terms of the victims and perpetrators, most of the papers come from the US; there is very little in the UK. It is telling that the only paper I quoted from the *British Journal of Psychiatry* is now 23 years old.

I accept that one does not want to medicalise this problem too much. On the other hand, there may be certain skills and there may be a certain benefit from trying to understand and find explanations of individual motivations and to see whether there are patterns that seem to generalise men who commit these acts of violence. Certainly, when you talk to the women, they describe very similar characteristics, patterns of behaviour, preoccupations and vulnerabilities of their partners. If you can identify those, then it is important, without pathologising what they do and denying their responsibility, to try to see whether that can give you some sort of entry into working with those individuals in order to reduce violence.

There is some evidence that therapeutic programmes for child sex abusers reduces the risk of them offending and protects victims. The important thing is to be able to assess perpetrators of domestic violence, to identify those men who are motivated to change and who can be helped, and to define effective interventions, rather than, on ideological grounds, dismissing the possibility of intervention ever being constructive or helpful.

Kerr-Wilson: On the subject of treatment, what positive things do you encourage in men to get them out of a cycle of thinking that it is macho to beat up their wives, that it is macho to go to prison? How do you encourage men to get out of this?

Mezey: This is partly to do with trying to induce shame, which many perpetrators lack. Some of them regard this as being perfectly acceptable behaviour and even necessary and desirable. You have to get them to realise what the disadvantages of behaving like this are, and what they stand to lose in their own personal life and in real terms is greater than what they stand to gain from stopping their violence. Non-violent means of conflict resolution can result in all kinds of concrete and powerful gains for the men involved. You have to convince them of such means.

Harwin: No work with such individuals will change anything unless something is tackled on a much broader scale. For example, a recent survey of young people in Manchester as part of a zero tolerance initiative found that 75 per cent of the boys and 74 per cent of the girls believed that it was likely that they would either use violence or experience violence in their relationships, a depressing finding after 25 years of increasing public awareness about domestic violence. Thus education and attitudinal change has to go beyond the individual.

Mezey: The approaches are not mutually exclusive. Of course individual work is not the whole answer. Addressing the problems requires multi-agency work, adopting an holistic approach and recognising that there is no single solution or single agency that is capable of solving this.

Cameron: This is really a comment about raising research issues and policies from the Royal College of Obstetricians and Gynaecologists. I was impressed with Richard Jones saying that he was able to approach this issue over the last four years with his patients and that he was not frightened of causing offence. Performance targets are often time related; gynaecologists in Britain are probably afraid of opening a can of worms and don't know about other agencies that are available and are unaware of how to address the problem if the situation arises. However, this shouldn't be seen as an excuse for inaction.

SECTION 3

THE ABUSED WOMAN

Chapter 7

Domestic violence: understanding women's experiences of abuse

Nicola Harwin

INTRODUCTION

Violence against women is a serious and prevalent global problem, the true proportions of which have only been acknowledged in the last decade. At the 1995 United Nations Fourth World Conference on Women held in Beijing, 35,000 women from non-governmental organisations (NGOs) all over the world identified violence against women as a fundamental and pressing human rights issue. The UN 'Platform for Action', adopted by governments at the Beijing conference, details the range of gender-based violence and abuse experienced by women world-wide, of which domestic violence is a key aspect.

Domestic violence is the physical, emotional and sexual abuse of one person (usually a woman) by another person (usually a man) with whom they have or have had some form of intimate relationship, such as marriage, in order to maintain dominance and control over that person. While such violence can also be carried out by other family members, for example in extended family networks, or occur in homosexual relationships, it is predominantly used by men against women.

In the UK as in other countries, domestic violence is extremely widespread. The single largest category of assaults uncovered by the 1992 British Crime Survey was domestic violence; 80 per cent of these assaults were against women, and such incidents were likely to be undercounted (Mayhew *et al.* 1993). Recent surveys, for example in Islington in 1993, have shown that up to a third of women regularly experience physical and associated abuse (Mooney 1994). In 1994–95, nearly 50,000 women and children stayed in refuges in England, and over 100,000 contacted Women's Aid for advice and support (Women's Aid Federation of England 1996).

Any woman is at risk of domestic violence, regardless of race, class, ethnic origin, religion, age, sexuality, disability or lifestyle. Such violence can affect every aspect of a woman's life: her physical and emotional well-being; her relationships with children, family, friends, neighbours and colleagues; her options for work and leisure. The violence may be life-threatening, systematic and long-term. It can and does occur anywhere, although the home is the main place. The popular idea of 'home' is synonymous with safety and sanctuary but for many women this is a myth and the home is a place of terror, injury, danger and sometimes death. An average of 100 women are killed by partners or ex-partners in England and Wales every year (Home Office 1995). Almost half of all female victims of homicide in England and Wales are killed by partners or ex-partners, compared with 6 per cent of male victims. Children may also be fatal victims of domestic violence, as recent cases of multiple killings of family members by violent men have highlighted. However, homicide statistics for children are not broken down by gender or cross-referenced to incidents of woman abuse.

WOMEN LIVING WITH VIOLENCE

Most abusive men use a range of behaviours, not all of which are inherently violent, to control partners or ex-partners:

> The thing is he wanted to be ruler of the house. He said there can't be two kings in one house, and on one occasion he said that I mustn't cook for the kids and don't cook for him, that he would buy separate shopping and sort of ban me from using the cooker. When we're fighting I wasn't to sleep on my bed, I wasn't to sleep on the kids' bed and I wasn't to sleep on the settee. One night he locked me in the toilet – sort of nailed it down. (Mama 1989)

> He stopped me from going to work. I got the sack because I wasn't at work for two weeks. He locked me in the flat for nearly two weeks and wouldn't let me out – my mother nearly had to bash the door down to get me out. (Homer *et al.* 1988)

The definitions of abuse shown in Table 7.1 come from training exercises done with women who are survivors of violent relationships, and activists working with abused women. It is important to name the problem, to say specifically what we mean when we use the term domestic violence. If we can avoid being voyeuristic or sensationalist, if we can overcome embarrassment, then we may make it more possible for women who seek our help to talk about their experiences.

These are only some of the many ways in which women are hurt, frightened, degraded, humiliated and intimidated. Talk to any refuge worker or survivor and the list would go on and on. Most women seeking help will not be able to talk easily about their experiences and may only tell us a little of what has been happening to them.

The impact of psychological and emotional abuse

Women coming to refuges frequently describe how psychological abuse and fear of violence are even more powerful in acting to limit and control their

Table 7.1. Definitions of abuse

Physical abuse

bruising	blacking eyes	breaking bones
hitting	punching	kicking
shoving	throwing	scratching
starving	shaking	burning with acid
burning with cigarettes	pulling hair	slapping
choking	pushing down stairs	smacking in the face
forced drug taking	spitting	biting
strangling	scalding	repeated banging of head
knifing	suffocating with a pillow	burning
being forced to sleep on the floor	being stripped of clothing and made to stand there	being made to eat horrible things
denying sleep	attempted murder	murder

Sexual abuse

rape	sexual assault using objects	sexual possessiveness
forcing sex in ways that hurt or abuse	forced sado-masochistic practices	enforced prostitution
forcing sex in front of children	forcing her to have sex with his friends	forcing sex in front of others
urinating on her	sexual abuse of children	forced tying up
forcing sex when she's tired or doesn't want it	forcing her to mimic pornography	forcing her to be photographed in pornographic sex acts
forced oral sex	refusing to have sex with her	sexual name-calling
denial of sexuality		

Psychological abuse

verbal abuse and criticism	being told she's worthless or ugly or useless	constant criticisms about the state of the house, cooking, appearance, etc.
swearing, shouting and screaming at her	intimidation by his family/friends	isolating her
preventing contact with her friends or family	preventing her from work or study	refusing to let her learn English
possessiveness	extreme jealousy	repeated interrogations
not allowing her out of the house or access to the phone	not allowing her any privacy, e.g. to go to the toilet alone	cutting up her clothes
destroying her personal belongings	humiliating her in front of others including children	making her lick the dinner plates clean

Table 7.1. *continued*

destroying her property or work	deliberately ignoring her	continually breaking promises
damaging the home	locking her out	degrading her
forcing her to clean household items that are already clean	forcing her to re-cook meals, because he says something minor is wrong with it	forcing her to polish the soles of his shoes
making her do housework in the middle of the night	being kept on edge all the time	making her think she's going mad
making her beg for money	being afraid to go to sleep	withholding affection
never knowing when the next attack will be		

Threats

to kill her	to kill or harm children or family or friends or pets	to take the children
to have the children taken away	to have her deported or committed	to hurt himself or commit suicide
to abuse her children sexually if she withholds sex	to tell someone that she's mad	to be violent
to throw her out of the home	to burn down the house	to mutilate her
to run her over	to withhold care if she is older or disabled	to destroy possessions and say, 'Next time it's you'
threatening letters and telephone calls, saying, 'I'll always find you'		

own actions than physical attacks, and this of course poses many problems when tackling domestic violence. An analogy has been drawn between the experiences of women living with abusive men and the psychological torture and 'brainwashing' experienced by prisoners of war (NiCarthy 1988). Abusive and violent partners can use methods similar to those of prison guards, who recognise that physical control is never easily accomplished without the co-operation of the prisoner, through the subversive manipulation of mind and feeling. In Women's Aid training we draw on the 'chart of coercion' developed by Amnesty International to describe the structure of this 'brainwashing':

(1) Isolation;

(2) Disability and exhaustion;

(3) Enforcement of trivial demands;

(4) Degradation;

(5) Threats;

(6) Displays of total power;

(7) Occasional indulgences;

(8) Distorted perspectives.

The experiences described above amply illustrate the first six categories. The last two describe some other aspects of women's experiences that can make it hard for them to leave the abusive relationship. Many women are caught up in confused feelings about their abuser. They may still love their partner but desperately want the abuse to end. Their partner may do something 'nice' or indulge and pamper them on occasions, especially after bouts of violence. Many women will put up with apologies for a long time before they wear thin. Buying her the odd gift or present, occasionally playing with the children, occasionally 'helping' with the housework, or 'allowing' her to see family and/or friends can all keep up hopes that things may change.

A violent man will often also seek to justify his behaviour and convince an abused woman that she is in some way at fault through her own behaviour or that he is doing it because he loves her. Some women may start, like hostages, to identify with the abuser's distorted perspective on why the violence occurs, partly as a means of survival. We accept that it may take prisoners of war many years to recover, if they ever can fully recover, yet most people find it hard to understand the impact of living with violence at home. The variety and wide range of methods used to undermine women's confidence, to put them down and prevent them from leaving, can be so pervasive that it is hard to believe that women do survive and manage to make the break.

As well as physical injury and disability, domestic violence may result in depression, mental illness or attempted suicide. Many women feel their situation is hopeless and experience disrupted patterns of eating and sleeping. Others have high levels of anxiety and experience panic attacks. Women also describe feeling demoralised, degraded, afraid, worthless, ashamed, angry and emotionally and physically drained (Women's Aid Federation of England 1989).

Nevertheless, if they are able to get away from the abusive situation, these effects can sometimes disappear very quickly and women survivors can display surprising resilience and hopefulness of spirit once they are safe. For many women, the experience of living in refuges, despite the difficulties, offers an opportunity to share experiences, to support and help each other, that can be both empowering and healing. For others, domestic violence can have long-term psychological effects that require more than mutual self-help, crisis counselling and support. In such cases, any longer term individual counselling or group work must be set within a feminist understanding of the nature of domestic violence that challenges victim-blaming stereotypes and myths.

UNDERSTANDING WHY IT HAPPENS

Many myths exist in popular culture (as well as amongst professionals) about the causes of domestic violence:

(1) That women's behaviour in some way causes abuse;

(2) That women provoke it;

(3) That women are bad housekeepers;

(4) That women enjoy abuse, and this is part of a particular sexual dynamic;

(5) That it only occurs in problem families, or in working-class or poor families;

(6) That it is caused by alcohol dependency, or poor anger management;

(7) That it is part of the normal give and take of family life;

(8) That women's sufferings are exaggerated.

Although all these myths are countered by research (Smith 1990), they continue to have currency. For women desperately seeking explanations for what is going on, these myths can seem to offer a possible way out: 'If only he could give up drinking'; 'If only he could get a job'; 'If only I could be a better wife and mother.'

When refuges were first set up in the early 1970s to tackle the problem of domestic violence, Women's Aid was often the only agency trying to meet the needs of women and children experiencing abuse, and challenge the victim-blaming stereotypes. Our long-standing approach has been to believe and support women and their children, and to understand the causes of abuse in the gender-based power relations existing within traditional models of family life. One hundred years ago it was legal to beat your wife in western countries. Now it is not, but many beliefs about men's right to chastise women still persist. Work since the early 1980s with abusive men in programmes for perpetrators in the United States and elsewhere confirms our approach. Domestic violence is intentional behaviour, based on an abusive man's belief that he has the right to control 'his' woman. Whilst other personal and situational factors and experiences may mediate his abusive behaviour, these beliefs originate from and are reinforced by everyday social attitudes. In one study in Islington, only 37 per cent of men did not see violence against their partners as an option, and 17 per cent admitted they had struck their partners (Mooney 1994).

The detailed description of the range of abuse women experience also helps to counteract mistaken perceptions that 'family violence' is equally carried out by men and women. (For a critique of 'Conflict Tactics Scale' and 'family violence' theories see Hague and Malos 1993; Dobash and Dobash 1992.) Violent and abusive behaviours cannot be divorced from the social context in which they occur – that of historically unequal relationships between men and women enshrined in laws and social structures, about which many traditional attitudes and beliefs about the respective (different) rights of men and women within, and outside, the family still persist.

WHY DO WOMEN PUT UP WITH VIOLENCE?

One reason is that it is very difficult for women to speak out about abuse. Abused women often blame themselves; they feel guilty about talking about family life outside the home; they feel ashamed that this has happened to them. Women may fear retaliation if they tell; they don't know if they are going to be believed; they don't know if they are going to be pressured to take action and they almost always fear that their children will be taken away. There are also many conflicts in relation to children. There is a pressure to keep the family together, both from women themselves and from others. Women may be seen by children as being responsible for the situation, especially if the man blames the woman, though this may differ amongst siblings, dependent on their treatment by their fathers. Men use children as a threat. It is very common for them to threaten abused women that the children will be taken into care, or that they will lose them if they tell anyone about the violence. But women's concerns about the effects of domestic violence on children, either witnessing it or experiencing it, are often, in fact, the key catalyst to leave and to seek help.

The reasons women stay in an abusive relationship include both love and terror. They may love the man but they hate the violence and abuse. They are often concerned about their children's well-being, education, welfare and safety if they leave. There are also many practical difficulties. Most women do not know where they can go: emergency housing is scarce; refuges are often full; many women do not know that they have any independent rights to money – if they have been dependent on their husband's income they may not know that they have a right to income support in their own name.

DIFFERENCE AND IDENTITY: COMPOUNDING FACTORS

We know that domestic violence cuts across all classes and communities. Yet, aspects of a woman's identity can be used against her in an abusive and undermining way. If she is being both abused and discriminated against on several levels, there are many additional difficulties to be faced and decisions to be made.

For black and ethnic minority women there are particular reasons why they may find it difficult to leave, or to seek help from agencies. They may be torn by family and cultural loyalties or fear ostracism or reprisals from their community. They may fear losing their cultural identity. There may be language barriers to accessing help and there are very few interpreting services in most of the formal agencies to which women may turn for help. It is often hard for black women to develop their own formal support and specialist services in the face of allegations of disloyalty within the community. They may have experienced racist treatment in the past from agencies such as the police or social services (Mama 1989) and therefore have expectations of racism if they seek help. They may fear deportation if their immigration status is used against them. Immigration regulations mean that some black women are unable to have access to the 'public purse' – housing, benefits, legal aid – and may be forced to stay with a violent partner who may hold their passport.

Women with physical, mental and psychological disabilities are often targets for sexual exploitation and abuse. Common perceptions of disabled women as non-sexual reinforce the power of men who abuse disabled women and such women often find that they are not believed. Yet the same level of violence can be perpetrated against women with disabilities as is perpetrated against able-bodied and able-minded women. Disabled women may be physically and emotionally threatened by abusive carers, who may withhold care, or medical care. Common feelings of rejection by society can reinforce the strength of the threats made by abusive carers. Women may be denied access to information about help by their carers, or such help may be inaccessible to them.

Lesbian women can be subjected to violence in much the same way as heterosexual women are, with the added burden of isolation caused through the social stigma of choosing a partner of the same sex. This violence may come from a male ex-partner or from a woman partner. Homophobic attitudes are prevalent and lesbians often encounter statements such as, 'She brought it upon herself.' It is not uncommon for men to subject lesbians to harassment, intimidation and physical and sexual violence as a way of humiliating them. Male ex-partners of women who are involved in lesbian relationships are often abusive and violent. This is often done in the name of 'teaching them a lesson'. It is particularly difficult for lesbians to ask for assistance because they are convinced they will not be treated sympathetically; being honest about their sexuality is already likely to have led to some form of physical or emotional abuse. Lesbians fear the possibility of a negative and unhelpful response from statutory agencies. Lesbians who are also mothers may fear losing their children should they report violence. Courts rarely give residence to mothers who are 'out' as lesbian, regardless of how good they are at parenting.

For women in rural areas the lack of infrastructure, poor transport, few support services, combined with their greater visibility, leave them vulnerable

– especially where key community leaders or agency representatives may be colleagues or friends of their abuser.

All women have particular problems and difficulties in taking effective action. To contemplate leaving their home, belongings, security, to go to an unknown destination is extremely difficult and it is a tribute to the courage of abused women that they often manage to do so.

MAKING THE BREAK: WOMEN LEAVING VIOLENCE

To get free from abuse, women need to be listened to, believed and have their experiences taken seriously. They need support, empathy, a non-judgemental approach and sensitivity to their different needs and experiences. Whilst it is important not to generalise about any woman's particular needs, at some point most may need the following:

(1) Information about where to get help and support;

(2) An emergency place of safety (for example, a refuge);

(3) Legal advice and protection;

(4) Long-term safe accommodation;

(5) Sanctions against their abuser;

(6) Financial support;

(7) Help and support for making safe arrangements for children.

Getting free of abuse is a lengthy process. Support over a prolonged period is often an important element in surviving domestic violence. Since the early 1970s, the role of Women's Aid has been to provide – through refuges, outreach and other support services – empowerment of abused women through mutual support and self-help with other women who have shared the same experiences:

> I used to be ashamed to talk about battering to people. I can really talk openly here because they've all been through the same thing.
>
> When I first left home, it happened in the night, and when I went to the police they put me in Homeless for the night. Of course I had an eye out here, and I had marks round my neck. The people they were looking at me and we were like fugitives there, hid away in our rooms. You know you want to cry, you want to ... you don't really know what's the matter with you, everything's so bad. If you go into a refuge you know that them other women that's in there have had it too, so you don't feel so bad and you can let out your feelings 'cos you know those people understand. They know exactly what you've gone through. (Binney *et al.* 1981)

Women's needs for help and support will vary over time, and we must not assume that we know best what any woman may need at any given point. A woman may request information about where she can get help but she may not use that information or take any tangible action for several weeks, months, even years afterwards, as she tries to balance the risks, dangers and advantages of different strategies or actions. It is often difficult for women to know who to trust. Some women may want police intervention, others may feel better protected by getting an injunction or leaving altogether. To help this process it is important that agencies should give women full information so that they can make their own choices based on their own needs.

Seeking help

When women do first try to talk about the violence, it is usually to a friend or close family member. In some cases they will be believed and supported; in others, especially in cases where there are no visible injuries or where the man has a charming and likeable public image, the woman may be regarded as causing trouble or exaggerating the problem. When women first try to get away, or to signal to their partner that they want the violence to stop, they are most likely to stay with family or friends. This rarely provides more than a temporary solution as they are often found and pressured to return.

Most women try to seek help or leave a number of times before they finally make the break. Women may try a range of agencies – health professionals, police, social services, housing departments and other bodies – but until very recently have received an inadequate response. The exception has been the responses from Women's Aid and women's voluntary sector services, who have consistently rated more highly in user feedback and numerous research studies since the early 1970s.

Some of the general difficulties encountered by women before they contact local refuges or the Women's Aid National Helpline can include a lack of understanding and support, unsympathetic and disbelieving responses and not being given information about their rights or other sources of support, for example, rights to help with emergency housing or information about specialist advocacy services like Women's Aid.

Until relatively recently, very few agencies had specific protocols on domestic violence or training in good practice. Women are often covertly blamed or men's behaviour condoned or excused and there has been an emphasis on keeping the family together. Meeting the needs of abused women does not form part of the statutory duty of these agencies and active intervention is often only aimed at the welfare of the children. Their needs are always important but such responses can serve to reinforce men's threats and women's fears that women will lose their children. However, there have been significant changes since the mid-1980s, partly as a result of the police and Home Office recognition of domestic violence as a crime and the development of formalised multi-agency work on domestic violence, but also because of the continuous pressure for change coming from activists in and outside the Women's Aid movement. Whilst these changes are most welcome and women's options for police intervention and help have improved in many parts of the country, we have also seen the negative impact of a number of social policy initiatives – social security, family policy, housing, immigration policy – which have created new obstacles for women trying to end violent relationships. Government initiatives in the criminal justice field have not been co-ordinated as a part of a strategy across other areas of social welfare response, especially refuge provision and advocacy services, and therefore we still provide a piecemeal response to domestic violence.

Somewhere safe to stay

Access to safe, secure permanent housing is one of the most important needs of women getting free from domestic violence. Since the early 1970s, the Women's Aid movement has provided a network of refuges offering emergency and temporary accommodation for women and children as well as other services. In areas where refuge provision is insufficient or non-existent, women may stay in local-authority bed and breakfast accommodation or hostels, but this does not provide the same level of support (James-Hanman 1995). Women are then faced with a number of options. Legal remedies, such as injunctions, can help some women oust a violent partner and return home but for the majority this option is ineffective and most do not feel safe going back to the same property.

Most refuge users who have decided to make the break prefer to make a fresh start and seek help from local-authority housing departments. Recent changes in homelessness law mean that, while women with children are still seen as homeless if they suffer domestic violence and are eligible for help with temporary accommodation, rights to help with long-term permanent housing have now been eroded. Finding long-term safe and secure ac-commodation is an increasing problem. Even in the north of England where they have traditionally been able to be rehoused within three months of going to a refuge, women are now having to wait up to a year. In London it is routinely two years. This creates a blockage in refuge emergency accommodation which undermines the service Women's Aid is trying to provide. Communal living for such long periods can also put intolerable pressure on women and children, though many value the support and safety.

In practice, local-authority responses vary enormously across the country; some women receive very sympathetic treatment from housing departments with clear policies and good training; other local authorities operate policies of 'minimal compliance' with housing law and the Code of Guidance. In practice this means excluding women without children or cases where the violence is coming from a non-resident partner or ex-partner, or women are advised to get injunctions and return home.

LEGAL PROTECTION

Protection under the criminal law has been the main focus of government action against domestic violence since 1990. The police have a key role as a 24-hour agency and as law enforcers, and with the development of domestic violence units across the country, women have had a much better response from police, though regionally this can vary. However, some women will hesitate about calling the police for a range of reasons. First, women can be extremely ambivalent about the whole issue of action under the criminal law – calling the police, going to court and being a witness to a prosecution. They may still love the man; they may not want him to have a criminal record; in some cases it may actually have a negative effect on their family income, if she ends up having to pay the fine herself; black and ethnic minority women are often ambivalent about whether they call the police or not because of concerns about police racism or community loyalties. Second, arrest and prosecution of a violent man rarely offers more than short-term protection to abused women. It takes a long time to go to court, and outcomes at court are often very unsatisfactory – usually a bind-over, or fine or a suspended sentence, with women often being left unprotected in the longer term.

To date, the criminal law has only been able to address the physical violence that has already happened; it can rarely provide protection from what might occur, or deal with sexual and psychological abuse. Women also need to be able to use the civil law, so that they can gain protection in advance. However, this too can be a problem:

> The first injunctions I got did not have power of arrest and was no good at all. My ex-husband came to my home on a number of occasions. Each time I phoned the police, he had gone by the time the police arrived. All they said was they would have to catch him on my premises first, even then they could only tell him to leave. I then applied to the courts for an injunction with a power of arrest, which I got. My ex-husband came back this time, and the police caught him, he was taken to court and given three months in prison for breaking the injunction and for actual bodily harm to me.
>
> After he came out of prison he still pestered me, I then applied for another injunction, which I was granted. The judge warned him if he broke it, he would be given a longer prison sentence. The same night he came back, smashed his way into my home. Twenty minutes later the police arrived by which time I was bleeding from head and face wounds and my leg was broke. He was arrested but let out on bail the same day. When he was took to court he was given six months in prison for breaking the injunction and for actual bodily harm to me. It couldn't be proved how I broke my leg because I had fallen down the stairs to get away from my ex-husband, so the judge ruled that it was my own fault, so he wasn't given any time for that. I have never applied for an injunction since, in my opinion they are a waste of time. (Women's Aid Federation of England 1988)

Injunctions against domestic violence were first introduced as free-standing remedies in 1976 but have been shown since then to be frequently ineffective in protecting women and children from violence. One of the main problems has been enforcement, partly because of courts' reluctance to attach police powers of arrest, partly because committal is rarely given and there are therefore no effective sanctions. Research shows that women often feel exhausted and frustrated by the process of trying to get injunctions (Barron 1990). Recent measures to improve and strengthen protection will be implemented in October 1997, as part of the 1996 Family Law Act. However, there may still be problems for several reasons:

(1) Under the new Legal Aid regulations, many women will not qualify for Legal Aid unless they are on income support and few women can afford £2000 for an injunction that may not work;

(2) Domestic violence awareness training is needed for the judiciary to improve understanding of the real dangers women and children face before they prescribe stronger remedies;

(3) The Children's Act must be brought in line so that women who have sought legal protection are not pressured to meet with violent ex-partners for the purposes of making and managing arrangements for contact with children.

KEEPING CHILDREN SAFE

Approximately two out of every three women who come into Women's Aid refuges, or who contact Women's Aid for advice and support, have young children who will almost certainly have been affected by the abuse their mother has suffered. We also know that over 150,000 women who contact Women's Aid each year are just the tip of the iceberg and many more children who experience the effects of violence do not come to our attention. Some of these children will have witnessed abuse, or actively tried to intervene to stop it, or will feel insecure and fearful without necessarily knowing why this is. A proportion of these children will themselves have been abused, physically or sexually, by their fathers, stepfathers or other adults (Stark and Flitcraft 1988). Social services may be involved and, however sensitive the social workers may be, the effect is likely to increase feelings of insecurity.

Research has confirmed Women's Aid experience of the impact and difficulties faced by children who have survived domestic violence (Jaffe *et al.* 1991; NCH Action for Children 1995). Table 7.2 lists some of these effects.

Even after a woman has left an abusive relationship, there are new difficulties to face, including sorting out benefits, housing and any legal matters, which all affect children directly and indirectly, and this exacerbates other problems. Prolonged stays in temporary accommodation carry health and safety risks and the stress associated with these risks.

Table 7.2. Effects of domestic violence on children

stress-related illnesses	confused and torn loyalties (i.e. to both mother and father)	fear of a repetition of or return to violence
unnaturally good behaviour	taking on the mother role	an acceptance of abuse as 'normal'
guilt	isolation	shame
anger	lack of confidence	lack of trust

When children come into a refuge with their mothers, they leave behind their home and many of their possessions. This results in them losing friends, who they may never see again, and needing to make new friends, in the refuge and at a new school. Other children go with their mothers into temporary accommodation, often a cramped room in a bed and breakfast hotel, with no facilities at all for children.

For women leaving abusive men, caring for children and trying to keep them safe can be very stressful, especially at a time when they are themselves feeling insecure or anxious. Work with children in Women's Aid refuges, which has been independently evaluated, has shown how important it is to provide positive attention and specialist services for children leaving an abusive situation, and how this can have a beneficial effect on children's sense of well-being and sense of self (Ball 1990). Domestic violence and child abuse frequently co-exist, but until recently child protection strategies did not take domestic violence into consideration, often leading to the worst child protection outcomes (Farmer and Owen 1995). Where there is child abuse, supporting abused women, as the non-abusing parent, is the best way to keep children free of abuse.

Sometimes, when a woman has left a violent relationship, taking her children with her, her partner will dispute her right to have the children live with her. Almost certainly he will want to have contact with the children. In some cases, the woman will be happy for this to happen and arrangements may be made without the need to go to court (in line with the presumptions of the Children's Act 1989). In many cases, however, where there has been domestic violence and in particular when the children have themselves been abused by their father, the woman will have good reasons to fear his attempts to see them. Sometimes the children themselves do not want to have any contact with their father and sometimes any contact will put the woman at risk, as it will reveal her whereabouts. In 85 per cent of cases, women and their children are further abused following contact orders made under the Children's Act 1989 (Hester and Radford 1996). Most of the women wanted their children to have contact with their fathers but they wanted this to be safe contact. Unfortunately, family proceedings still tend to ignore the continuing dangers facing women who have experienced domestic violence. Where contact is awarded to abusive fathers and the mothers feel the children will be neglected or abused on contact visits, this can sometimes lead to women feeling forced to be present during contact to protect the child or even, sometimes, going back home to live.

STARTING AGAIN

Leaving an abusive relationship is a long process that can take many years. Even then harassment may not stop and many women are traced through their address being given out in court proceedings or by other means. Whilst not all women continue to face threats, harassment and sometimes life-threatening violence long after they have left their violent partner, many do experience the mixed blessings of starting again. Life can be hard, especially if they are now living on benefit, or in low-income, part-time work because of lack of child-care provision. Many women find they have been rehoused on hard-to-let estates, with few amenities and inadequate resources to manage:

> The school playleader came round and says: 'Oh you've not got a carpet.' – I says: 'I know I haven't.' She says: 'Why not?' and I says: 'I can't slap a bit of Axminster between two pieces of bread and say to my kids there's your tea!' (Binney *et al.* 1981)

But equally, escape from violence has meant the freedom for many women to live their lives without fear of violence, and to make a new start:

> You're your own boss. Nobody to pick you up on your faults and give you a black eye for it. You can shop for what you need and the kids can go on school trips and to youth clubs. (Binney *et al.* 1981)

THE CHALLENGE OF MULTI-AGENCY WORKING TO END VIOLENCE AGAINST WOMEN

The needs of abused women – for information, advice, legal protection, emergency refuge, permanent accommodation, financial support and safe arrangements for children – cross the boundaries of agency roles and services. We need a multi-agency approach that can:

(1) Prioritise women's and children's safety;

(2) Support women's empowerment and choices;

(3) Deliver specific and appropriate integrated services;

(4) Offer effective legal protection within the civil and the criminal law;

(5) Develop strategies for dealing with perpetrators;

(6) Raise community awareness of the issue.

In effective multi-agency working, all agencies – including health services, local authority housing and social services, police and other criminal justice agencies, community workers and benefits agencies and, of course, the women's voluntary sector – need to develop clear policies and monitor practice. We have to be prepared to challenge and change existing assumptions and practices. We must be aware of and emphasise the social roots of domestic violence, not individual inadequacies, in all our policies, guidelines, training and practice. Domestic violence has existed for a very long time and is rooted in very ingrained and deep social assumptions about relationships between men and women and our respective rights and abilities.

For all of us addressing the question of domestic violence, of woman abuse, means that we have to grapple with our own notions and expectations of family life, of intimate relationships, and with our own feelings and experiences of power and abuse. It presents a very personal challenge to all of us which we must confront at the same time as we attempt to improve laws and develop services, if we are to ensure the safety and empowerment of abused women and children in their own homes.

REFERENCES

Ball, M. (1990) *Children's Workers in Women's Aid Refuges: A Report on the Experience of Nine Refuges in England.* Bristol: Women's Aid Federation (England) (WAFE)

Barron, J. (1990) *Not Worth the Paper . . . ? The Effectiveness of Legal Protection for Women and Children Experiencing Domestic Violence.* Bristol: Women's Aid Federation of England

Binney, V., Harkell, G. and Nixon, J. (1981) *Leaving Violent Men: A Study of Refuges and Housing for Abused Women.* Bristol: Women's Aid Federation of England

Dobash, R.E. and Dobash, R.P (1992) *Women, Violence and Social Change.* London: Routledge

Farmer, E. and Owen, M. (1994) *Child Protection Practice: Private Risks and Public Remedies – Decision Making, Intervention and Outcome in Child Protection Work.* London: HMSO

Hague, G. and Malos, E. (1993) *Domestic Violence: Action for Change.* Cheltenham: New Clarion Press

Hester, M. and Radford, L. (1996) *Domestic Violence and Child Contact Arrangements in England and Denmark.* Bristol: Policy Press

Home Office (1995) *Domestic Violence Homicide Factsheet 1990–1994.* London: Home Office

Homer, M., Leonard, A. E. and Taylor, M. P. (1988) *Private Violence: Public Shame.* Bristol: Women's Aid Federation of England

Jaffe, P. *et al.* (1991) *Children of Battered Women.* California: Sage

James-Hanman, D. (1995) Unpublished paper for Islington Women's Equality Unit, London

Mama, A. (1989) *The Hidden Struggle: Statutory and Voluntary Responses to Violence Against Black Women in the Home.* London: Runnymede Trust

Mayhew, P., Maung, N.A. and Mirrlees-Black, C. (1993) *The 1992 British Crime Survey.* London: HMSO

Mooney, J. (1994) *The Hidden Figure: Domestic Violence in North London.* London: Islington Police and Crime Prevention Unit

NCH Action for Children (1994) *The Hidden Victims: Children and Domestic Violence.* London: NCH Action for Children

NiCarthy, G. (1988) *Getting Free: a Handbook for Women in Abusive Situations.* London: Journeyman

Smith, L.J. (1990) *Domestic Violence: An Overview of the Literature.* London: HMSO

Stark, E. and Flitcraft, A. (1988) Women and children at risk: a feminist perspective on child abuse. *International Journal of Health Services* **9**, 461–53

Women's Aid Federation of England (1988) *Women and Children in Refuges: You Can't Beat a Woman.* Bristol: Women's Aid Federation of England

Women's Aid Federation of England (1989) *Women's Education Project. Breaking Through: Women Surviving Male Violence.* Bristol: Women's Aid Federation of England

Women's Aid Federation of England (1996) Report from Annual Survey of Refuges and Helpline Services (unpublished)

Chapter 8

Domestic violence – a physician's perspective

Richard F. Jones III

Domestic violence occurs in 25 per cent of American homes each year, affecting at least four million battered women in the United States. When wife abuse is present, at least 50 per cent of their children are also abused. When child abuse is present, at least 50 per cent of their mothers are abused. Battering can be the cause of up to 30 per cent of Emergency Room visits by women, but fewer than one out of ten such women are identified by emergency department personnel (Stark *et al.* 1981). Over 2000 women each year are murdered in association with battering (30 per cent female homicides) and at least 25 per cent of women suicides in this country are related to battering. Battering occurs in as many as 25 per cent of America's homes each year.

There is no typical victim and no woman who is immune. Ninety-five per cent of battered partners are women, and their batterers are overwhelmingly men. However, it is estimated that there are approximately 100,000 men who are battered in their relationships. This is undoubtedly an under-reported figure.

MEDICAL IDENTIFICATION OF DOMESTIC VIOLENCE

Although the medical community in the United States is responding, it has been a 'hard sell'. Domestic violence is underdiagnosed in Emergency Rooms and general medical settings (Kurz 1990) where, although the diagnosis was made about 3 per cent of the time, it should have been made 25 per cent of the time. Physicians are not responsive to abuse problems in the Emergency Room. One study (Kurz 1990) reported that in 40 per cent of abuse cases, the physician did not respond. In another emergency department, physicians failed to give any referral or follow-up planning in 92 per cent of domestic violence cases. Ninety per cent of women who are abused do not discuss this with their physician and over 50 per cent don't discuss this with anyone. But the real problem is that **physicians don't ask!**

Surgeon General Koop (1985) declared that domestic violence is a public health epidemic affecting the lives of millions. The direct cost to society is enormous in terms of medical expense and time lost in the workplace. The social and personal 'cost' to battered women and men is incalculable.

If domestic violence is as important a health factor as smoking cessation and use of seat belts, then why have physicians been reluctant to include this problem as part of routine queries in their offices and clinics? Would any other condition that resulted in this much illness be neglected by medicine? One would think that the ethical principles of respect for persons, autonomy, beneficence and non-maleficence would lend further impetus to the involvement of physicians. So, the question is: **Why?** Why don't physicians ask the question?

In the first place, physicians, like everyone else, are a product of their own particular environment: their gender, their age, their culture, their education, their family, their religion, their economic and social situation, their own exposure to violence in the home, and so on.

As such they believe many of the following myths that non-physicians believe:

(1) Battering occurs infrequently;

(2) Battering is limited to certain women;

(3) Battering is a private matter;

(4) Battering is caused by drinking and drugs;

(5) Battering is not a crime;

(6) Battered women cause their abuse;

(7) Battered women can just leave;

(8) Once a victim, always a victim;

(9) Once a batterer, always a batterer.

Yet even when the myths are dispelled, reluctance persists. Physicians understand the ethical principles mentioned earlier but are troubled by the competing principles of respect for privacy and confidentiality. Physicians may also be reluctant to endanger their patients since, in some States, there is mandatory reporting of domestic violence. Further, physicians are concerned that documentation in the medical records will take time and may involve them in future legal entanglements such as testifying in court.

Sugg (1992) studied 38 primary-care physicians in an effort to uncover the barriers to domestic violence intervention. Most didn't want to become involved with this issue because it 'opened a can of worms' or 'opened Pandora's box', unleashing a myriad of evils. Other reasons cited included:

(1) Too close for comfort;

(2) Fear of offending;

(3) Powerlessness;

(4) Loss of control;

(5) Time constraints.

Describing these obstacles in greater detail, Sugg found that physicians who come from a white, middle-class background, with no experience of domestic violence, often assumed that patients with similar backgrounds would not be at risk of violence. These physicians were more inclined to ask patients of lower economic status about abuse even though research has shown that this economic bias is largely unfounded.

There is no reason to suspect that the prevalence of child abuse (either direct or witnessed) among future physicians is any more or less than that of any other segment of children. Further, it is well known that in any hierarchical system (the military, for example) or institution, abuse may occur.

Komaromy and colleagues (1993) sent questionnaires to 133 residents in internal medicine at the University of California at San Francisco, asking about abuse. When asked about a previous history of child abuse or physical violence with an intimate partner, 14 per cent of male physicians and 31 per cent of female physicians acknowledged this as a personal problem and 73 per cent of female residents had been harassed during their training. Thus, physicians are not immune to abuse and for those physicians so affected, this may prevent them from making the necessary enquiries of their patients and describing the issue openly.

Over 50 per cent of the physicians in Sugg's (1992) study felt that questions about domestic violence might offend their patients. Some felt that such questions might betray or jeopardise the doctor–patient relationship. Those experienced in this work know that patients are almost always pleased and relieved that their doctor makes the effort and cares enough to ask. Many physicians voiced frustration and feelings of inadequacy when discussing intervention or they felt they had inadequate 'tools' to 'fix' the problem, 61 per cent saying they had no formal training in this area. Forty-two per cent of physicians felt frustration because patients would not change their circumstances in spite of being advised to do so. Hence, attempts at intervention were useless. Further, medical paternalism is still around. Many physicians still believe that they should be in a position to tell patients what to do (even if benevolently) and, moreover, that patients should follow their advice. These physicians feel powerless to control their patients' actions and are not content merely to educate and advocate.

Physicians are also concerned that enquiry into such matters can involve a significant time commitment that may not be reimbursed by the patient or her insurance carrier. They also feel that this problem occurs so infrequently that routine questioning is a waste of time.

Experienced physicians know that routine questioning is not time consuming. In fact, in the long run early diagnosis may decrease the number of visits required in order to investigate vague, non-specific psychosomatic complaints and possibly reduce irrelevant or unnecessary treatment.

THE PHYSICIAN'S ROLE

First, all patients must be asked about domestic violence, rather than limiting the questions to certain types of patients or just to obviously injured patients. Such limitations will miss many of those affected.

Physicians should attend lectures on this issue to learn about how to take a history and do an examination on these patients. They need to know how these patients present. What about injury maps? They need to be familiar with documentation and reporting and know what to look for in gynaecologic or obstetric patients. If a patient is going to be asked the question, the interviewer must be prepared to respond to both the 'Yes' and the 'No' answer.

If the patient answers 'Yes,' the physician may wish to follow up on their response by asking:

(1) Would you like to talk about what has happened to you?

(2) How do you feel about it?

(3) What would you like to do about this?

In some ways the 'No' answer is even more complicated, particularly if the physician believes that the patient has been battered. But the physician must be willing to step back and try to understand the patient's perspective. A variety of explanations may pertain:

(1) Trust relationship not yet established;

(2) Inappropriate setting;

(3) Lack of privacy and confidentiality;

(4) Inappropriate history taking;

(5) Inappropriate format;

(6) Not emotionally ready;

(7) Acceptance of blame;

(8) Admission of failure;

(9) Fear of rejection;

(10) Feels ashamed;

(11) Fantasy it will not happen again;

(12) Fear of reprisal and escalation;

(13) Believes no viable alternatives exist;

(14) Believes no solution to her problem;

(15) Unaware of community resources.

Once the diagnosis is made the physician must assess the degree of injury and current danger. This should also include an assessment of the entire family at risk: children, other dependants such as elders, etc. (Salber and Taliaferro 1995).

Finally, a safety plan should be discussed with the patient:

(1) Is it safe to go home?

(2) Are the children/other dependants safe?

(3) Is there a need for immediate sheltering?

(4) Are there family/friends to stay with?

(5) Is there a need for urgent crisis counselling?

(6) Does she know about community resources?

(7) Is there a specific plan for a quick exit?

The physician should try to evaluate the severity of the situation through specific enquiry, for example, in the following ways (Campbell 1986):

(1) Has your partner ever threatened to kill you, your children, your relatives or himself?

(2) Are there weapons in the house?

(3) Does your partner abuse alcohol or use drugs?

(4) Is your partner violent outside the home?

(5) Does your partner hurt the family pets?

(6) Were you beaten when you were pregnant?

(7) Has the violence increased in frequency or severity over the last year?

Finally, it may be useful to prepare an 'action plan' with the patient. This should include:

(1) Providing phone numbers – police, rescue squad, Domestic Violence Hotline;

(2) Spare pair of keys – home and car;

(3) Emergency money;

(4) Essential documents.

Clear and detailed documentation of medical records is imperative. Correctly done, it may save the physician time in court and may be critically important to the patient. The records should include the following details:

(1) Date, time of domestic violence incident;

(2) Patient identifying information;

(3) Patient's statements;

(4) Findings on physical examination;

(5) Medical opinion/diagnosis;

(6) Treatment required;

(7) Follow-up and referral plans;

(8) Photographs taken at the time with the patient's consent, where appropriate.

As physicians, our involvement in this issue must go beyond aiding the individual patient in the clinic setting. Each of us must become an agent of change, ensuring that our offices and clinics are safe and sensitive places where patients can get help.

We must educate ourselves about the resources in our communities and must be actively involved in our local groups and shelters. We must be positive examples for our residents and students and have zero tolerance for abuse in the work place as well as in the homes of our patients.

These observations reflect a United States perspective. Whilst this perspective may be similar to many other countries, societal norms vary enormously. Further, in many parts of the world physicians are not as influential as they are in the United States. In courts that are dominated by men, in countries where women are regarded as little more than possessions, these observations on domestic violence may be viewed as unrealistic and parochial at best. Nevertheless, we must start somewhere. Society, all of us, must 'own' this problem because it is everyone's problem.

REFERENCES

Campbell, J.C. (1986) Nursing assessment for risk of homicide with battered women. *Advances in Nursing Science* **8**, 36–51

Komaromy, M., Bindman, A.B., Haber, R.J. and Sande, M.A. (1993) Sexual harassment in medical training. *N Engl J Med* **328**, 322–6

Kurz, D. (1990) Interventions with battered women in health care settings. *Victims and Violence* **5**, 243–56

Salber, P. and Taliaferro, E. (1995) *The Physician's Guide to Domestic Violence*. Volcano, CA: Volcano Press

Stark, E., Flitcraft, A., Zuckerman, D., Grey, A., Robinson, J. and Frazier, W. (1981) *Domestic Violence: Wife Abuse in the Medical Setting. Monograph 7*. Washington, DC: Office of Domestic Violence

Sugg, N.K. and Inui, T. (1992) Primary care physicians' response to domestic violence: opening Pandora's box. *JAMA* **267**, 3194–5

Surgeon General (1985) *Report of the Surgeon General's Workshop on Violence and Public Health*. Washington, DC: US Department of Health and Human Services

Chapter 9

The abused woman

Discussion

Walker: I wondered whether Richard Jones thought that the different healthcare system in the United States has relevance as to how our Royal College should react? In the UK, the obstetrician and gynaecologist is neither a public health physician nor a primary care physician, nor is he responsible for the continuing lifelong care of women. He acts as a specialist who is referred to, usually to address a specific obstetric or gynaecological issue, to provide an episode of care. He then returns that individual woman to the care of her primary health physician. The question is, do you think that within our healthcare system, the role of obstetric and gynaecological consultants is different?

Jones: The short answer is that I do not believe it makes any difference at all. The somewhat longer answer is that you are primarily a physician and a consultant specialist secondarily, at least in my view. It seems to me that it is incumbent on any physician whose obligation is beneficence, non-malificence and respect for persons, to look after the total care of his patient, i.e. if you see a woman who you think may have a problem, it is easy enough to ask. I see myself as a specialist as well, and I see patients referred to me all the time by family doctors. I sometimes ask the questions other doctors have not but that I very much feel all doctors should ask. Interestingly enough, in our country, ophthalmologists, who you would think would be uniquely focused on just one area, ask about domestic violence because they see orbital injuries and they know that one common cause of a busted orbit is that the patient has been punched in the eye.

Another reason it is important is that a very common cause of pelvic pain is stress. Let me give you an example. A woman came to our office about a month ago. She had a large vulval haematoma. I went to examine her and the haematoma was turning yellow/green, meaning that this did not happen yesterday. Most women with a vulval haematoma would come to the office immediately. Once upon a time, I would have said to her, as a specialist, 'How did you get this?' and she would have told me that she was riding her son's bicycle and she slipped under the bar of the bicycle, or she was putting up the curtains and fell on the step-ladder. She would have known that I did not want to know, so she would not have told me. Instead, I went round to the head of the examination table and I said, 'This injury occurred some time ago, didn't it?' and she said, 'Yes, doctor.' I said, 'Did somebody at home do this to you?' and she said, 'Yes, my husband hit me with a hammer.' Now, the patient had been referred to me as a specialist for treatment of the vulval haematoma. Once upon a time, I would have treated the vulval haematoma as a vulval haematoma and sent her on her way. This way, because I knew something about this issue, I was able to ask her specifically what had happened, and who did it and I was able to refer her on to the proper agency.

My point is that I do not see how you can get out of the loop. It always has to be part of every health professional's armoury. I am often asked by people, 'Aren't you putting yourself in some danger from the batterers?' My answer to that one is that batterers are very much into understanding authority and control; that is their game. I do not think we are in much danger. I have only been threatened once.

In terms of how the patients feel, it is a very strong message to a battered woman when her doctor asks the right question, tells her, for example, 'This is not your fault, it is his problem, not yours,' and then starts to discuss the issue with her. It is a very strong message when a figure in authority is on her side, takes time to explain and to understand her.

Harwin: That is the point. The issue came on the public agenda because there were women addressing issues for women, doing things for women. Refuges started by women coming to women centres and saying, 'I can't go home, can I sleep on the floor?' and women there saying, 'Yes,' and accepting, believing them, taking them seriously. The fundamental thing is recognising that this is a real issue, that can be happening to anybody who might come to you and that you will only know if you give that person the opportunity to say what is happening to them. The most important thing is to do it, exactly as you were saying, in a very routine way.

We do not have any health visitors at this conference which is a pity because, over the years, the only health professionals who have consistently identified domestic violence and referred women to refuges have been health visitors. I know that, in some areas of the country now, they are starting to ask routinely: 'Are you frightened of the person you are living with? Have you been hit or threatened?', even when there is no obvious evidence.

Friend: I would like to ask Richard Jones how much influence this approach has had on his colleagues in obstetrics and gynaecology in the States, in relation to getting them to do what we all feel should be done. A second point is that, in the United States, there are some areas where it is mandatory both to document and to report domestic violence. Does he feel this is of benefit or not?

Jones: The educational part of the campaign does appear to have influenced the physician community. In 1990 we did a survey of obstetricians and gynaecologists and 6 per cent said they asked about domestic violence. We asked the same question last year, and 90 per cent said they asked the question; at least that is a start.

In terms of documentation and reporting, these are two different things with different requirements. Documentation is critical and sometimes will save the woman's life. Physicians are always worried about the documentation issue because they do not want to go to court and it is too much bother, but if the records are complete, the records will go to court and the physician does not have to testify.

Reporting is another hot issue, as I am sure it is here. In the United States, if you are aged under 18 or over 65, there is mandatory reporting and, of course, if somebody is incompetent and they have been harmed, that has to be reported. That has to do with informed consent-type issues. Between 18 and 65 there is a big debate around this. Five states now have mandatory reporting. All states require reporting for felonies. We had a woman with an ice-pick stuck in her pregnant abdomen last winter, and that sort of thing naturally has to be reported but standard domestic violence is not reported in most states, and most domestic violence experts say that is correct because it may put the woman in greater jeopardy. Very commonly, women will not talk about the issue if they think you will report them to the authorities.

Stanko: It seems to me that there is no other profession that is in a better position to make a statement that they are about the promotion of women's health than the Royal College of Obstetricians and Gynaecologists. Part of your mission statement could be to recognise that violence is common and to begin to find ways of promoting positive practice around these issues. My sense is that a policy statement is something that might be worth doing.

C. Bewley: Since about 1990 I have been raising awareness with midwives using literature from North America along the same lines that Richard Jones has been doing. I feel that what has hampered us somewhat is the lack of a medically-sanctioned opinion on the subject. I am very hopeful that what will come out of these two days is a policy statement which will give a lead in this area.

Richardson: I wanted to make two points to follow up what Richard Jones was saying in reply to Patrick Walker's questions. First, speaking as a GP working in primary care, the obstetrician definitely has a role in asking women whether they have experienced violence when they are seen in secondary care. You cannot assume that people are being asked the question in primary care, either by their GP or midwives. The second point is in relation to women that you may be seeing for ongoing care during their pregnancy who are experiencing complicated pregnancies. They may well be having those complications as a result of the violence that they are experiencing. Another good reason for asking.

Yearnshire: In the area of substance abuse, we now have what we call DATS, which is a Government White Paper called *Tackling Drugs Together*. That very firmly gave the responsibility to the health authorities to move away from purely purchasing into prevention and, dare I say, enforcement. It is seen as a community service strategy and it directs that all the professionals – those in education, social services, police and the probation service – work together. We are now working holistically to try and tackle the whole scenario. I would not be surprised if a similar approach was adopted in connection with domestic violence.

SECTION 4

INSTITUTIONAL RESPONSES

Chapter 10

The law and domestic violence

Susan S.M. Edwards

INTRODUCTION

Domestic violence against female intimates is a problem encountered by health professionals and specialists in their care of women. For the obstetrician and gynaecologist there are specific presentations in women, both mental and physical, which have their origin in domestic violence. Where physical trauma is inflicted on pregnant women, harm is perpetrated both on the expectant mother and her unborn child. The purpose of this paper is not to provide a detailed recitation of the pertinent legislation but to identify some of the key medico-legal issues of specific relevance to health care professionals and obstetricians and gynaecologists in particular.

What is domestic violence?

Domestic violence is widely recognised as a punch, slap or a kick. The Domestic Violence Prevention Project (1992) in Hammersmith states that physical violence includes a range of conduct:

> Slap, punch, grab, kick, choke, shake, push, restrain, pull hair, pinch, bite, rape, use of force/threats/coercion to obtain sex. Use of weapons against her, keeping weapons around which frighten her. Throwing objects at her or near her, destroying her possessions or the furniture. Standing in doorway during arguments, preventing her from leaving, menacing or threatening gestures, use of your size to intimidate, standing over her, driving recklessly, uninvited touching. Harassment through uninvited visits or calls, following her, checking up on her, not leaving when asked. Isolation, preventing or making it hard for her to see or talk to friends or relatives and others.

The criminal law, however, recognises only certain forms of domestic violence including physical injury and under certain circumstances, mental assault.

In assessing the responsibility of the offender when determining the seriousness of the offence, the law is concerned with his intent rather more than the consequences of the act.

Violence against the pregnant woman

Violence to the pregnant woman often results in violence to the unborn child. Whilst there is a wealth of literature on the problem of violence in pregnancy (see Chapters 4, 21 and 23) and the dangers posed to mother and unborn child, few cases result in a criminal prosecution. In *R v Virgo* (1988) the appellant was charged with child destruction and grievous bodily harm with intent against his girlfriend. He forced her to remove her clothes, piled snow upon her naked stomach, said he was going to kill her and the baby. When she tried to run away he caught up with her and threw her to the ground kicking her in the stomach causing intra-cranial haemorrhage and death to their unborn child (Edwards 1996, p. 183). In *Attorney General's Reference No 3 (1994)*, the defendant stabbed his girlfriend causing an injury from which she died some weeks afterwards. The injury caused the unborn child to be born prematurely and die some weeks later from the injury inflicted (Smith 1996). In *R v Bakhshish Kaur Sangha* (1977) where a wife had stabbed a violent and adulterous husband the court were to hear a catalogue of the deceased's abuse – 'Incidents involved her being punched, kicked, almost strangled, struck with a walking stick and with a pan, beaten whilst she was pregnant . . .'

Violence – physical force and weapons

Domestic violence against women includes physical assault either by brute force or through the use of a weapon (Edwards 1996, p. 181). In *R v Di Palma* (1989) the victim was attacked by her boyfriend with a hammer causing an extensive compound, depressed comminuted fracture of the skull and the destruction of an eye. In *R v Casseram* (1992), following other previous incidents of violence which were explained as a manifestation not of his repeated violence towards her but as the expression of a 'deteriorating marriage', the husband attempted to strangle his wife and poured petrol over her, setting her alight. In *R v Dearn* (1990) the husband admitted tying a piece of electric flex around his wife's neck causing irreparable brain damage. Assaults may also result in homicide (Table 10.1)

The genitalia as a target for violence

Research on domestic violence in Portland, Maine in 1996, including a study of all homicide cases, revealed one case where a wife had been killed, the body was mutilated and a glass bottle was pushed into the vagina (Edwards 1997).

Table 10.1. Homicide of female intimates: England and Wales 1988–1995 (Source: Criminal statistics England and Wales (1995) Table 4.4.)

Victims	1988	1989	1990	1991	1992	1993	1994	1995
(a) intimate	102	109	95	122	107	92	100	93
(b) all	547	524	556	626	583	566	639	699
(c) (a) as % of (b)	17	21	17	19	18	16	16	13

Violence against women is frequently directed at the genitals. Sexual assault includes fisting, buggery and the insertion of objects into the vagina and anus. In *R v Boyea* (1992) the defendant was convicted of indecent assault. He inserted his hand into the complainant's vagina causing injuries. In *R v McAllister* (1997) a husband performed all manner of indecencies and assaults upon an ex-wife which included inserting objects into her vagina and anus. A charge of indecent assault was upheld and a sentence of 220 hours community service ordered!

Consent, submission and assent

In many cases of domestic violence, especially where the violence is directed at the genitalia and/or is accompanied by sexual acts or intercourse, the defence alleges consent. Until 1991 a married woman had no legal redress against a husband's rape. In 1991 the House of Lords ruled that the three-hundred-year ruling of Chief Justice Hale was no longer good law (*R v R* 1991).

Consent and sexual assault

Where the defence is one of consent the Court of Appeal has recognised that a woman may submit out of fear or duress but this may not be true consent. In *R v Olugboja* (1982), where a young woman was raped, Lord Justice Dunn explained, '. . . every consent involves a submission but it by no means follows that a mere submission involves consent.' Out of fear of retaliation and as a strategy for survival, women may submit or even fake consent. In *R v McFall* (1994), the complainant pretended she was enjoying what was happening to her. Lord Justice Farquharson explained 'This is a situation that is not altogether unfamiliar as in a number of rape cases girls who are in that position find it more politic to pretend to co-operate with the aggressor in case he becomes violent to her'. In cases where women are forced to fellate men and forced into buggery the defence alleges consent. Until *R v Kowalski* (1988), the courts had assumed that men were also immune from criminal liability for fellatio on the basis of the matrimonial consent of a wife (see *R v Caswell* 1984). The defence in such cases relies on the argument that consensual sexual practice in the past is an indicator of present consent. In *R v Boyea* (1992) the defendant was convicted of indecent assault having inserted his hand into the complainant's vagina. The defence did not rely on consent, relying instead on intoxication. Interestingly, it was the judge in his summing up who introduced consent. The Court of Appeal added to this ideology of sexual violence: 'The court must take into account that social attitudes have changed over the years, particularly in the field of sexual relations between adults ... As a generality, the level of vigour in sexual congress which is generally acceptable, and therefore the voluntarily accepted risk of incurring some injury, is probably higher now than it was in 1934' (see Edwards 1996, p. 352).

Here again, the ideology of female masochism is given credence in the courts lending legitimacy to the construct of the ever consenting female (see Edwards 1981). Where women bring charges of buggery and violence the court has on occasion recognised that she may not be consenting. In *T v T* (1964), where a husband forced sodomy on his wife the Court of Appeal recognised 'the wife's consent ... was not real consent, she had not complete freedom of choice' (see also *R v Krause* 1989; *R v Stapleton* 1989). However, where rape is accompanied by buggery and the defence succeeds in establishing that he thought she was consenting to rape, buggery is also regarded as consensual (*R v Cawley* 1988; *R v Bush* 1989). In such cases the defence is often one of honest belief in her consent where the defence have argued that they thought 'no' meant 'yes' and that women like the 'additional thrill of a struggle' and that a wife who bit her wrists to endure the pain of anal intercourse was actually biting them out of pleasure (*R v David Malcolm W* 1994).

Lord Justice Russell held that a husband who tattooed his wife's buttocks with his own initials had committed no offence and 'consensual activities between husband and wife in the privacy of the home was not a proper matter for criminal investigation' (*R v Wilson* 1996).

Somewhere deep in the public and legal viscera is the belief that women are fundamentally masochistic. Medical discourse did much to create and sustain this idea (Edwards 1981, pp. 73–114) to the extent that minor assault in sexual relationships has been regarded as an indicator of consent and not of resistance. Such beliefs surface in the legal defence discourse as in *DPP v Morgan* (1975), where the defence alleged that a wife's resistance to three of her husband's friends raping her was to create an additional thrill of struggle. Edwards details a rape case where the defence explained the minor injuries sustained by the victim were the result of the victim saying 'Hit me, hit me, I'm kinky' (Edwards 1981, p. 166). Such ideologies are impediments in the effort to protect women from domestic abuse in all its forms.

Consent and manslaughter

In 1848 the wife of William Hetherton died when eight months pregnant of a wound to the urethra following assault with a stick. It was concluded that the injury might have been caused by being kicked. Found guilty of culpable homicide at Edinburgh he was transported for life (*Monthly Journal of Medical Science*, (1848–9) September, p. 199). In *R v Slingsby* (1995), the victim died of septicaemia. The appellant had sexual intercourse with her, buggered her and penetrated her vagina and anus with his hand, inflicting the injuries from which she died. In *R v Williamson* (1994) a four year sentence was reduced to three years. The appellant claimed that he had killed the victim during consensual 'pseudo-masochistic' sexual intercourse in which she enjoyed having a pillow held over her head. The pathologist for the Crown accepted this version and the plea to manslaughter. Williamson went on to abuse other women and to kill his mother (see Edwards 1996, p. 354).

THE LAW AND THE LEGAL PROCESS

In examining current law and remedies available to women, limitations arise first in respect of the law itself and what forms of violence are recognised and second in the application and implementation of law by police, prosecutors, judges and magistrates.

Assaults

Where a physical assault has been committed, criminal charges may be preferred depending on the severity of the injury, ranging from common assault and battery under s. 39 of the Criminal Justice Act 1988 to offences under the Offences Against the Person Act 1861, including assault occasioning actual bodily harm (s. 47), grievous bodily harm (s. 20), grievous bodily harm with intent (s. 18), and attempted murder.

Fear of s. 47 and s. 20 assaults

Until recently, mental assault has been largely ignored, since the criteria for assault has relied on apprehension of, or actual, physical injury. Recent case law has expanded the law beyond the stricture of physical injury to include behaviour which leads to psychiatric injury. The recent introduction of the Protection From Harassment Act 1997 is intended to be used to deal with those cases where there is harassment or where the victim is in fear.

s. 47 assault

In *R v Ireland* (1996) making a number of telephone calls and staying silent when the telephone was answered was held to constitute s. 47 assault where psychological injury following on from immediate fear was occasioned. In *R v Constanza* (1997) the Court of Appeal upheld a conviction for s. 47 assault where the appellant made telephone calls, sent his victim more than 800 letters and repeatedly visited her house late at night. In defining assault, the

Court of Appeal (Lord Justice Schiemann) held that it was enough to prove 'a fear of violence at some time not excluding the immediate future' and that an assault could be committed by words alone, thus expanding the law beyond earlier cases rejecting the previous requirement of 'immediacy'.

s. 20 assault

Stalking is often part of domestic violence, especially when the relationship has ended. In *R v Burstow* (1996) a conviction under s. 20 for unlawful and malicious infliction of grievous bodily harm through psychiatric damage was upheld by the Court of Appeal following stalking which included making nuisance telephone calls, breaking into her house, sending her a soiled sanitary towel and sinister notes, stealing her underwear and pouring solvent on her car. The victim suffered psychiatric injury. Both prosecution and defence accepted that the infliction of psychiatric injury through causing fear constituted a s. 20 assault, the appeal court rejected the appellant's submission that 'inflict' required the application of 'physical force'. An appeal on the certified point to the House of Lords was refused.

Murder-manslaughter

'Provocation', 'diminished responsibility' and 'involuntary' are the legal defences invoked when men kill female intimates. 'She provoked me', 'I didn't know what I was doing', or 'it was an accident' are the all-too-common justifications and excuses relied upon. Men who kill female intimates (Edwards 1996, pp. 365–419) have been involved in continuous violence against women.

The modus operandi of men who kill intimates – lethality indicators and prevention

Health care professionals, obstetricians and gynaecologists and all those working with women who experience domestic violence can learn from what is known about the *modus operandi*. In cases of the homicide of female intimates, the method most frequently used by men is strangulation and asphyxiation. This method of assault has been largely ignored since any women who survive such attacks may manifest little or no corroborative signs of injury (Edwards 1996, pp. 368–9).

The *modus operandi* will be taken into consideration when assessing criminal liability. The killing of another by brute force (including strangulation and asphyxiation) rather than with a weapon, is legally considered less likely to indicate intent. When men kill women, brute force is used in the majority of cases, but women killing male spouses use weapons because of their relative strength and socialisation. Women therefore find difficulty in persuading the court that their action was without intent.

Domestic violence, anxiety, despair and depression

Living in continual fear of domestic violence results in a deterioration in mental and physical health. Not knowing when and where violence is going to happen next results in physical and mental symptoms. The law has recognised that the impact of domestic violence on a woman's mental state may be a relevant factor in considering responsibility when women kill their abusive partners. Women in this state have gone on to kill in self-defence, although the courts have not recognised the self-defensiveness of their action in the legal sense. The mental health of these women becomes only of interest to the law if it reduces their responsibility for the crime, constituting an abnormality of mind under a defence of diminished responsibility, (*R v Ahluwalia* 1992; *R v Bakhshish Kaur Sangha* 1997)

THE APPLICATION OF LAW – THE CRIMINAL JUSTICE PROCESS

Investigating domestic violence

The extent of domestic violence against women is largely unknown for reasons of under-reporting and under-recording. The reasons for women's silence are well documented and they include: fear that children will be removed from their care, that the marriage will be effectively over, that they have nowhere to go, or the fear of further violence (Edwards 1989, p. 169). Women are socialised into minimising male violence which erodes their ability to report and to challenge their abusers. The criminal justice system continually condones and minimises and colludes with male violence, sending a symbolic message out to both victims and perpetrators. Whilst patriarchy and family honour bind all communities, the manifestations of these systems of power have their own consequences. This is compounded for ethnic minority communities by a lack of faith in the police whom they regard as protectors of white indigenous society:

> The majority of women have no faith or confidence in the police, but because of a lack of any alternative, women have had no choice but to make demands for protection and safety from them. For black women, challenging an issue like domestic violence within our own communities and challenging the racism of the police at the same time is often fraught with contradiction. (Southall Black Sisters 1989)

The economic and political vulnerability of these communities further compound their reluctance to involve police, for fear of extending the net of corporate policing.

Recording domestic violence is a function of police policy. In 1984–5, the Metropolitan Police Department (MPD) recorded as few as 384 cases of domestic violence for a population of 7.5 million. These recorded cases represented prosecutions, and not notifiable offences as was originally sup-

Table 10.2.   Domestic violence incidents in the MPD for selected years only (Source: Metropolitan Police for 1985, 1990, 1991, 1992 and Performance Information Bureau for 1995 and 1996)

Year	1985	1990	1991	1992	1995	1996
No.	384	8510	9660	7800	51,929	49,828

posed. By 1987, following pioneering research (Edwards 1986), public criticism, and an internal police inquiry, the Metropolitan Police issued a Force Order, directing police to recognise that domestic violence in the home was as serious as violence in the street. This led to an increase in recorded cases regardless of their prosecution potential or prognosis. In 1996, 49,828 domestic violence incidents were recorded due to changes in police recording practice, supported further by the recent introduction of Minimum Operational Standards of Performance (1996) which followed on from the recommendations of the Domestic Violence Working Party (Metropolitan Police 1993) (Table 10.2).

There is some concern that whilst officers working in domestic violence units are sensitively aware of the domestic violence situation, this is not necessarily true of beat officers who are in the front line of such police work (again the MPD have insisted on training for front line officers in their Minimum Operational Standards (1996)). The collection of evidence is even more critical in cases where the prosecution and outcome is uncertain. More could be done to gather evidence at this point, given that complainants are reluctant to give evidence in court to support a prosecution (*R v Bird* and *Holt* 1996). The gathering of photographs and statements, medical reports and other witness statements is critical. Few cases will ever reach court if they remain dependent on the testimony of the victim. A further deterrent to women proceeding against abusers is that the abuser has the right to conduct his own defence. This has led to victims facing prolonged ordeals in the witness box during cross-examination and to victims withdrawing charges. In one case the defendant had poured lighter fuel over the victim's genitals. When served with the papers he took the photographs down the pub to show his friends. Inevitably traumatised, she withdrew the charges and the case was withdrawn. In addressing these problems the Sexual Offences (Protected Material) Act 1997 now provides that disclosures to the defendant shall be regulated (s. 3(1)), and the defendant's legal representative must take reasonable steps to ensure that relevant material is protected (s. 4(1)).

Police, until recently, have rarely arrested perpetrators of domestic violence. Police have powers to arrest in accordance with common law, breach of peace, and for crimes including assault or criminal damage. Force guidance and the Home Office Circular 60/90 (1990) states, '... all police officers involved in the investigation of cases of domestic violence regard as their overriding priority the protection of the victim and the apprehension of the offender.' Once arrested, an offender is taken to the police station where a decision regarding preferment of a criminal charge: breach of the peace; a decision to caution; or to terminate the matter with no further action, is made by a custody sergeant. In the past, the tendency with domestic 'incidents' has been to discharge the offender and in some cases to proceed with a 'breach of the peace'. Metropolitan Police Guidelines (1987) indicate that where the offender admits the offence, he may be dealt with by way of a caution. Figures are not available regarding the extent of the use of a caution in domestic violence, although cautions for offences of violence against the person have increased by 126.7 per cent, from 9000 in 1985 to 20,400 in 1995 (Criminal Statistics 1995). The obvious advantage of a breach of the peace charge is that offenders can be detained in custody and released later without a court appearance, or may be brought before magistrates during the following session. Under the Police and Criminal Evidence Act 1984, police may detain a suspect in custody for up to 24 hours, with extensions up to a maximum of 96 hours following renewed applications to a magistrate. When charged, Home Office Circular 60/90 (1990) encourages police to remand domestic violence suspects in custody. Police powers regarding remand were further extended by the Criminal Justice and Public Order Act 1994 s. 27, providing a police power to impose bail conditions by amending the Bail Act 1976 s. 3 and omitting the restriction on imposition of bail 'only by a court'. Under Schedule 1, bail may be refused where the defendant is likely to fail to surrender to bail and will commit further offences including interference with witness(es), and/or obstructing the course of justice, whether in relation to himself or any other persons. These last two conditions provide compelling grounds for bail refusal in the case of domestic violence where the offender is in continuous close contact with the victim and is likely to interfere or commit further offences against her.

In 1987, the Metropolitan Police Force Order stated that it is vital to offer 'every support to victims' by identifying a local referral point such as a women's refuge, involving other agencies, warning the victim when the suspect is to be released from custody, making follow-up visits and giving increased training emphasis on arrest and prosecutions. The police have responded in setting up domestic violence units (DVUs) in the MPD, although they are varied in the work they do.

Prosecuting domestic violence

Since 1985 the decision whether to continue an action and what charge to prefer is taken by a prosecutor. The Crown Prosecution Service (CPS) are directed to consider whether the evidence will afford a 'realistic prospect of conviction', and what impression a jury may make of the evidence and the witness(es). When the prosecutor decides in favour of a prosecution, he or she must then consider whether it is in the 'public interest' to prosecute. The CPS policy document on domestic violence (1995) states:

5.1   Crown Prosecutors always think very carefully about the interests of the victim when they decide where the public interest lies. But we also have to think about the wider interests of the public and not just the interests of the individual.

5.2   There may often be difficulties in striking this balance. For example, there is one side of public interest which condemns all personal violence, and another which recognises the benefit of keeping a family together.

The 'public interest' factors *against prosecution* (emphasis added), include:

(1) The chances of the abuser offending again;
(2) The victim's continuing relationship with the abuser; and
(3) The effect on that relationship of continuing with the prosecution against the victim's wishes (para 5.4).

The public interest considerations *in support of a prosecution* (emphasis added) include:

(1) The history of the relationship, particularly if there has been any other violence in the past;
(2) The seriousness of the offence;
(3) The victim's injuries;
(4) If the abuser used a weapon;
(5) If the abuser has made any threats since the attack;
(6) If the abuser planned the attack; and
(7) The effect on any children in the household.

Few cases of domestic violence are in fact prosecuted. Cretney and Davis (1996) found a discontinuance rate of 29 per cent in non-domestic cases, compared with 39 per cent in domestic cases (where the parties were not cohabiting), and as high as 60 per cent in cases where both parties were living at the same address. Cretney and Davis also found that women wishing to drop charges were asked to go into the witness box to retract the statement in open court. This practice, although motivated by the concern to establish the victim's genuine desire to retract her statement, is not capable of ascertaining that fact with any certainty. It places the onus on the victim to decide whether a prosecution will or will not go ahead, reinforcing once again the transference of responsibility for prosecutions from the public on to the private – from the state to the individual. The interpretation placed on her retraction demonstrates a misunderstanding, since her denial may be actuated by fear. Lord Salmon similarly misunderstood the reasons why battered women do not continue with a prosecution if not legally 'compellable' '. . . if she does not want to avail herself of this protection, there is, in my view, no ground for holding that the common law forces it upon her' (*Hoskyn v Commissioner of Police for the Metropolis* (1979). Since 1984, s. 80(3)(a) of the Police and Criminal Evidence Act abolished the rule of spousal immunity, over-ruling *Hoskyn*. In this case, a conviction for grievous bodily harm was quashed by the House of Lords since the wife was wrongly compelled to give evidence against the husband. Lord Salmon proclaimed on behalf of the majority, 'It seems to me altogether inconsistent with the common law's attitude towards marriage that it should compel such a wife to give evidence against her husband and thereby probably destroy the marriage' (p. 149). Lord Wilberforce similarly asserted, '. . . to allow her to give evidence would probably give rise to discord and to perjury and would be, to ordinary people, repugnant' (p. 159).

A woman's reluctance to give evidence is occasioned by fear. Some judges have misunderstood her fear and need for protection, enforcing her compliance with the threat of imprisonment for contempt of court whilst others have imprisoned women when they have persisted in their refusal to give evidence (Edwards 1989; *R v Renshaw* 1989). Since 1988, s. 23(3)(b) of the Criminal Justice Act has provided for the submission of a written statement in the absence of oral testimony where the witness is in fear. The same rules governing the admissibility of a written statement, i.e. that it is in the interests of justice and not prejudicial to the defendant, are relevant here. Whether to admit the written statement or not depends upon magistrates at committal or hearing, and the trial judge at a trial on indictment. With the exception of one or two cases, this section has been rarely implemented. Judges are reluctant to use it (see *Ashford Magistrate's Court ex parte Hilden* (1993)) concerning a charge of grievous bodily harm with intent which local police said was more akin to attempted murder), and the CPS have not proceeded with cases on this basis (except for *R v Waters* (1997)). Following *R v Bird* and *Holt* (1996), the Court of Appeal has given some indication of the circumstances under which it considers its use appropriate. It will be a matter for police to gather evidence and prepare the case cognisant that a witness may not appear. It will be for prosecutors to proceed in the absence of witnesses and for courts to rule that admission of other evidence is in the interests of justice.

Sarah Holt suffered serious injuries at the hands of her partner, Alex Fryatt, who punched her, stamped on her face, and kicked her to the floor. When police arrived and the flat was examined there was blood over the walls and Sarah Holt was drifting in and out of consciousness. Sophie Bird, in refusing to give evidence said:

> I am in fear of what Alex's family and friends will do when they find out I have given a statement. I have visited Sarah in hospital and have been to her flat since the attack and I cannot believe that someone could do this to a woman. When I saw Sarah in hospital I did not recognise my friend due to her horrific injuries. I am willing and able to attend court as a witness if so required.

When the case came to court both Sarah Holt and Sophie Bird refused to give evidence. The judge said, '. . . I am quite satisfied that *prima facie* your unwillingness to give evidence in this case is deliberate.'

The Court of Appeal found that CPS procedure (Crown Prosecution Service 1995) was not followed, despite the fact that the appellants had, in the week preceding 16 September 1996, indicated their wish to withdraw the complaint and not to give evidence. This should have sent the CPS down the route of considering whether to proceed with a prosecution applying compellability or alternatively without a witness applying s. 23 (3)(b) of the Criminal Justice Act 1988. There was a further failure, said the Court of Appeal, that despite indications by the appellants in the week before the trial that they wished to withdraw their statements, the CPS's sensible procedure did not operate. The Court of Appeal considered that such a case might be one for a prosecution application under s. 23(3)(b) of the Criminal Justice Act 1988 for the witnesses' s. 9 statements to be used as evidence, because the appellants were witnesses who did not give oral evidence through fear. The court asserted, 'We would draw attention to this provision and express the hope that greater use will be made in future of it in cases like the case from which these proceedings emerge.' The court nevertheless upheld the conviction for contempt and a sentence of imprisonment, but reduced the time spent in prison from three months to two weeks. The Court of Appeal has clearly acted as a beacon for encouraging prosecutions, even in the absence of victims.

There is also evidence of crime reduction, where the charge of grievous bodily harm with intent, grievous bodily harm, or assault occasioning actual bodily harm is reduced to a lesser offence. Evidence of this was seen in the Streatham study where assault cases were reduced to charges of common assault and battering under s. 39 of the Criminal Justice Act 1988 (Buchan and Edwards 1991). The 1995 CPS policy statement states that charges resulting from domestic violence should reflect the seriousness of the abuser's behaviour and that Crown Prosecutors should use the Charging Standards on Assaults. In *DPP ex parte Tasmin C* (1995) a decision of the Department of Public Prosecutions (DPP) not to prosecute was reviewed by the divisional court. The complainant was forcibly buggered and assaulted on several occasions by her husband. Mr Naunton for the CPS, in defending the decision of the CPS said in evidence, 'I concluded in all the circumstances the complainant's grievance could be more appropriately dealt with in the matrimonial court, and that the public interest did not require the institution of criminal proceedings.'

The belief that domestic violence is a lesser violence continues to be articulated throughout sentencing decision-making, including the appellate process. Sentencing is guided by the statute governing the offence itself, although within this there is a tremendous scope for discretion. The Criminal Justice Act 1991 s. 1(2)(a), (b) places restrictions on passing a custodial sentence:

> ... the court shall not pass a custodial sentence on the offender unless it is of the opinion –

> (a) that the offence, or the combination of the offence and one or more offences associated with it, was so serious that only such a sentence can be justified for the

offence: (as amended by the Criminal Justice Act 1993 s. 66(1)) or
(b) where the offence is a violent or sexual offence, that only such a sentence would
be adequate to protect the public from serious harm from him.

The Criminal Justice Act 1993 amends s. 29 of the Criminal Justice Act
1991 to provide:

(1) In considering the seriousness of any offence, the court may take into account any
previous convictions of the offender or any failure of his to respond to previous
sentences.
(2) In considering the seriousness of any offence, committed while the offender was
on bail, the court shall treat the fact that it was committed in those circumstances as
an aggravating factor.

Consequently the domestic violence offender is rarely sent to prison (see *R
v McAllister* 1997).

Sentencing practice in domestic violence is guided by the Court of Appeal
in appeals against sentence and through decisions made in Attorney General's
References. Research for the documentary *Till Death Do Us Part* revealed
that no cases of domestic violence were referred to the Attorney General.
The Court of Appeal demonstrates little unanimity and previous cases can
be departed from by the art of distinguishing the case before the court on
the basis that it involves different facts. In *R v Cutts* (1987) the judge said:

In the view of this court it is high time that the message was understood in clear terms
by courts, by police forces, by probation officers and above all by husbands and
boyfriends of women, that the fact that a serious assault occurs in a domestic scene
is no mitigation whatsoever and no reason for proceedings not being taken and condign
punishment following in a proper case.

Yet, in the majority of cases the court does not consider the aggressor to be
'a threat to the public' (Edwards 1996, p. 208). Sentence is reduced in
accordance with that philosophy. In the case of *R v Nicholas* (1994), where
the appellant attacked his wife on two separate occasions, a longer-than-
normal term of imprisonment was imposed under s. 2(2)(b) of the Criminal
Justice Act 1991. In this case the Court of Appeal held that a longer-than-
normal sentence was not precluded for the protection of a 'single member
of the public.' The case of *R v Oudkerk* (1994) again underscores the fact
that domestic violence would not usually be a case where s. 2(2)(b) would
be applied.

In the lower courts there is a general reluctance to send a domestic violence
offender to prison. As *R v McAllister* (1997) shows, the courts prefer non-
custodial sentences; perpetrators are regarded as no threat to the public.

Moving forward with regard to evidential matters and sentencing depends
quintessentially on judicial and magisterial training. Judicial training in this
country is provided largely by judges. The Bridge Report identifies the most
important objective as being 'To convey in condensed form the lessons which

experienced judges have acquired from their experience' (Judicial Studies Board Report 1995). The constitutional position of judges and their need for independence from political interference is continually stressed. Yet in contradistinction the Royal Commission on Criminal Justice Report (1993) recommended: 'There should be an increased effort to improve and extend the existing training of judges in awareness of race issues and consideration should be given to extending this training to awareness of gender issues.' The Commission also recommend, in contrast to the Lord Chancellor's comments cited above: 'Training courses involving a mix of persons from different agencies and disciplines in the criminal justice system should be held wherever possible.'

CIVIL AND FAMILY LAW

This problem of the law and its application is further compounded by the introduction of new civil legislation (Family Law Act 1996) which returns the protection of the victim of molestation to a balancing act between the harm done to the applicant in refusing an injunction and the harm done to the respondent by granting one. The Family Law Act 1996 continues to restrict the remedy of civil law to those who are, or have been, living together. Eligibility for protection depends on parties being 'associated persons' defined as:

> [I]f they are or have been married to each other; they are cohabitants or former cohabitants; they live or have lived in the same household, otherwise than merely by reason of one of them being the other's employee, tenant, lodger or boarder; they are relatives – a term which is itself widely defined; they have agreed to marry each other (whether or not the agreement has been terminated) they are the child's parents (or connected with a child in other defined ways); they are parties to the same family proceedings.

Whilst eligibility criteria are no longer sex-specific, thereby recognising same-sex relationships and no longer depend on marriage prioritising present or past cohabitation, contemporary partners who are not living together are still excluded. Buchan and Edwards (1991) indicated that 52 per cent of women calling police were girlfriends, thereby falling outside the protection afforded by the Family Law Act.

Part IV of the Family Law Act

Part IV of the Family Law Act provides that the court may make occupation orders with respect to the regulation of the occupation of the family home and non-molestation orders prohibiting molestation (Cretney and Masson 1997).

Occupation orders

The Act differentiates between persons entitled and persons non-entitled discriminating between those who have a legal, recognised or statutory right. A person entitled is a 'person with matrimonial home rights'. Spouses who have matrimonial home rights have a right of occupation, a right not to be evicted without a court order and a right to register the right to protect them from eviction by third parties without a court order. A person entitled occupies a dwelling house by virtue of an interest or contract giving her the right to remain in occupation. In both these cases the property must be or have been intended to be the home of the person entitled or the home of a person with whom she is associated. This latter person includes spouses, former spouses, cohabitants, former cohabitants, relatives, persons who live or have lived in the same household, certain children and parties to the same family proceedings. Declaratory orders state that the applicant is entitled to occupy the property. Regulatory orders require the respondent to permit the applicant to enter and remain on the property or part of it and regulate the occupation of the property by either or both parties, prohibit, suspend or restrict the exercise by a person entitled to occupy the property by reason of beneficial interest or contract or by virtue of any enactment giving her the right to remain in occupation; require the respondent to leave the dwelling house or part of it, or exclude the respondent from a defined areas on which the property is included.

The court must consider:

(1) The housing needs and resources of each party and any relevant child;
(2) The financial resources;
(3) The likely effect of any order or decision of the court not to grant any order on the health, safety or well being of the parties and of any relevant child;
(4) The conduct of the parties in relation to each other.

The court is under a duty to make an order if the application or any relevant child is likely to suffer significant harm if an order is not made, unless it appears that the respondent or a relevant child would suffer as great or greater harm than that suffered by the applicant.

A non-entitled person is a cohabitant, former cohabitant or former spouse. Non-entitled persons may be given occupation rights taking into account the parties, any relevant child's housing needs, and financial resources of the parties. The order may regulate the occupation of the property, require the respondent to leave or exclude the respondent from a defined area.

With a non-entitled cohabitant or former cohabitant, the court must regard the balance of harm and take into account the nature of the parties' relationship, length of relationship, children and length of time since the parties ceased living together.

Non-molestation orders

Section 42(1) provides that the court may make a non-molestation order prohibiting the respondent from molesting another person who is associated with the respondent. The term molestation includes a wide range of behaviour, including where a husband continually called at his wife's home and workplace (*Vaughan v Vaughan* 1973).

The Family Law Act 1996, Part IV, which addresses domestic violence and consolidates previous legislation on injunctions, is also considered to put women at risk. Under s. 42 the court may make a non-molestation order to protect the applicant and/or child of the applicant. In deciding whether to exercise powers under this section the court shall have regard to the health, safety and well-being of the applicant or any relevant child, and under s. 47 the presumption is in favour of making a power of arrest unless the court is satisfied that the applicant or child would be adequately protected without it. Under s. 46, undertakings have now been elevated and expressly provided for in statute despite the wholesale criticism of the use of this practice. With regard to occupation orders and powers of excluding a violent person under s. 33, the court will consider first whether the child or applicant is likely to suffer significant harm if an order is not made and then weigh up the significant harm likely to be suffered by the respondent. In this respect see the House of Lords in *Re H and R* (1996) in respect of the standard of proof required for 'is likely' in connection with orders under the Children Act 1989. This standard may well be applied in cases under the Family Law Act 1996 which uses the same language including 'significant harm' and 'is likely'. The test or standard seems to be whether the applicant's harm outweighs the harm of the respondent. The harms suffered are of course distinctly different. The applicant's harm is violence to the person; the respondent's harm is related to a temporary suspension of rights to occupy certain property, and the inconvenience of finding temporary alternative accommodation. This reverses the reasoning of *Davis v Johnson* (1978):

> It is highly likely that respondent threatened with ouster on account of his violence would be able to establish a degree of hardship (perhaps in terms of difficulty in finding or unsuitability of alternative accommodation or problems in getting to work). But he is unlikely to suffer significant harm, whereas his wife and children who are being subjected to his violence or abuse may very easily suffer harm if he remains in the house. (Law Commission 1992, para 4.34)

In *Khorosandjian v Bush* (1993) a young woman was pestered by the defendant with whom she had had a social but not sexual relationship. The court held that the tort of nuisance had been committed and granted an injunction. In *Patel v Patel* (1988) a son-in-law harassed his father-in-law by continually visiting the vicinity of his property . The court refused an injunction as there is not English tort of harassment. In *Burris v Adzani* (1996) the Court of Appeal held that it had the power to grant an injunction in divorce or other proceedings.

Current civil legislation places the child's welfare as the paramount consideration with regard to contact and is frequently thought to put mothers at risk. Currently the Children Act 1989 prioritises the need to keep families together wherever it is possible and is in the child's best interests. Where parents have separated, the view is that one parent shall have the day-to-day care of the child, shall have a residence order (s. 8) and a contact order (s. 8) which requires the person with whom the child lives or is to live, to allow the child to visit or stay with the person named in the order. Contact orders are made to ensure that there is contact between parent and child and are granted irrespective of violence between the spouses. Indeed in very few circumstances has the court seen to refuse contact (including where the father was a transsexual). Domestic violence between spouses has not been an exercising consideration.

The Protection from Harassment Act 1997 promises to offer protection to persons who do not live together and would be excluded by the Family Law Act. Section 1 prohibits a person from embarking on a course of conduct which he knows harasses another. Section 4 creates the offence of aggravated harassment when a complainant is in fear of violence. The implementation, operation and interpretation of the Protection from Harassment Act will be examined through tracking and monitoring of cases from the original complaint through to:

(1) The police and prosecutorial decision to proceed to trial under s. 4.1 (causing another to fear that violence will be used against him) or s. 2 (the offence of harassment);
(2) The solicitors' interpretation of the civil provisions in the Act through the advice given to clients and analysis of cases being brought under s. 3.1;
(3) Use made by the courts of s. 5 restraining orders in accordance with s. 2 and s. 4.

This will offer protection to those who do not come within the category of associated person. This is especially useful to domestic violence situations involving girlfriends and boyfriends. It makes harassment a summary offence punishable by a term of imprisonment. Where the complainant is put in fear of violence it creates the offence of aggravated harassment which is punishable with up to five years' imprisonment. Section 3 creates a statutory tort of harassment for those offences anticipated.

Domestic violence remains a major health issue affecting the lives of thousands of women and their families. The health community has a responsibility to intervene in this escalating spiral of violence which results ultimately in the homicide of many women and, indeed, of some men, whom women kill in self-preservation and self-defence.

REFERENCES

Ashford Magistrate's Court ex parte Hilden [1993] 2 All ER 154
Attorney General's Reference No 3(1994) [1996] 2 All ER 10, [1996] Crim LR 268.
Buchan, I. and Edwards, S.S.M. (1991) *Adult Cautioning for Domestic Violence.* London: Police Requirements Support Unit, Home Office Science and Technology Group
Burris v Adzani [1996] 1 FLR 266 CA
Cretney, A. and Davis, G. (1996) Prosecuting domestic and non-domestic assault. *Criminal Law Review* p.167
Cretney, S. and Masson (1997) *The Principles of Family Law,* p.244. London: Sweet and Maxwell
Criminal Statistics England and Wales (1995). London: HMSO
Crown Prosecution Service (1993) *A Statement of Prosecution Policy: Domestic Violence.* London: Crown Prosecution Service
Crown Prosecution Service (1995) *Policy for Prosecuting Cases of Domestic Violence,* p.4. London: Crown Prosecution Service
Davis v Johnson [1978] 1 All ER 1132
DPP ex parte Tasmin C (1995) 1 Cr. App R 136
DPP v Morgan [1975] 2 All ER 347
Domestic Violence Prevention Project (1992) *DVIP Violence Prevention Checklist,* p. 1. Hammersmith, London: Domestic Violence Intervention Project
Edwards, S.S.M. (1981) *Female Sexuality and the Law.* Oxford: Martin Robertson
Edwards, S.S.M. (1986) *The Police Response to Domestic Violence.* London: Polytechnic of Central London.
Edwards, S.S.M. (1989) *Policing 'Domestic' Violence.* London: Sage
Edwards, S.S.M. (1996) *Sex and Gender in the Legal Process.* London: Blackstone Press
Edwards, S.S.M. (1997) *Policing Portland's Domestic Violence Problem* (in press)
Home Office (1990) *Home Office Circular 60/90 on Domestic Violence.* London: HMSO
Hoskyn v Commissioner of Police for the Metropolis [1979] AC 474
Judicial Studies Board Report (1995) *Judicial Studies Board Report 1991–1995,* p. 5. London: HMSO
Khorosandjian v Bush [1993] QB 727
Law Commission (1992) *Domestic Violence and the Occupation of the Family Home.* No 207 HMSO
Metropolitan Police (1987) *Domestic Violence Best Practice Guidelines.* London: Community Involvement Policy Unit, TO30
Metropolitan Police (1993) *Domestic Violence Working Party.* London: Metropolitan Police
Patel v Patel [1988] 2 FLR 179
Re H and R [1996] 1 All ER 1
R v Ahluwalia [1992] 4 All ER 889
R v Bakhshish Kaur Sangha [1997] 1 Crim LR (S) 202, [1997] 1 Cr App R (S) 202
R v Bird and *Holt* (1996) Transcript
R v Boyea [1992] Crim LR 574
R v Burstow (1996) Times Law Reports 30 July 1996, [1997] Crim LR 452
R v Bush (1989) 11 Cr App R (S) 295,
R v Casseram (1992) 18 Cr. App R 384
R v Caswell [1984] Crim LR 111
R v Cawley (1988) 10 Cr App R (S) 452
R v Constanza (1997) Times Law Report, March 31

R v Cutts [1987] Fam Law 311, Lexis Enggen,Transcript
R v David Malcolm W (1994) 15 Cr App R (S) 561).
R v Dearn (1990) 12 Cr. App R (S) 527
R v Di Palma (1989) 11 Cr App R (S)329
R v Ireland Times Law Report 22 May 1996, [1997] Crim LR 434.
R v Kowalski (1988) 86 Cr App R 339
R v Krause (1989) 11 Cr App R (S) 360
R v McAllister [1997] Crim LR 233
R v McFall [1994] Crim LR 226
R v Nicholas [1994] Crim LR 77
R v Olugboja [1982] QB 320
R v Oudkerk [1994] Crim LR 700,
R v R [1991] 4 All ER 481
R v Renshaw [1989] Crim LR 811
R v *Slingsby* [1995] Crim LR 570
R v Stapleton (1989) 11 Cr App R (S) 364
R v Virgo (1988) 10 Cr. App R (S) 427
R v Waters (1997) The Times March 10 CA
R v Williamson [1994] 15 Cr App R (S) 364
R v Wilson [1996] 3 WLR 125
Royal Commission on Criminal Justice Report (1993) Cm 2263, rec. 247. London: HMSO
Smith, J.C. (1996) *Smith and Hogan Criminal Law*, p.339. London: Butterworths
Southall Black Sisters (1989) 'Two Struggles: challenging male violence and the police' in C. Dunhill (Ed.) *The Boys in Blue*, p.38–44. London: Virago
T v T [1964] P 85
Vaughan v *Vaughan* [1973] 1 WLR 1159

Chapter 11

Government direction

Gwyneth Lewis and Anne Spence

Lewis: This was intended to be a presentation from the Home Office. We are from the Department of Health. We would have been here anyway, but unfortunately the Home Office's representatives were not able to come.

We both work in the Maternity Services Policy Branch of the NHS Executive. Because the Home Office cannot come, I have my colleague, Anne Spence, who liaises with our Social Security branch and she will give you a run down, as far as we know it, of our new government's policy on inter-sectoral working.

We have not been able to prepare a paper for you, partly because we stepped into the Home Office breach rather late, and partly because it is a little difficult for us to determine what the new government will do during the next few months.

Spence: I would like to set out the background to the government's decision-making structure on domestic violence as it has been and where it looks as though it is going.

In general terms, policy responsibility for domestic violence rests with the Home Office. They chair the Inter-Departmental Group on domestic violence and membership of that group includes all government departments with key interests. The Lord Chancellor's Department, for example, deals with civil law remedies; the Department of the Environment has responsibility for housing legislation and homelessness; and we, the Department of Health, have responsibility for both the health and social care aspects of domestic violence.

The purpose of the Inter-Departmental Group which was set up in late 1992 was to ensure a shared understanding of the nature of the problem and to co-ordinate responses across government as a whole. In the early 1990s the main developments resulted from the Home Affairs Committee. The Inter-Departmental Group responded with an action plan to that committee. Much of that is out of date and it is interesting that none of the 42 recommendations that the Select Committee made were related to health.

Probably the main achievement of this cross-government group has been the production and widespread distribution of the inter-agency circular, *Domestic Violence: Don't Stand for It,* which was produced in August 1995 to assist the development of a framework for local inter-agency co-ordination.

I have distributed [to the Study Group] a résumé of commitments that the Labour Government has made in strategy statements on domestic violence. They were drawn from a number of Labour Party documents and although it may not be clear exactly how government policy will mirror these, it gives a useful idea of their likely priorities and attitudes. The main issues are publicity and public awareness, refuge provision, inter-agency co-ordination, children and domestic violence, and training of key professionals.

It is interesting to note that the agenda for women states that Labour intends to conduct a full review of the law governing domestic and sexual violence towards women. That will be principally for the Home Office and Lord Chancellor's Department, but the Department of Health will have an input.

In the Department of Health, the lead for domestic violence has historically been in the Social Care Group. They house the Social Services Inspectorate and are responsible for social care policy. They hosted two major conferences in 1995 to stimulate thinking and assist in the development of a framework for the local inter-agency co-ordination. Recently there has been an increasing recognition of domestic violence as a major public health issue and a significant and often unmet or inadequately met health need, and there have been strenuous and successful attempts to focus thinking in the NHS Executive, of which we are a part.

Lewis: One of the things that you did not mention was the revision of the Family Law Act later in 1997.

Spence: It is Part IV of the Family Law Act 1996 which comes into effect on 1 October 1997 and much of our efforts are geared around that date.

Lewis: One of the key features of the Act is that the man can be removed from the house rather than the woman having to remove herself from the house. The new government may well want to look at the wording of that before it goes to Parliament.

Speaking from my perspective, I am not just a civil servant in charge of maternity, but I am also a public health doctor. I run the UK Confidential Enquiries into Maternal Deaths, so I look at domestic violence from a large number of areas.

I will first talk about my Maternal Deaths Enquiries, because its relevance struck me when I took it over two years ago. Under the chapter heading *Fortuitous*, and in fortuitous deaths there is a long list of deaths from causes not related to pregnancy, there is a table which breaks down the cases. At the bottom it says 'murder' or 'suicide' and nothing else, just one figure. At least we have started to analyse the deaths from postnatal depression. This time we would like to look at deaths from domestic violence, but they are not always reported. In fact, only nine deaths in the last three years have been reported to us as being a result of domestic violence. Therefore, one of the recommendations I would make as part of this working group is that in terms of collecting data, coroners should be requested, if not required, to inform us in confidence of deaths of women who have had babies or who are pregnant and who died by violent means.

Internationally, I do a lot of work on maternal deaths as well and although this is a meeting of this College in England, I would like to propose that there is a section on the international issue. As Dr Jones said this morning, and following a conference in Morocco on maternal deaths, the figures are horrifying and people from other countries look to this College as a leader. Some sort of international recognition of the problem would be helpful.

Turning to the NHS Executive, it is one of three branches of the Department of Health. The second branch is the Social Care Group, which covers services and the third is the wider department which covers broad issues such as AIDS, HIV, communicable diseases, BSE and international issues. Domestic violence was not very high on the Executive's agenda until a couple of years ago but it has been moving up rapidly since then.

One reason is the initiatives that certain colleges and groups have been showing and the increase in letters that we have been receiving. Secondly, there has been a gradually increasing awareness of the public health needs of these women and of the impact of domestic violence on public health and on NHS expenditure. Nobody has done a needs assessment in England of the cost of domestic violence – not just to the women and their children or to the penal service, but also how much it costs the National Health Service.

Fortunately, in Scotland, there have been the beginnings of a needs assessment in Glasgow which is very helpful. I hope that as one of our initial responses to the new government, we will be able to look at how we can start costing this out, because we need to know the financial position as well as the effects.

We do not yet know where we are going in terms of specific actions but I can tell you that our ministers have already signed up enthusiastically to what was in their manifesto.

We will certainly wish to continue to facilitate and raise consciousness amongst professionals. This College has taken the initiative amongst all the Royal Colleges on domestic violence and training for professionals – and others are following suit. We look forward to the publication of these Proceedings. In determining policy the Department of Health listens to views from a number of angles, not least the medical colleges. That is why your work is so crucially important to the work that we will be doing in the future.

Chapter 12

Police practice

Stephanie Yearnshire

INTRODUCTION

The role of the police is perceived by the public as the protection of life and property. Police resources have, however, been focused on areas such as house burglary and youth disorder rather than domestic violence. In recent years, recognition of domestic violence crimes has increased, following pressure from a variety of sources including women's groups and media exposure. This has led to the production of Home Office circulars which include guidelines on domestic violence and encourage the police forces to adopt a formalised strategy to deal with this crime.

Nevertheless, for several reasons, the ways in which the police deal with victims of domestic violence have been the subject of some justified criticism. Although police practice has improved, there is still room for further development in the present situation. This chapter will focus on certain problems within police practice, discuss the actions which one force, Northumbria Police, have adopted to address these shortcomings and outline the strategy which has been formulated to tackle domestic violence crimes.

Any examination of domestic violence issues will fall short in making any recommendations for change unless it encompasses a discussion of the present state of the English law. Before police practice is discussed, it is useful to outline the differences between the public domain of the criminal court and the more private domain of the civil court, since both affect the police response to domestic violence and explain why so many victims feel cheated when they seek legal redress.

THE LEGAL SYSTEM

Incidents of domestic violence can, depending on the circumstances, fall within several aspects of law. The two main branches are criminal law and civil law. Generally, civil law relates to rights, duties and obligations between two or more people and can result in a financial settlement between the two conflicting parties. In contrast, criminal law is concerned with wrongs affecting the community at large, contrary to order, peace and the well-being of society. These criminal offences attract a range of punishments ranging from a police caution to imprisonment.

Many victims are frustrated with the outcome of police and court involvement in their case, without realising that both are bound by the legal definitions, rules and principles which support them. Decisions made in English courts can have far-reaching consequences for men and women in violent relationships. It is misleading to speak only of 'the law', since the law is multi-faceted and it is to some of these facets that this chapter now turns.

Criminal law

Police expertise is centred upon the application of criminal law and so victims often feel let down since they have an expectation that automatic legal and police support is available in every circumstance. This is sometimes not the case, due to the restrictive civil and criminal definition of an offence. For example, domestic violence is widely regarded as including physical, sexual and psychological abuse. There is a plethora of unlawful criminal acts which may be involved in the various forms of physical and sexual abuse. There are no criminal laws which reflect psychological abuse, though effects of this type of abuse can be just as debilitating.

In criminal law, the burden of proof requires that the weight of evidence against a man accused of domestic violence proves his guilt 'beyond all reasonable doubt' before a court will convict him of an offence. This is acknowledged as a high standard. Criminal law takes into account a number of factors, including the intention or 'state of mind' of the person carrying out the offence. The classification of crimes is often based on the degree of harm done to the victim, their property or public rights.

Civil law

A victim applying for separation, protection orders or injunctions to protect themselves from a violent partner will find that they become subject to civil law rather than criminal law. Civil law includes family law, the law of property, contract and tort.

The rules of evidence in civil law cases are not as strict as those in criminal law. Here, the case need only be proved on the principle of 'balance of probability'. If, based on the evidence, it is probable that one person is at fault, then the court will 'find' the case in favour of the person who is not at fault. We have seen this in some high profile cases where the criminal courts have found an accused not guilty, only to have the case proved in the civil courts. The hearings are in a separate venue from the criminal courts and, in the main, the police are rarely, if ever, involved.

Civil courts make a variety of orders to be obeyed by one or both parties but these are problematic if there is not enough protection offered to the groups or individuals at risk, because powers of arrest are not always attached to such orders and last on average for only three months.

Progress of a case – key issues

In the main, all court proceedings must be held in public.

Many complainants are frustrated that their word alone, without supporting independent evidence, is not enough to take the case to court. It must be remembered that judges, faced with one person making an allegation and another person denying that allegation, will not be able to convict. The ethos of the criminal court centres on fairness and support to the person accused of the crime rather than the victim.

It is important to prevent 'false witness' testimony and false conviction. In seeking to ensure this does not happen, many evidential rules appear to work against women suffering emotional, sexual and physical abuse. If there is no injury to see, no independent witnesses and the accused gives a plausible explanation, it is virtually impossible to rule against the accused. In fact, in such circumstances it is unlikely that the case would reach the courts. Conversely, where there is strong supporting evidence, a case will be robustly pursued to court.

Crown Prosecution Service (CPS)

Because of the problems outlined, the police must consider all available information when preparing the case file. The file is then forwarded to a solicitor in the CPS. Their brief is to examine further the contents of the police case file against their own criteria for prosecution. If there is a high probability that the accused may be found not guilty, the costs of prosecution may not be justified.

The CPS has been subject to criticism for failing to prosecute certain domestic violence cases. Organisations including Women's Aid, Victim Support and the Southall Black Sisters have all reported to the House of Commons (1992) what they saw as a reluctance to prosecute. However, in recent years the CPS has made efforts to ameliorate the situation. Their recent policy guidelines, which link with those of the police, undertake that a charge should adequately reflect the seriousness of the offence and that a 'domestic' background should not be a factor in reducing the seriousness of that 'charge'.

Magistrates' court

Once the file has been passed on to court by the CPS, the case proceeds to the magistrates' court where it is heard by three people who are respected members of the community. Magistrates may have little legal training and are advised by a legally qualified magistrates' clerk. Due to the volume of cases waiting to be heard and the time involved in preparing case papers, there is generally a delay of a number of weeks between the incident and the actual court hearing. In cases involving domestic violence, the delay may lead to threats, intimidation or, indeed, reconciliation between partners in the intervening time period.

Crown Court

In certain categories of criminal offence, particularly those carrying a sentence of imprisonment, the case may go to a higher court and be heard by a judge and jury. Here, the victim, expecting to have the matter finalised at the magistrates' court, may instead have to attend Crown Court many months later, which adds stress to an already worrying situation. In both courts the case may be adjourned several times, often on the set date of the hearing, further adding to the victim's trauma.

Victimisation compounded by the legal process

In both legal arenas the defence is entitled, by an Act of Parliament created in 1865, to defend their clients in any manner they wish. In real terms, this often means a direct attack on the victim, challenging their veracity, lifestyle and motivation. Victims rarely expect or respond well to this onslaught by lawyers who, by comparison, are articulate, educated and practised in defence skills. It is widely acknowledged that women report this as leaving them shocked and demoralised.

DIFFICULTIES SURROUNDING POLICING DOMESTIC VIOLENCE

Having placed the crime in the legal framework, it is now important to highlight the policing problems which have been present when taking action against domestic violence. Strategies which have been formulated by Northumbria Police to rectify these problems will then be discussed.

There have been many specific problems, including reluctance to get involved, indifference to the crime, inaccurate recording and general lack of knowledge regarding domestic violence.

Perhaps the most salient criticism levelled at the police was their willingness to activate all of their powers in respect of an attack by a stranger and yet reluctance to intervene when that attack took place in a domestic situation.

Officers were more comfortable operating in the public arena, with the offence and the perpetrators clearly defined. However, in the relative privacy of the home, officers may have lost the clarity of role and thus attempted to deal with the situation in ways which may not have supported the victim.

The complexity of the situation and the intimate relationship between perpetrator and victim often impinges on the decision-making discretion of the officer. Indeed, police officers are part of the wider society which tolerates domestic violence and are likely to have absorbed some of the social mores which foster a lenient view of partner abuse.

Perhaps a more substantial explanation for police indifference in the past is because officers see arrest as pointless, citing many cases where women return to their partners the next day and request no further police action. It must be understood that in criminal matters such as assault, the absence of a complaint by the victim will effectively end the prosecution case. The arrest, investigation and interview process takes an officer, often with a high workload, off the street and away from policing other criminal activities.

Some officers have complained that they feel let down, where they have supported the woman throughout her complaint, preparing the case for court in an effort to protect her, only to be told that she has reconsidered, wants no further action and willingly returns to the battering environment. There are many legitimate reasons why the victim wishes that no further action should be taken. She may fear negative repercussions once her partner is out of custody; she may lose her source of income or may fear for her children's safety. Often the victim has nowhere to go, no money and little support and, indeed, she may still care for her partner. It is not surprising that victims often withdraw their statement, ending the prosecution. However, for the officer concerned, this may have a negative effect on his or her motivation to help. The next domestic violence situation may not receive the same dedication from that officer.

There has also been criticism of the recording of domestic incidents by the police. If the previous history has not been recorded properly and comprehensively for the attending officer, there is an increased likelihood that the next incident will be treated as an isolated event. If the incidents are treated as isolated events, the level and frequency of repeat victimisation may not be recorded and thus not acted on appropriately. An instant decision to mediate rather than to take positive action may result. Police only have powers to arrest in certain situations. The courts demand evidence and this is where the issue of an injury becomes important. If the evidence is not present, then the likelihood of arrest for assault becomes unrealistic. Indeed, if the officer were to arrest in these circumstances, without evidence, then the perpetrator may be able to successfully launch a civil claim against the police for false arrest. There are other offences for which a perpetrator may be arrested. Creating an immediate situation of disorder is one such area but, as usual, police powers are conditional. Often the police are called after the actual incident has taken place, when the perpetrator may have 'cooled down' and is no longer using threatening behaviour. This amelioration of behaviour cancels out the officer's right to arrest.

Finally, the police force, as an organisation, have been criticised for their general lack of knowledge in dealing with domestic violence which is perhaps related to their reluctance to become involved. In any case, where there has been some form of abuse, whether it be a sexual or violent attack, the initial response to the victim is crucial, in order to obtain an accurate account of the incident. Unless they are well trained, police officers may lack the skills necessary to help the victim and, perhaps more importantly, they may lack the knowledge of where to send the victim for support. If the officer lacks knowledge about other agencies involved in supporting victims, the abuse may continue because the victim is ignored or powerless to take action herself.

In theory, police powers are extensive; in reality, there is little an officer can do in some situations other than to facilitate separation of the offender and victim. Due to the nature of the abuse and the human factor, there is every possibility that the situation will recur in the months to come. The police, however, are mandated to attend every call they receive promptly, within the constraints of the volume of emergency calls being received.

NORTHUMBRIA POLICE RESPONSE TO DOMESTIC VIOLENCE

Background

Strategies aimed at domestic violence have in the past been piecemeal and performed on a local rather than a force-wide basis. However, the impetus to set up a domestic violence policy gained momentum partly as a result of the Home Office circular (Home Office 1990) but more importantly as a result of a trial domestic violence unit set up in 1989 within the South Tyneside Police Area Command. This was a three-pronged initiative, where officers were directed to arrest where there was evidence, magistrates agreed to hear cases the next morning and unit officers contacted victims, offering information, advice and initial counselling in respect of the victim's social, legal and civil rights. Calls over each 24-hour period were monitored by unit staff ensuring proper police action.

The unit itself had varying levels of success but, perhaps most importantly, paved the way to a more formalised, force-wide strategy to tackle domestic violence. An internal working party and separate thematic inspection, in 1993 and 1995 respectively, resulted in policy formulation (Broughton 1993; Northumbria Police 1995).

Northumbria Police policy and strategy

Policy highlighted that the police response must be cognisant of the needs of the victim, i.e. there needs to be:

(1) A prompt response;

(2) An understanding of the danger that the victim is in;

(3) An appreciation of the impact of repeated abuse;

(4) Positive action.

In this policy, domestic violence is defined as physical, sexual or emotional abuse by partners and ex-partners, whether married or not.

It is emphasised that police officers attending such incidents must take heed of the vulnerability of the victim and the prevailing climate of fear in which they are forced to live. The immediate duty of police officers who are called to attend domestic violence incidents is to secure the protection of the victim and any children from further abuse. This will normally involve referral to another agency and may necessitate conveying the victim to a place of safety. Refuges run by Women's Aid are of great importance in providing a secure environment. Medical assessment of the victim should always be considered, even if no injuries are apparent.

Officers should not attempt conciliation, especially where the victim has been or claims to have been violently assaulted. It is the officer's duty to investigate any allegations thoroughly, ensuring that full use is made of the legal powers available. The arrest and detention of the perpetrator should be a primary consideration, and the reasons for any failure to effect an arrest as a result of a domestic incident must be recorded.

It is imperative that all reported domestic incidents and their outcome are recorded properly and in an easily retrievable format in order to provide a full relationship history. The seriousness of such offences should not and cannot be underestimated.

Training

An important aspect of the strategy was to develop the training needed to deal with domestic violence situations effectively and consistently. Although it can be said that attitudinal problems pervade through the whole of society, there was a need to address police training to standardise police behaviour.

Various training schemes were set up, which included training at all levels, but with particular emphasis on probationers and constables. The training packages aimed to ensure that officers had comprehensive knowledge and understanding of domestic violence issues (an attempt to rectify the earlier problem that officers were ill-prepared). These areas of training included an awareness of the non-physical and non-apparent physical injuries. It was felt that since officers tended to cite bruising and cuts alone as evidence of abuse, it was critical to equip them to recognise other forms of abuse.

A second area of training highlighted an awareness of local agencies and support organisations and generally enhanced the officers' understanding of the problem, the vulnerability of the victim and an appreciation of the impact of repeated abuse.

Information systems

A third aspect which formed part of the strategy of Northumbria Police was the role of information systems in helping to record data more accurately. In the past, an important problem facing officers attending a domestic violence incident was lack of information regarding the background of the case and inconsistent record-keeping.

There was little attempt to build profiles of the most vulnerable households. However, with the increasing role of information systems in Northumbria Police, the coding system used for identifying domestic violence incidents provided a more accurate picture of the problem within an area.

A consistent response

The fourth aspect of Northumbria Police's strategy was aimed at producing a consistent response to domestic violence and an effective arrest strategy. Experience indicates that a proactive police policy which favours arrest is the most effective intervention to reduce repeated violence. Where arrest is not appropriate, positive action by means of direct referral can take its place. However, this approach must be driven by a change in the traditional attitudes of officers in terms of just 'calming things down' and 'giving advice'. This strategy has clear links to the role of training in seeking to change the behaviour of officers in domestic violence situations. Again there was a requirement that the officer justify his or her action if an arrest did not take place.

Multi-agency approach

Finally, perhaps the most important aspect of Northumbria Police's strategy regarding domestic violence was the provision of a multi-agency approach, now encapsulated under the umbrella of the highly innovative Northumbria Community Safety Strategy partnership. It is now accepted that neither the police nor, indeed, any other agency alone can properly address the diverse arena of domestic violence. The police role in domestic violence is that of law enforcement. Whilst it was recognised that counselling forms an important factor in this type of crime, other agencies are better qualified at providing this service. Therefore, seven multi-agency domestic violence forums were set up under the Northumbria Community Safety Strategy in order to develop the inter-agency response.

The forums hold regular meetings for information exchange between agencies, thus providing a co-ordinated response to domestic violence. The broad objectives of the forums were to develop and implement an inter-agency strategy on domestic violence which seeks to:

(1) Promote and maintain co-operation and joint action;

(2) Increase awareness of domestic violence in the community;

(3) Improve services and responses to victims who have experienced or are experiencing domestic violence;

(4) Take positive action against perpetrators;

(5) Maximise resources available to achieve the above.

Members of these forums include the local authority, social services, housing departments, police, Women's Aid, Victim Support, probation, CPS and other professionals, together with a range of other voluntary organisations.

The forums are matched with the local authority boundaries, with the result that local officials take responsibility for families resident in their geographical areas. The Sunderland Forum has already developed intervention programmes for men. Funding, however, remains a key issue in all such developments.

CONCLUSION

This chapter has highlighted the problems faced by the police in dealing with domestic violence and some of the measures being implemented to reduce these problems. But when considering this subject, the legal aspects cannot be ignored, in particular the fact that there are few measures that deal with domestic violence as a specific crime. As a result we have to fall back on general legislation which deals with crimes such as assault.

Changes in the law regarding injunctions were passed in 1996 and took effect in October 1997. All existing legislation on injunctions under the Family Law Acts was replaced with one system, thus speeding up the process. Courts were also given increased powers to attach bail and arrest conditions.

The Law Commission Report (1992) recognised limitations in all forms of legal action. There are social and psychological problems which can be eliminated only by fundamental changes in societal attitudes to women and children.

Domestic violence is likely to be high on the police agenda for a long time to come. The approach of Northumbria Police is an illustration of one way of dealing with this type of crime. However, constant monitoring and evaluation is needed to minimise the gap between policy and practice. Ongoing training of officers and revisitation of the current policy are essential in monitoring the appropriate approach to domestic violence. Police practice will always be constrained in areas such as the law and court systems; and, indeed, the complexity of the crime itself has, in many cases, set its own constraints. Nevertheless, a systematic approach, together with liaison with other agencies, will help to reduce the negative effects and increase positive police response to this crime.

REFERENCES

Broughton, J. (1995) *Responses to Domestic Violence.* Newcastle-upon-Tyne: Northumbria Police Internal Report

Home Office (1990) *Home Office Circular 60/90 on Domestic Violence.* London: HMSO

House of Commons (1992) *Domestic Violence: Memoranda of Evidence to the Home Affairs Committee.* London: HMSO

Law Commission (1992) *Family Law, Domestic Violence and the Occupation of the Family Home. Law Commission 7.* London: HMSO

Northumbria Police (1993) *Working Party on Domestic Violence.* Newcastle-upon-Tyne: Northumbria Police Internal Report

Chapter 13

Institutional responses

Discussion (1)

Kerr-Wilson: Can I ask Stephanie Yearnshire a question? Do you have any evidence that what you have implemented so far has had any effect? It is probably early days, but what targets do you have? What limits are you setting?

Yearnshire: Bearing in mind that this is developmental, what we should be evaluating initially are the forums and how they are developing. Having said that, no money has been made available under the single regeneration budget which funds community strategy or domestic violence, so progress depends very much on the genuine goodwill of the people involved. Certainly they are taking on the counselling roles and they are influencing police policy. If you are asking about police officers and how well they are responding, from time to time we support MPhil students who are looking at a range of aspects.

An MPhil student from Durham University has just finished looking at how women were dealt with in the police service. She ended up by going out with our police officers virtually every day in various shifts over three months. As a side issue, she said she was pleasantly surprised to find the way in which the women were dealt with at the time of the incidents: referring them to a refuge, giving them advice, making sure that the man was no longer in the vicinity and arresting in far more cases than she had previously thought.

If you are asking whether there is any direct information that I can give, the answer is, not yet.

Hepburn: There is a national Scottish needs assessment programme. This means that all centres in Scotland are devising their own policy within a national framework and that is very important for the kind of consistency that Stephanie Yearnshire was talking about.

Friend: I would like to ask Stephanie Yearnshire about the avenues down which victims travel and the help that they can get. For example, I understand that police surgeons could be general practitioners or they could indeed be specialists.

How often do these doctors become involved in these problems? Secondly, you mentioned the multi-forum agencies and several categories of individuals, including professionals, but you did not identify whether doctors are involved. Do we, in fact, need a better networking structure whereby, for particular doctors and particular expertise, avenues should be opened to reach these people – and how should we set about that?

I notice, for example, that the multi-forum agency document has a very small paragraph on health care, mainly because it states that the health-care professions have not been involved in this at all. How should we move in that direction?

Yearnshire: I certainly feel that health care has been slow to come on board and I separate the women surgeons and police surgeons from that category. It was recognised that the male police surgeons were not doing a very good job with victims; they were not very sensitive and a bit brusque. For some time now we have called on women doctors. But, of course, it is not just a case of using your GP or specialist knowledge to give evidence in court. You have to recognise what it is that the court is looking for in your description of what you are seeing, and then you have to have the skills to match yourself against these extremely professional defence lawyers who seek to undermine what the doctors are doing.

As far as the rape investigations in 1996 were concerned, our figures show that the doctors were called out 130 times to deal with these cases, but you have to bear in mind that women can go to the refuge centres without telling the police, so I would expect the figures to be much higher.

Women doctors who are much more specialised than general police surgeons carry out these examinations. A specialist training day was held recently at Headquarters, when the CPS had a session by a doctor who was a specialist in genitourinary tract injuries and I am told that the feedback was tremendous. The training day was attended by some of our women doctors and the CPS and the information was so good that one of the superintendents who had produced our previous recommendations said I had two of them wrong! We are jointly probably now giving a better service than we have done in the past.

Evaluation also needs to be considered and Durham University is currently looking at the community centre strategy. Their report is due very shortly.

As to multi-agency forums, you have to bear in mind that the police are the enforcers if it is a criminal environment. The support comes from Victim Support or Women's Aid and we also advise that people should see a solicitor. I am moving back from that point of view because seeing a solicitor is not enough. An injunction without a power of arrest attached to it is not worth anything and even one with the power of arrest attached usually has some wording written inside which gives the police officer discretion based on the scenario. I am very sceptical these days of any written policy because the small print inevitably does not help.

Wilson: I am horrified that both Stephanie Yearnshire and Susan Edwards pointed to the role of law in obstructing society dealing with domestic violence by bringing questions of consent into it. I wondered whether either, or both, of you would like to comment on how you think we could improve matters and whether there is any scope for using the decision in the *Brown* case; whether we can raise this issue using that case as an example, saying it is not acceptable to start talking about consent in issues of sexual violence?

Mezey: Is everyone familiar with the *Brown* case?

Wilson: It is also known as the Spanner case.

Stanko: It is a case where men were prosecuted and convicted for participating in sado-masochistic sex and the case came to light almost as a matter of chance. The police followed up an investigation and found video tapes. The case was based on tapes of activity which was participated in consensually.

Wilson: Of course, the key point in that case, both domestically and in Europe, was that there are elements of sexual practice which one cannot consent to because they are so violent. I am very depressed and very pessimistic about what can be done given that consent is and must be a defence; it is a defence to rape, it is a defence to indecent assault, it is a defence to assault and actual bodily harm, and if the Law Commission had had their way it would have been a defence to causing serious physical harm, even to the level of grievous bodily harm.

There are Bar Council rules but they have very rarely, if ever, been used when defence counsel has gone over the line. Where is the line where a defence counsel will say this is a legitimate strategy, a chance to gain, everyone plays to win and that is what I am going to do? I offer that as a warning because there are so many cases. One of the cases I mentioned was of a man called Williamson which I reported in something I have written. It was an unreported legal case, a sexual asphyxiation case, where of course the dead cannot speak and she could not say 'no, he was strangling me'. He said in his defence, 'this is what she liked, she was physically excited by this,' and he got off. Interestingly, the very same man went on to batter his next girlfriend and ended up killing his mother and he is now in Broadmoor. It is a pity we did not have the benefit of hindsight when he got off for the killing of the girlfriend.

There are a number of cases of assault. Although in the *Brown* case I accept that the European Court upheld the decision of the House of Lords, the problem is that in the dissenting judgement of two of the judges, they tended to say, 'Well, we must look at consent in the area of sexual relationships.

We must recognise that what happens in private is a matter for those two people.' That takes us back into the conundrum that we face when we try to look at domestic violence.

Finally, the whole issue of consent has never been properly explored. We know that a woman's consent may be submission, it may be assent but it is not consent and we have to look at the whole issue of power relationships within domestic violence and, more broadly, when we come to ask, what is consent? On the issue of the *Brown* case, I wonder whether they ever really consented and whether it was a matter of assent, but certainly for domestic violence victims, I would think in a majority of cases it is not consenting but assenting and submitting, and we have to be very careful about this when the argument is put up that in fact they consented.

Langley: This is a point for all multi-agency forums and perhaps the police, from the woman's point of view. One of the key issues that should come out of any study day like this is the issue of communication. We communicate with each other and often professionals communicate between themselves and with each other across agencies and within their own agency. Very often, they do not communicate very well with the women. From my point of view, working with women, both in a refuge and counselling them on a long-term basis, one of the things that is most difficult for them is that they feel that professionals are making policies, procedures and practice which does not involve them and is not communicated to them.

On multi-agency forums and health professionals' involvement, one thing I would like to plug is the health visitor. Certainly in Kent where our domestic violence forums are not yet off the ground, we have had a good response from health visitors, perhaps less so from other health professionals; but certainly health visitors and community midwives – the people who are in the community, in people's homes – are absolutely vital.

Harwin: Picking up on the issue of multi-agency work, it is vital that a national lead is given through the various medical Royal Colleges. There were a number of very well-developed multi-agency forums even in 1992 and several of them were saying that the probation service could not be involved. As soon as there was a national position statement, then local probation officers, at quite senior levels, became involved in multi-agency work and there have been a number of initiatives in terms of programmes for perpetrators and partnerships with the voluntary sector in terms of support services for women. It is vital that a national lead is given.

Picking up on what Stephanie Yearnshire said, injunctive protection is still pretty ineffective. I am afraid that, despite Part IV of the Family Law Act, it was very watered down from when it was originally drafted by the Law Commission in 1989. Unless it is beefed up and, in particular, unless there is specific training for the judiciary and the magistrates in terms of the way they implement the law, women will not get a much better deal.

We have heard how the criminal law and the civil law do not protect women very well. We have to come back to saying that there are alternative strategies for safety for women, i.e. alternative safe housing, looking at family policy and how contact arrangements force women back into abusive relationships. We have not had time to go into this, but we need to.

Longer-term strategies for making women safe are vital. One thing nobody has mentioned is that on the very last day of the old administration, a new Bill was passed – the Protection from Harassment Act, otherwise known as the stalking legislation, which may offer some hope because it introduces two new criminal offences of harassment and fear of violence which means that the police may be able to intervene on women's behalf after they have left abusive relationships but where they still continue to be harassed.

Lloyd: I wanted to make a couple of points which go back to what Stephanie Yearnshire said. The first is about communication – not just communication between professionals but between professionals and the woman concerned. Research reports have repeatedly stated that women do not know what is happening once they get into the system as prosecution proceeds. We need to stop and remember that and look at that area again.

The second point is in relation to the question of who does the policing. It is all very well to acknowledge that police attitudes have changed hugely over the last ten years but there is a vast difference between the policy-makers within the police and the practitioners on the ground.

When it comes to the implementation of Standing Orders, a couple of years ago a colleague and I researched all the specialist units in Scotland and found a number of things that were disquieting within the framework of change and new departures. Amongst the police themselves, domestic violence units and female and child enquiry units were called things like the 'Women and Waifs', or the 'Nappy Squads', or much more derogatory names as well. There were issues in relation to resources for these units. Very often they had cramped office space, they were sharing cars or did not have cars, they were often borrowing lifts across town, there were questions about how records were kept, where they were kept. There were issues about how the units were staffed, whether they were only 9 am–5 pm units, during the daytime only, not at weekends, and then the work reverted to the CID who had much less training than the specialist officers.

Lastly, there was the really important business of how police officers are appointed to do this work. Are they appointed because it is work that they want to do, that they actively support the women who are lodging the complaints, or are they doing it unwillingly and they would rather be doing 'real' police work somewhere else, or do they see it as a career opportunity? This research was conducted a couple of years ago, so is still valid.

Jones: Perhaps I can expand on the idea of medical 'informed consent'. This used to be based on whatever the physician felt the patient needed to know. Now the model of informed consent is what the patient needs to know as defined by the patient. If there is an analogy here, it seems to me that the standard in terms of violence needs to be what the victim thinks is all right and not what the perpetrator decides is all right. That is a slight shift.

The College should certainly be involved in identifying domestic violence in the Maternal Deaths Enquiries. We deal with maternal deaths all the time and the statistics are appalling. As I mentioned in my presentation, the most common maternal deaths result from murder and not ruptured uterus, and therefore that is a worthwhile thing for the College to do.

Anti-stalking laws in the USA have been an abominable failure. They just do not work, nor do restraining orders. In the USA a woman has to pay to file a restraining order and she has to pay the county sheriff to serve the order and that costs $50 or $75. Most of these women do not have that money; furthermore, these orders do not work. Restraining orders and anti-stalking laws sound right, but they are not easy to police.

Finally, police departments across the United States have been riddled with macho guys and the thing that they least like to do is go out on what they call 'a domestic'. Domestic disputes are at the bottom of the pile – they are for the young recruits. In Connecticut that attitude resulted in a legal case where the police did not bother to respond for two hours and the woman is now a quadriplegic resulting from secondary beating by her husband. The woman had called and called and called.

Mezey: I would like to make a point in relation to the Enquiries into Maternal Deaths. There is also a national committee (Confidential Enquiry into Stillbirths and Deaths in Infancy – CESDI) looking at causes of stillbirth. They have failed to separate out trauma from intentional, malevolent violence, for example, differentiating between a stillbirth due to a violent assault and from a road traffic accident. Perhaps this is something that needs to be looked at.

Lewis: Can I come back to CESDI and the Maternal Deaths Enquiries as there are significant differences. With the Maternal Deaths Enquiries, we fortunately have far fewer numbers and can get to the bottom of every case. CESDI are overwhelmed with case numbers, but they are trying to look at how they can get better information. The process is being refined all the time.

Chapter 14

Voluntary agencies

Anne Viney

The United Kingdom is characterised by its rich and diverse voluntary sector. But by 'voluntary sector' do we mean organisations run by volunteers, charities, non-profit-making organisations, or all of these?

One way of characterising voluntary agencies is by function, as follows:

(1) Service providers;

(2) Research, advocacy and action groups;

(3) Self-help groups;

(4) Intermediary bodies (Handy 1988).

Of course it is not uncommon for voluntary agencies to fulfil more than one of these functions, as is the case with Women's Aid and Victim Support.

It is important for medical professionals to obtain clear information about the function of voluntary agencies in order to liaise on behalf of patients. Service providers such as Women's Aid provide vital support services such as emergency refuges and advice. Victim Support can help women who may be considering whether they should report a crime to the police. Citizens Advice Bureaux (CAB) will be able to provide advice on housing and benefits. Self-help groups may help women who have had a traumatic experience to regain personal autonomy and a feeling of self-worth by helping others in a similar situation. Agencies undertaking research and advocacy give women a chance to contribute to knowledge in this difficult field by sharing their experiences.

IDENTITY

In the voluntary sector, identity is as important as function. The following are some very general characteristics which are relevant to the identity of voluntary sector organisations:

(1) Importance of strong ethical value base;

(2) Empowerment of staff, volunteers, customers;

(3) Value of small, flat, flexible organisations;

(4) Teamwork;

(5) Participation in decision-making;

(6) Inter-agency co-operation (Courtney 1996).

Values will tend to have a strong effect on the organisation's history, origins, and current structure and working methods. Federated structures are common and provide an opportunity for local autonomy in fairly small local organisations. Such local organisations are linked to a national code of practice, statement of aims and values or other conditions which bind them to one broad remit with local variations.

What can voluntary agencies provide? The range of help available is too complex to list in detail here – the following are examples only:

(1) Housing;

(2) Benefits;

(3) Support;

(4) Advocacy;

(5) Refuges;

(6) Legal advice;

(7) Support with police and courts;

(8) Family and child care issues;

(9) Counselling for individuals, couples or families.

This chapter will focus on the work of Victim Support schemes, as one of a number of relevant agencies.

VICTIM SUPPORT: A NATIONAL CHARITY

Victim Support schemes operate a nationwide service with 890 staff and 11,000 volunteers. Witness services are provided in the Crown Courts in addition to local schemes. Victim Support has developed a national code of practice for standards and training and has recently published a number of influential documents on its work.

Victim Support's national network grew from one local initiative which was then supported by Government funding (Rock 1990), as is the case for many voluntary agencies. Those who started the first local group in Bristol in 1974 were members of NACRO (National Association for the Care and Resettlement of Offenders), an organisation for offenders. They had enough experience of the reality of the effects of crime to recognise that victims were largely neglected.

In this early initiative, the police were persuaded to refer victims of burglary, and volunteers were trained to provide support for the unexpectedly high levels of distress, confusion and mistreatment by the system that were found.

Victim Support's work with victims grew in volume and scope to include victims of serious violent and sexual crimes. This has not been done without investigation of the implications of this expansion, or preparation for the consequences. Most voluntary agencies in my experience do not move into new areas of work without careful thought, including talking to other agencies in the field. Before accepting referrals of women who had been victims of rape, we convened an expert working party to advise on practice and training. The resulting training programmes have since been tried, tested and updated, and local groups work in co-operation with Rape Crisis and Women's Aid.

Research and advocacy are important functions of voluntary sector groups. Most voluntary agencies have statistical evidence drawn from their records which provides unique evidence about the problems of violence against women. In 1995/6, local Victim Support Schemes offered help to 3431 women who had been raped. In November 1996 we carried out a survey of our members in relation to this important work (Victim Support 1996). The survey provided information about 646 rape referrals, 506 of which had been reported to the police. Despite the relatively high reporting level in this sample, a lack of protection and the women's vulnerability to further attack were illustrated by evidence of the following:

(1) Harassment/assault by friends and family of the defendant;

(2) Harassment/assault by the defendant (often a former partner);

(3) Enforced house moves (reported by 23 per cent of the Victim Support schemes who responded to the survey);

(4) Threats to the victim's children;

(5) Damage to the victim's home/property.

This survey is an example of the valuable information voluntary agencies can provide; it used no additional outside research resources, having been compiled from Victim Support's own confidential records. Eleven women also agreed to provide individual anonymous interviews.

Inter-agency collaboration is essential in the voluntary sector given scarce resources and ever-increasing demand. Inter-agency work helps to break down misunderstanding and provides a multi-faceted service to women, whilst still allowing each agency to keep within its own specialist remit. Victim Support convened its working party on Domestic Violence in response to demands placed on local schemes to provide a service in this area (Victim

Support 1992). Members of the working party included Women's Aid, Relate, the Royal College of General Practitioners, the British Association of Social Workers, the Law Society, the Institute of Housing, Probation Services, the police and Dr Susan Edwards of the University of Buckingham. Evidence was taken from an even wider range of individuals and organisations, illustrating the range of expertise which is needed to deal with this very difficult issue.

The resulting report strongly recommended the formation of local Domestic Violence forums. The suggested terms of reference were to:

(1) Compile information about local services;

(2) Co-operate so as to make best use of local resources;

(3) Distribute information for women as widely as possible, including information in minority languages;

(4) Promote suitable training, include inter-agency training if appropriate;

(5) Raise public and professional awareness;

(6) Develop and improve services;

(7) Encourage and promote crime prevention.

Input from medical professionals is vital if local forums are to succeed.

Victim Support's own response to domestic violence was further developed as a result of the working party. We recognised the need for workers to understand the complexity and range of problems for women, and why abuse continues for so long before women are able to seek help. Victim Support therefore had to institute appropriate training. We needed to elicit co-operation with other agencies, especially Women's Aid. In cases of domestic violence we also had to be acutely aware that confidentiality is also a safety issue.

In addition we had to reconsider the issue of worker safety. Like some other agencies which may be giving help in this field (such as CAB, law centres, Relate), Victim Support addresses and telephone numbers are public and workers could be subject to threats from violent men.

Many victims of crime find the decision of whether to report a crime a difficult one, and this is particularly the case for victims of domestic violence. Where women seek help from Victim Support about this, our task is to explain criminal justice procedures and the possible consequences and to provide support to women in their decision. Should a case reach the Crown Court, help is available from our witness service.

Lastly, I offer some suggestions as to how medical professionals can work alongside voluntary agencies.

(1) Get to know local organisations and keep updating information. This may not be easy if the catchment area for referrals is a wide one. Most

Councils of Voluntary Service (local umbrella bodies) publish a directory, and these are worth subscribing to.

(2) Obtain and display voluntary organisation publicity material in waiting rooms, clinics and wards.

(3) Develop a policy for responding to disclosures of domestic violence, offering advice, reporting, etc.

(4) Offer to assist local organisations. Is there an organisation in your area which would appreciate your help, advice, or input to training?

REFERENCES

Courtney, R. (1996) *Managing Voluntary Organisations*. Hemel Hempstead: ICSA Publishing

Handy, C. (1988) *Understanding voluntary organisations*, London: Penguin

Rock, P. (1990) *Helping Victims of Crime: The Home Office and the Rise of Victim Support in England and Wales*. Oxford: Clarendon Press

Victim Support (1992) *Domestic Violence: Report of a National Inter-Agency Working Party*. London: Victim Support

Victim Support (1996) *Women, Rape and the Criminal Justice System*. London: Victim Support

Chapter 15

The role of Women's Aid and refuge support services for women and children

Nicola Harwin

INTRODUCTION

For nearly 25 years, Women's Aid refuge services throughout the UK have given practical and emotional support to women and children living with violence and abuse. In the absence of legal or statutory provision, the first refuges were set up in response to women's desperate need for a place to stay with their children, where their violent partners could not find them. Since those early days, Women's Aid has continued to be the key support agency for women and children experiencing physical, emotional and sexual violence and abuse in their homes, and has expanded the range of services and improved the quality of refuge provision.

The Women's Aid Federation of England (WAFE) is the national organisation which supports and resources the English network of 240 local refuge projects. There are also sister organisations in Wales, Scotland and Northern Ireland. We offer a unique national network of safe accommodation, specialist help, advocacy and residential and outreach support.

In England alone, over 42,000 women and children use refuges each year and there are over 100,000 calls to Women's Aid services for advice and help (Ball 1994). Research shows that refuges are the only services which are consistently praised by women who have experienced violence (Smith 1989). Refuges are not simply a resource for 'when all else fails', but an integral part of the process of obtaining protection under the criminal and civil justice systems. This role is clearly recognised by the Inter-Agency Working Party Report (National Inter-Agency Working Party 1992) and the Home Affairs Select Committee Report into Domestic Violence (Home Office 1993).

THE WOMEN'S AID APPROACH: OUR VALUES AND PRINCIPLES

(1) To believe women's and children's experience of abuse and make their safety a priority;

(2) To support and empower women to take control of their own lives;

(3) To recognise and care for the needs of children affected by domestic violence;

(4) To promote equal opportunities and anti-discrimination in all our work and services.

The work and standards of local member groups are informed by these principles and by other policy statements and good practice guidelines. The majority of our members are local refuges and agencies that run support services for women and children. Refuges offer a safe breathing space for women and children escaping domestic violence.

Local Women's Aid groups provide a range of services that benefit women and children, including:

(1) 24-hour access to emergency refuge;

(2) Information, advice and support;

(3) Outreach support to women who may not want refuge;

(4) Advocacy: legal and welfare rights;

(5) Specialised services for children;

(6) Aftercare and follow-up;

(7) Education and public awareness.

PRIORITISING WOMEN'S AND CHILDREN'S SAFETY

A key role of refuges has been to offer women safe, confidential help and safe emergency accommodation. A crucial part of this is protecting the secrecy of refuges and the confidentiality of telephone numbers and addresses. This safety can be threatened if other agencies do not understand the realities of abuse, women's experiences and how charming and devious abusive men can be in order to find women.

The concern of Women's Aid groups to protect the safety of women and children escaping domestic violence is an important feature of the Women's Aid refuge network. It offers safety and security to women and children who may need to move out of their local area to another part of the United Kingdom, where they cannot easily be found by their partners. If a woman's whereabouts are discovered, she can very quickly be moved to another refuge and will be given support in settling herself and her children in the new area. It is for this reason that telephone numbers and addresses of refuges are kept confidential.

Women's Aid national office has clear guidelines on confidentiality, including confidentiality in relation to women users (whether or not they use the refuge), children, employees, management members, etc. Women's Aid groups do not disclose information to other agencies without women's knowledge and consent. If confidentiality has to be limited or breached then this is made clear to women. Limits to confidentiality are primarily in relation to children and child abuse issues.

Women's Aid also operates an 'open door' policy, which means that no woman or child needing refuge will be turned away without assistance. Women can refer themselves to a refuge, rather than having to be reliant on an official organisation and Women's Aid refuges do not require women to offer proof. This does not mean that a refuge, however full, will accept all referrals; it means Women's Aid will not turn women away without assistance and will offer an emergency place overnight, find another refuge place or help with other emergency accommodation, e.g. bed and breakfast.

WORKING WITH ABUSED WOMEN: PROMOTING EMPOWERMENT

Being in a refuge, or in contact with other women survivors, gives women a breathing space from an abusive situation. They have time to reflect on their own needs and to overcome their isolation and sense of shame which many women feel at being abused by a partner, ex-partner or family member. A vital aspect of ending an abusive relationship can be the opportunity to share experiences with other survivors – through talking, discussion and mutual support when dealing with day-to-day problems and practical tasks. Many women who use refuge services have remained involved with Women's Aid and later become volunteers or paid staff themselves.

For women who have been in abusive relationships with men, becoming empowered means taking control back from the abuser. They are able to gain self-esteem, self-confidence and the financial, material and emotional resources to control their own lives, rather than living under the influence or control of a violent man. For this reason, the principle of the women-only group – women helping women – can support this process by providing powerful role-modelling. Many women also prefer to receive services from female staff in helping agencies (Hague and Malos 1993). Finally, refuge services run by women for women can contribute to maintaining safety and security procedures within the refuge or advice centre. This need not compromise inter-agency working or the individual support needs of users, as male professionals, such as solicitors or doctors, can visit or be involved by prior arrangement.

THE RANGE OF SERVICES OFFERED BY WOMEN'S AID

The refuge

A refuge is the basic building block of provision. Safe emergency accommodation is one of the most vital needs of women and children escaping violence. Women can stay in a refuge from one night to two years, and many women will use refuges more than once as part of the process of ending an abusive relationship. However, if refuge security has been breached and the address becomes known to the violent partner of a woman wishing to re-enter the refuge, she may have to be referred elsewhere. Individual refuge policies on this vary.

Refuge provision varies enormously from purpose-built houses for five or more families, to three-bedroom semis let on short-term lease from a local authority. In recognition of institutional racism as well as the specific cultural or practical needs of some women, there are a number of specialist refuges; for black women (African women, Asian women), as well as other specific ethnic groups (e.g. Turkish women, Latin-American women).

Although refuges have to be operated as safe emergency accommodation for many women, often with a high turnover, Women's Aid refuges become a home to women and children. This means supporting women to learn to live co-operatively with other women and children and to share responsibility for the management of the house on a day-to-day basis. Staff facilitate regular weekly house meetings to air problems and discuss issues, as well as agreeing rotas for cleaning and other tasks. In some refuges, children's support workers facilitate similar meetings for children, to help empower them and to encourage non-aggressive resolution of problems and conflicts.

Advocacy and support with all aspects of legal, welfare and housing rights

A key element of all our work is providing support for women and children and advocating on their behalf with all the agencies with which they have to interact as part of the process of ending the violence. Emotional and practical help and support is offered with all aspects of legal, welfare, housing and financial matters. A refuge is often used as a safe place from which to apply for legal protection, or as a last resort when injunctions fail (as they do so often). Access to safe alternative accommodation is often the only way to live free from abuse and Women's Aid has worked for many years to improve public housing policy and local authority responses to women and children homeless because of violence.

Day-to-day experience of the ineffectiveness of legal protection for abused women and children under both the civil and criminal law has meant that Women's Aid has consistently lobbied for better provision and enforcement.

From the beginning we have also been 'institutional advocates', lobbying for improvements to law, policies and practice in relation to domestic violence and working with other agencies and practitioners to initiate and implement change in criminal justice, social welfare and housing responses to violence against women and children in their homes.

Outreach

There has always been a demand for help and support from women who, for whatever reason, do not want to use refuges, as well as from women in temporary accommodation, such as bed and breakfast or local authority hostels, where no support or help is provided. In practice this has often been difficult to meet, because of the discrepancy between our resources and level of demand. This demand on Women's Aid services has increased since the improvement of responses by some other agencies, notably the police.

The range of outreach work has expanded through a number of recent initiatives: for example, the development of separate advice centres, specialist projects for Asian women and a number of rural initiatives. Outreach work in conjunction with primary health care services such as Health Visitors and GPs is also being developed. The success of mutual support systems in refuges provides a model for the development of support groups of women survivors within the community. In some areas these groups have operated from Women's Aid drop-in centres and been run for both non-residents and ex-residents of refuges. On average, refuges give aftercare support to 24 families each year, although only 10 per cent have specific staff for this work (Ball 1994).

Work with children in Women's Aid

Many children coming into refuges have been abused; some may have been forced to watch or take part in abuse of their mothers; some will have tried to intervene and stop the violence; most will also have suffered indirectly from the abuse their mothers have experienced. Research into work with children in refuges has shown, however, that the effects of witnessing or experiencing domestic violence can be alleviated or reversed if child-centred activities and adequate support and resources are available (Ball 1990).

All refuges provide specific services and resources for children in refuges and over 75 per cent of refuges have children's support workers. These staff are not just 'play workers' but do one-to-one work, group work, run holiday schemes as well as provide advocacy for children to outside agencies, liaise with schools, education and welfare departments, health visitors, etc.

Since the early 1990s, WAFE has developed a national training programme for refuge staff and external agencies to improve policy development and service provision to abused women and children. Underlying all work with children both in and after their stay in refuges is a recognition of the need to promote non-violent relationships, to support women and children to develop non-violent strategies for managing family life, as well as to challenge traditional sex-role stereotyping which can reinforce and support abusive relationships.

Refuges have often had a key role since the 1970s in identifying child abuse, as children may disclose for the first time to child-workers. Many Women's Aid groups in England are jointly developing child-protection policies and procedures with their local social service departments. These aim to satisfy both the needs of social services to protect children and our commitment to protecting and empowering both women and children. Our guiding principle is that the safety and empowerment of the non-abusing parent (usually the mother) is the most effective form of child protection.

EDUCATION, PUBLIC AWARENESS AND INTER-AGENCY WORK

Education and public awareness have always been a key focus of local and national activity, as the biggest problem we encounter is the prevailing attitude to domestic violence. Unhelpful stereotypes abound about the 'types' of women, 'types' of families or alcohol, drugs and poverty being the cause of violence. All of these are discounted by research (Smith 1989) and the practical experience of the Women's Aid movement since the early 1970s. Local groups have for many years tried to raise awareness of the extent of the problem through local talks, media contact and joint initiatives with specific local voluntary and statutory agencies. More recently, Women's Aid has been in the forefront of multi-agency initiatives to tackle domestic violence, although their development has not been unproblematic, given difference in status and knowledge of participating agencies (see Hague and Malos 1996). The specific expertise of Women's Aid and our unique status as the only agency to offer independent advocacy for women and children escaping domestic violence, makes our participation vital. The Home Office Inter-agency Circular of August 1995 recommends that statutory agencies, with more resources, should look at how they can enable this.

REFERRAL AND CONTACT

Referral procedures vary locally. Many local groups now have separate public numbers but the addresses and phone numbers of refuges themselves are confidential and may only be given out to specific agencies or individuals where it is clear that they must not be passed on without permission or given out to violent partners or other family members in any circumstances. Women frequently self-refer via word of mouth and Women's Aid refuges rarely require women to offer proof of violence.

Many groups also have separate public telephone numbers and can be found in the telephone directory. Outside normal working hours, some groups have 24-hour contact via telephone switch-over systems, or pagers; others organise out-of-hours referrals through other 24-hour services such as the police or Samaritans or emergency duty teams of the social services who then contact the refuge; some groups only have resources for answerphone systems at night with police and other numbers on them. However, over 50 per cent of groups do provide 24-hour contact systems or helplines, using rotas of staff and voluntary members. Thirty per cent of refuge projects have separate offices or advice centres which offer a public drop-in point for face-to-face help and advice; others will arrange to meet women in safe locations if they just want to talk.

If the local refuge is full, staff or volunteers will either support the woman in applying to the local housing department for emergency accommodation, or find her a place in a refuge out of the area until space becomes available. For some women, referral on to another refuge is the preferred option if they have friends or family elsewhere or feel it is too dangerous to stay in their local area.

To support this national network of provision, Women's Aid national office publishes and regularly updates the only UK-wide telephone contact list which is used by over 300 refuge groups to find women somewhere to stay. Access to local services and support is also facilitated by the Women's Aid National Helpline (0345-023-468) and by other regional, and locally-based, helplines.

Any agency or practitioner is advised to contact their local refuge to find out their local referral procedures, or for more information on specific policy aspects of referrals. Admissions policies will vary, although member groups within WAFE strive to operate an 'open door' policy, whereby no woman or child needing refuge will be turned away without assistance in finding some safe accommodation. However, project guidelines may vary – some refuges have admissions policies which limit access for families with teenage boys, or women with substance dependence. 'Open door' may be limited in practice by access for women with disabilities or by lack of provision for women with specific language or cultural requirements.

FURTHER LIMITS TO THE HELP WE CAN OFFER

The range of services offered by refuge groups, and in particular the balance between direct services to women and children and associated education and interagency work, is maintained with difficulty because of limited resources. An independent study into refuges concluded that funding is grossly inadequate, inconsistent and insecure (Ball 1994). All refuges are heavily dependent on volunteer input – averaging 129 hours per month. Most groups can only function by relying on the goodwill and commitment of both voluntary and paid staff working extra hours.

There are still less than a third of the refuge spaces recommended by the 1975 Government Select Committee Report on Violence in Marriage (Home

Office 1975). Existing refuge services are located very unevenly throughout the country and are virtually non-existent in rural areas. The 1992 Home Affairs Select Committee recommended that: 'the first priority for Government action on domestic violence should be the establishment of a central co-ordinated policy for refuge provision throughout the country.'

THE WORK OF WOMEN'S AID NATIONALLY

Women's Aid aims to promote the protection of women and children who have suffered from, or are exposed to, domestic violence. This includes the preservation and protection of their mental and physical health, the relief of need and the promotion of research and education about domestic violence.
   Our work includes:

(1) Running the Women's Aid National Helpline for women experiencing domestic violence. The National Helpline deals with thousands of calls from women experiencing domestic violence. Helpline volunteers and staff give advice and information, as well as a much-needed listening ear.

(2) Co-ordinating and supporting the network of 240 local refuge groups throughout England. This area of work includes:

   (a) Helping groups to develop refuges and other support services for women and children;
   (b) Providing advice and information on all aspects of refuge work, including management, children's work, housing, legal issues, publicity and fund-raising;
   (c) Providing refuges with training on all aspects of domestic violence and refuge work;
   (d) Producing the only UK-wide Directory of Refuge and Helpline Services;
   (e) Organising networking events and conferences for all refuge groups to enable them to meet, share good practice and develop their services.

(3) Training and educating the public, media and relevant professionals about domestic violence.

(4) Providing information and research about all aspects of domestic violence.

(5) Lobbying for relevant policy and legislative changes to improve the safety of women and children experiencing or leaving domestic violence.

(6) Raising awareness of domestic violence among the public, policy makers, practitioners and the media.

(7) Providing Women's Aid's members with a package of benefits to support their work with women and children experiencing domestic violence.

REFERENCES

Ball, M. (1994) *Funding Refuge Services*. Bristol: Women's Aid Federation of England

Hague, G. and Malos, E. (1996) *Multi-agency Responses to Domestic Violence*. Bristol: Policy Press

Smith, L. (1989) *Domestic Violence*. Working Paper No. 107. London: HMSO

Home Office (1975) *Government Select Committee Report on Violence in Marriage*. London: HMSO

Home Office (1993) *Home Affairs Select Committee Report into Domestic Violence*. London: HMSO

National Inter-Agency Working Party (1992) *Domestic Violence*. Report of a National Inter-Agency Working Party. London: Victim Support

Chapter 16

Institutional responses

Discussion (2)

Edwards: There is a need for resources to be allocated from central government. In the USA the Violence Against Women Act 1994 has resulted in a lot of money being pumped in for refuges, shelters and a whole range of projects. Uniquely and importantly, they have redefined domestic violence as a civil liberties issue for women, in the sense that the majority of victims of domestic violence are women and they get a poor service, whether it is from criminal or civil justice agencies, housing provision, etc.

Lloyd: I wanted to echo what Nicola Harwin was saying about rural women. I was pleased to see that being mentioned today, as I come from a part of the world where we have a huge rural hinterland. A conference in Aberdeen in 1996 looked at women's access to all sorts of services and resources in rural areas. When it came to the issue of domestic violence, a number of important things came out. One was the double isolation that women in these areas feel. If they were being attacked in their homes, then very often no-one could hear; there was no-one next door or in the flat below or above. There was then the whole question of where to go.

Research done in Tayside, around Dundee, in 1996 suggests that there are a couple of simple and important things which can significantly affect women's mental health and their ability to get support in rural areas. One of these is access to telephones; we know that rural telephones are not thick on the ground. Secondly, access to public transport, which again is difficult in rural areas. Thirdly, the fact that resources are away from the environment rather than in it or near it. Of course, Women's Aid in rural areas of Scotland, and particularly in the Island communities, have all these issues and more to face.

S. Bewley: I wondered whether the national telephone helpline is a free phone? I know that in the USA there is a toll-free line which the whole country knows about and is encouraged to ring, primarily so that it enters the public knowledge and consciousness. Does the Women's Aid Federation encourage the central number that everyone can use?

Harwin: Our number has recently become an 0345 number because that is all we can afford. We would make it 0800 if we could, but we are unable to bear the cost.

Regarding the issue of a national helpline, we feel that it is important that there is one, but equally the best access for women should generally be to something local. We feel that women need to have proper 24-hour access at a local level and a national line needs to back that up. Very often we find that women use a national helpline to talk about things that they do not feel at that point able to talk about to anybody locally, or they do not know who to talk to locally. They do not necessarily want refuge. Some of them keep the number and use it from time to time. It would be wonderful if there was a national system that could immediately give the woman access to information from a computer, for example, 'yes, there is a refuge down the road and it has four bed spaces', but we are a long way from that at the moment.

S. Bewley: That would seem something not terribly expensive which this new government might be interested in funding. It is very public, it is very simple and it cannot cost that much.

Harwin: Yes, they might. The problem is that we already have 20,000 women a year phoning us. If they want refuge space and there is no refuge in the area, or it only has one paid staff member who cannot be at the end of a phone 24 hours a day, then the system breaks down. It works all right for the women who do not want immediate refuge or immediate counselling services, which do not exist, unless they are the ones attached to refuges. But there simply aren't the resources or counselling services available for more.

Friend: In terms of the helpline, I cannot help feeling that it must be very important, not only for helping people but also raising public awareness as well. I wondered whether this has been very effective in the USA, in what way it has been effective and should we be going for a higher profile helpline? I am in no way undermining what is happening in Women's Aid, but should it be on a different level altogether?

Jones: If you are going to have a national helpline, you had better do it right because we did it wrong the first time. We had a number up and running and when women called it they would get a recording which said that this number was no longer in service. At 3 am when a woman thinks she is going to be murdered, that does not work. If you are going to do it, get the funding and do it right.

As it is currently funded, all that is being offered in the USA is a local telephone number, sometimes a local agency or a local shelter, but there is currently no counselling. They just do not have the personnel to do it. The number of calls is just overwhelming but it is federally funded and I am pretty sure it will stay on-line.

Stanko: It is important not to think that there is a quick fix or a quick solution. It is very important to recognise that Women's Aid is hanging on by the skin of its teeth and with great effort. I set up a shelter in the United States in 1978 and connected with that was a 24-hour hotline and 13 paid staff, in a small town in Massachusetts. The thought of reproducing that in every refuge in this country would be a tremendous expense and when you begin to think of the kinds of services that are needed and the personnel to do that, you are talking about a fairly hefty financial commitment which does not exist at the moment. Even Victim Support cannot keep up with the demand. We are basically saying that there are some things which exist which help some women, but everyone has to be involved in providing some kind of support.

Mezey: I wanted to ask a question about child victims. My understanding is that there is some kind of age limit on bringing children into refuges, particularly for adolescent boys. This represents a real problem for women who are trying to leave home with their children because there seems to be no place for them. They are potentially allied with the perpetrators of domestic violence.

Harwin: There is no national policy on boys not being allowed in refuges. In fact, the national policy in terms of Good Practice guidelines for Women's Aid is the opposite. There should be no age limit to adolescent males coming to a refuge. There is a general guideline that probably over 16 years is inappropriate and that has developed for a number of reasons. One is because of the co-operative living arrangements. The problem has been exacerbated with the change in social security regulations, which meant that 16-year olds were unable to get any independent income. It was possible before to accommodate young men of 16 and upwards and women could still come to the refuges. The other problems have been to do with young people and children in refuges who can exhibit the most difficult behaviour to handle, particularly if they are big and strong. There are some refuges, however – and they are mainly in London – which have policies about age limits on boys, but it is not a national policy.

Friend: Do the voluntary agencies and other community resources have any direct input to hospitals except via the Social Services Department? In other words, should we be looking towards someone within various directorates or departments that has a responsibility to link with these voluntary agencies, because they are often the organisations which can provide the help?

Harwin: There should be some link. But I wanted to say something more fundamental which I did not have a chance to say earlier. One of the problems in terms of health response which has come to the attention of Women's Aid year after year is getting women onto doctors' registers at all, getting doctors to take on board women who are in refuges. Very often, if you have several women and a lot of children in a refuge, it can have quite an impact on local practices. There is a problem of not being able to get women in a refuge seen by local doctors. That is something that certainly needs to be taken up.

SECTION 5

THE HEALTH PROFESSIONALS

Chapter 17

The health professionals: an overview

Helene Langley

INTRODUCTION

The 1990s have seen the reappearance of domestic violence as a serious issue at a national level. Home Office studies, local surveys, changes in police recording and intervention have all contributed to a growing awareness of the scale of domestic violence, the still inadequate resources and procedures available to women and children and the necessity for agencies to produce an integrated service which will provide for the complex needs of those women and children living in abusive households. The growth of inter-agency forums and the corresponding recognition of the value in multi-agency co-operation is beginning to create a greater understanding among professionals of some of the major issues which must be addressed as well as the acknowledgement that many women experiencing domestic violence fail to receive the response they need when seeking help. One main reason for this failure is the *partial* nature of agency response. While an agency continues to treat only the aspect of the woman's experience which falls within its own remit, the totality of the woman's experience of violence remains invisible.

HEALTH SERVICE'S RESPONSE TO DOMESTIC VIOLENCE

The fragmentary nature of agency response is nowhere more obvious than in women's experience of health professionals. Community health-care teams (health visitors and community paediatric and midwifery services) have, by the nature of their role, greater access to and involvement in a woman's world and may develop more empathy and understanding of the difficulties and fears with which a woman has to cope in her daily efforts to manage her life and that of her children. However, the greater number of medical personnel still remain largely fixed within a medical model of intervention which ignores or marginalises the social context in which a woman's physical, emotional and psychological wounds occur. The non-medical aspects of an abused woman's experience – her fear, isolation, humiliation and shame – framed within silence, largely escape the medical gaze and, in so doing, both reflect and reinforce the woman's own experience of abuse (Warshaw 1989):

> By not asking . . . questions, physicians . . . were unable to address the etiology of the patient's medical condition, could not engage in any preventive measures and . . . did not open up the possibility for the battered woman to discuss what may have been her most important reason for seeking help. They chose to medicalise her chief complaint and address only the physical symptoms, thus reinforcing whatever feelings of helplessness, isolation and futility at not being seen or responded to that the woman may already have felt.

The medical and allied professions are often the first formal agency to which abused women turn for help. Although the scale of domestic violence is not known, current estimates of between one in five and one in three are generally accepted as the likely number of women who have experienced or are experiencing violence from a present or ex-partner. In 1985 Stark and Flitcraft reported that battering may be the single major cause of injury among women in the USA and that between 22 per cent and 35 per cent of all emergency department visits by women are related to battering. Many researchers in the USA and the UK have documented the discrepancy between the large numbers of women coming to health-care settings with symptoms related to living in abusive relationships and the low rate of detection and intervention by medical staff. Lack of training and information on the subject of domestic violence leaves health service professionals unable and unwilling to interact confidently and effectively with women experiencing violence. Research in the UK (Dobash and Dobash 1985; Pahl 1995) has shown that although 80 per cent of battered women went to a doctor at least once during a violent relationship, they did not necessarily report the violence. Those that do disclose abuse to a GP rarely receive time to discuss their experiences or receive practical safety advice. Dobash and Dobash (1980) found that 75 per cent of GPs treated only the injuries and were likely to prescribe tranquillisers and anti-depressants as a palliative measure. This failure to identify and intervene effectively is also true of accident and emergency (A&E) departments. A self-report questionnaire (National Inter-Agency Working Party 1992) completed anonymously by women in A&E departments showed that 24–35 per cent had experienced violence, yet relatively few personnel identify the real cause of women's injuries and distress. There is no formal process to aid identification of female patients presenting with trauma as abused women. Brady and Taylor (1990) found that only one in 25 women who come to an emergency room are identified as battered on their medical records. My own work with women living in a refuge in Kent bears this out. Figures show that out of 208 women living in this refuge during the period January 1995 to January 1997, 63 per cent reported to A&E departments with injuries consistent with battering. Of these, 12 per cent volunteered the cause as domestic violence and 4 per cent were asked how the injuries had been received. The remaining 84 per cent gave no explanation and were not asked. Of the 16 per cent whose injuries were known to be caused by violence, only 10 per cent received further help and advice.

EFFECTS OF VIOLENCE

The effects of domestic violence bring women into contact with the entire spectrum of medical and allied professions. The most common physical assaults involve punching, kicking, biting, hair pulling and hitting with objects. The numerous injuries that women receive include bruises, cuts, fractured bones and internal injuries and miscarriages (Dobash and Dobash 1980). However, abused women also suffer disproportionate rates of general medical and psychiatric problems including pregnancy-related problems, drug abuse, alcoholism and suicide attempts. Pregnancy is a common starting point for domestic violence and a number of research surveys carried out among obstetric services have shown an alarmingly high incidence of abuse among pregnant women. Helton *et al.* (1987) found that 37 per cent of obstetric patients were at risk of abuse during pregnancy. Bowker and Maurer (1987) found that 48 per cent of abused women were assaulted while pregnant. Andrews and Brown (1988) showed that violence tends to worsen during pregnancy and may double the risk of miscarriage. Stark and Flitcraft (1996) found that battered women in their Yale Trauma Study were 15 times more likely to have suffered a miscarriage than non-battered women and Lent (1991) found that typical injuries to pregnant women are to the breast, chest and abdomen. In their chapter on discharge planning, Stark and Flitcraft (1996) suggest that 'persistent gynaecological complaints, particularly abdominal pain, miscarriages and divorce or separation during pregnancy are important presentations of abuse, particularly in obstetric or gynaecological admissions.'

Many female 'mental health' problems such as acute anxiety or panic attacks, agoraphobia, depression, drug or alcohol dependency and suicide attempts can be traced back to domestic violence but will be placed within the psychiatric medical model and treated accordingly. Jacobson and Richardson (1987) found that 64 per cent of hospitalised female psychiatric patients had a history of being assaulted while Stark and Flitcraft (1996) found that one in seven battered women were institutionalised in psychiatric hospitals or received psychiatric referrals without the experience of violence being recorded on their referral notes. The symptoms resulting from living with violence are often treated as if they lie solely in the individual rather than in society and in the abuser. The Yale Trauma Study 1991 (see Stark and Flitcraft 1996) also found that women who had been abused were:

(1) Fifteen times more likely to abuse alcohol;

(2) Nine times more likely to abuse drugs;

(3) Three times more likely to be diagnosed as depressed or psychotic;

(4) Five times more likely to attempt suicide.

They also estimated that 45 per cent of female alcoholics started out as battered women and that about 25 per cent of all female suicide attempts can be traced back to domestic violence.

Women's adaptive responses to the violence, stress and isolation of an abusive relationship with its pattern of coercion and control may result in or mimic psychiatric disorders, particularly those associated with depression or anxiety. The psychosocial aspects of abused women are outside the framework of medical intervention. Instead, the psychosocial consequences of living in an abusive relationship provide the medical services with *labels* that they can organise around and which render the cause of such disorders (the violence) invisible. As Mullender (1996) writes:

> Abuse is more likely to be taken seriously where the woman was seen to be in immediate danger, was not evasive about what had happened, was taking action to leave her partner, was not under the influence of drugs or alcohol and was not acting in a bizarre or dramatic manner but was pleasant and normal.

MODELS OF WORKING PRACTICE

The explanatory model adhered to by those who come into contact with domestic violence will construct a framework within which policy and working practice takes place. The dominant model adhered to by most health service professionals is a medical model in which individual (psycho)pathology is the primary focus of assessment and treatment. Within this framework, the individual pathology of the battered woman is also taken as a causal factor, underpinned by commonly-held myths and stereotypes of domestic violence, and a corresponding 'treatment' programme is provided which may deny or minimise the woman's experience of violence altogether. Most GP and A&E responses to violence are usually confined to treating wounds, prescribing medication and referral to psychiatric services, thereby fitting complex social, psychological and physical problems into neat, clear-cut symptoms that can be defined as treatable. Violence is rarely noted and almost never selected as the focus of intervention.

Many women do not seek help because of the very real fear that they will be neither listened to nor believed. A woman's silence about violence is often mirrored by the medical profession which, by discounting her reality, may reinforce her feelings of isolation and helplessness. A medical model which treats only the physical presentation and removes it from the framework and context in which it takes place may succeed only in repeating the dynamic of abuse that has brought a woman to seek help in the first place. The woman's lived reality will be discounted (Warshaw 1989):

> ... [her] ongoing need to distort her sense of reality in order to survive the pain of abuse ... reinforced by the demands of the medical encounter. Great emphasis needs, therefore, to be placed on the nature of the relationship between health professionals and the woman which takes account of the woman's experience rather than constructing a medical model, controlled by a physician and which extracts events from their context and fixes them in a discrete moment without relationship to either past or future.

As one woman I worked with said in relation to her visit to her local hospital A&E department:

> I wish I'd been asked what had happened. I was so ashamed but I really wanted to tell them. They didn't ask me though and I didn't have the courage to tell them myself. Even though he wasn't there I lied for him just like I always did. They just gave me some painkillers and sent me home. It wasn't any good though, because he thought I'd told them anyway and hit me even though I hadn't. Nobody seemed to believe me.

A feminist critique presents domestic violence within the context of a gender power model which locates women abuse within the unequal power relations in society that are mirrored at the micro-familial level. As Stark and Flitcraft (1996) write:

> Domestic violence has at its core a pattern of coercive control over key aspects of the woman's life. Once the gendered nature of domestic violence disappears, coercive control disappears as the identifiable core, a woman's experience of violence is fragmented into a myriad of more or less serious medical ... events. Without a gender perspective on violence we lose the capacity to recognise the links between one trauma episode and the next.

The feminist critique of present health service interventions presents the case for an empowering model, where the woman's voice may be heard and believed, the right questions asked and the necessary advocacy and support offered. Such a model asks health professionals to reframe their understanding and treatment of the battered woman, to link cause and effect and to look beyond the presenting symptom to the whole person and the totality of her experience. For a woman experiencing violence, it is the violence and fear of further violence that may become the organising principle of her daily life. It is in this context that all her experiences, actions and coping strategies take place. Any attempt to treat one part without an understanding of the whole will place the woman back in her abusive dynamic until the next, possibly fatal, attack.

CHILDREN AND DOMESTIC VIOLENCE

It has already been shown that pregnant women are especially at risk of abuse, with a corresponding risk to the unborn child. Children, too, suffer significant difficulties as a result of living in a violent household. Hughes (1992) indicates that in 90 per cent of incidents of domestic violence, children are in the same or the next room. Children may be caught up in the abuse dynamic in a number of different ways:

(1) Some may be used as pawns to threaten or humiliate the woman;

(2) Some may intervene directly to try to stop the violence and themselves suffer injury;

(3) Some may be abused themselves.

Whichever level of involvement a child has, it is generally agreed by researchers, clinicians and children's workers in refuges that children from violent households are likely to suffer psychological damage, behavioural adjustment difficulties and a range of other health and social adjustment problems. Many of these bring children into contact with health service professionals. A model of working – one which recognises and understands the impact of domestic violence, gives a child permission to break the silence and locates the problem in the abuse rather than in the woman – is vital. Children rarely find an opportunity to talk freely and openly about their fear, anger, hurt and confusion. The silence that constructs their reality places heavy burdens on them. A six-year-old girl I worked with told me that she liked being in a refuge better than being at home because she felt she was the same as everybody else. She said, 'I don't have secrets now. My friends are the same as me. In my other school I had to keep secrets about my Daddy hitting my Mummy. I've got lots of friends now.'

There is increasing evidence that woman abuse and child abuse are linked. In 1994, the National Children's Homes (NCH) found that in 25 per cent of cases the male partner had also been violent to the child (Abrahams 1994) and a London Borough of Hackney research project in 1993 found that one third of children on the child protection register had mothers who were experiencing domestic violence. It becomes increasingly important, therefore, to identify and support women who are being abused at an early stage in order to minimise further harm to both women and children.

THE WAY FORWARD – NEW INITIATIVES

The traditions of a medical–social divide have been an obstacle to the fully effective response by health service providers to the problems posed by domestic violence. In the absence of institutionalised policies and procedures for diagnosing and treating women who have been abused staff may either resort to commonly-held myths and stereotypes or maintain their reluctance to take on multiple role responsibilities under the pressure of time, overwork and limited resources. Although injuries are apparent and unexplained and distress obvious, medical personnel do not generally feel equipped or have the confidence to deal with the complex social problems presented by a battered woman so do not ask key questions or pursue the matter in the face of a woman's reluctance: 'Policy makers need to support staff with adequate training, resources and information, clear guidelines and systematic co-operation with other agencies' (Mullender 1996). In particular, there is increasing evidence that lack of training in the issues surrounding domestic violence for all health professionals and lack of clear protocols for dealing with domestic violence in hospitals lies at the root of the failure of many health service providers to document, identify and offer appropriate woman-centred intervention to patients experiencing abuse.

Domestic violence is only now being identified as a major public health problem. The National Crime Survey in the USA (Inter-University Consortium for Political and Social Research 1981) showed that, in 1980, as a result of battering, there were 28,700 emergency department visits, 39, 000 physician visits, 21,000 hospitalisations and 99,800 days of patient hospitalisation. Total health-care costs associated with battered women came to US$44.4 million. The financial burden placed on the health-care system has largely been ignored, although 'the UN (Beijing Conference), the World Health Organisation and the World Bank are all beginning to indicate the global impact on women's health and on the call made upon health, disability and care services by the injuries and stress male abuse causes to women' (Mullender 1996). In 1991, a major campaign in the USA relating to domestic violence was launched by the American Medical Association. At the same time the American College of Obstetricians and Gynecologists took the lead in producing a leaflet, 'The Abused Woman', as part of its Women's Health Series. The Australian Government's policy statement on women's health also identifies violence as a priority. Research into the extent and cost to the health service of domestic violence is still at an early stage in the UK but it is quite clear that the accumulated costs to all sectors of the health service are high. A new collaboration between epidemiologists, policy makers, researchers, practitioners and health professionals could lead to a more successful method of reducing abuse and empowering women to take control of their lives. Such changes rely on encouraging and enabling abused women to break their silence in a context of appropriate and non-punitive support and advice by professional agencies to whom they may go for help.

PROGRAMMES AND INTERVENTION

In the UK not much is known about the numbers of abused women who visit A&E departments and about the way they are treated. However, Stark, Flitcraft and Frazier (1979) examined the medical records of 481 women at the Yale-New Haven Hospital who had been treated for injuries. Physicians were asked to estimate the number of abused women they treated in a sample month and their estimates were compared with data from the records. During this month, 14 women were identified (2.8 per cent). However, from the full records the researchers were able positively to identify 10 per cent as battered, with another 15 per cent who had trauma histories pointing to the likelihood of abuse: 'What physicians described as a rare occurrence was really an event of epidemic proportions.' The study was also able to examine how battered women were perceived and treated by health staff. There was a high incidence of psychiatric referral and a failure to respond to the context as well as the discrete injuries.

A study of the clinical notes of all patients attending the A&E department of the Leicester Royal Infirmary in 1988 with a history of assault were studied (Smith *et al.* 1992). The study did not exclude patients suffering abuse on the basis of gender. Many of the patients had no details noted about the circumstances of the assault or who had assaulted them and the authors state that the study undoubtedly underestimated the number of abuse cases presenting to the department. They point to the inadequate training received by medical students about family violence, with no in-service training for medical and nursing staff employed in A&E and no protocol for dealing with domestic violence in the hospital. The authors conclude:

> Although the health authorities may not be able to prevent adult domestic violence, they should acknowledge the problem and provide victims with appropriate help and facilitate secondary and tertiary prevention, e.g. counselling and refuge. The development of working protocols and the education of personnel involved in the primary and hospital services should achieve these aims.

TRAINING INITIATIVES

There has been considerable progress in the setting up of working protocols in the USA which focus on identifying abused women, validating their experience, training health-care staff in the issues about domestic violence and appropriate forms of multi-agency resources and raising awareness and challenging attitudes among staff in order to improve detection and response. A study by McLeer and Anwar (1989) in the emergency department of the Medical College of Pennsylvania looked at the results of administering a protocol aimed at identifying battered women. The protocol contained a number of questions and directly asked if the women had been injured by someone. It was administered by triage nurses who had been trained in the issues of domestic violence and received information about community resources. In 1977, after a year of administering the protocol, the positive identification of battering rose from 5.6 per cent to 30 per cent. Most health-care professionals have received little or no training about domestic violence and lack the confidence to ask direct questions or intervene effectively with battered women. A programme in Minnesota provided an integrated approach which brought together medical and non-medical staff, initially in the emergency department but later throughout the entire hospital. The key to the programme's success was seen as ongoing training for medical staff. Other programmes in the USA to train nursing staff aim to dispel myths and stereotypes held by students, encourage nurses to view domestic violence as a health problem and enable them to ask direct questions within a framework of greater awareness of the issues. Nurses who have completed the course have been used to develop assessment tools in specific medical areas such as maternity clinics (Mandt 1993).

CONCLUSION

Domestic violence is firmly on the health agenda. Battered women can no longer be ignored in health-care settings and new initiatives are being developed in all areas as the result of greater co-operation between agencies through inter-agency forums and multi-agency training groups. Statutory agencies such as Social Services and Probation are beginning to develop policy and procedures around domestic violence. The fragmentary nature of the health service, with community teams and hospital teams rarely meeting, may make it difficult to develop a co-ordinated approach to the identification and treatment of battered women. However, health-care professionals are in a position to give direct support to women experiencing abuse even if that support merely takes the form of listening, believing and understanding the woman's reality. As Mullender (1996) writes: 'The health professional who understands abuse as part of a continuum of unwarranted, coercive, cruel and gendered behaviours is more likely to appreciate what a woman has been through and is thus better able to give her a model for survival.'

REFERENCES

Abrahams, C. (1994) *The Hidden Victims: Children and Domestic Violence*. London: NCH Action for Children

Andrews, B. and Brown, G.W. (1988) Marital violence in the community. *Br J Psychiatry* **153**, 305–12

Bowker, L.H. and Maurer, L. (1987) The medical treatment of battered wives. *Women and Health* **12**, 25–45

Brady, M. and Taylor, W. (1990) Break the vicious circle. *The Health Service Journal*, June, **882**

Dobash, R.E. and Dobash, R.P. (1980) *Violence against Wives*. London: Open Books

Dobash, R.E., Dobash, R.P. and Cavanagh, K. (1985) 'The contact between battered women and social and medical agencies' in J. Pahl (Ed.) *Private Violence and Public Policy*. London: Routledge and Kegan Paul

Helton, A.S., Anderson, E. and McFarlane, J. (1987) Battered and pregnant: a prevalence study with intervention measures. *Am J Public Health* **77**, 1337–9

Hughes, H. (1992) Impact of spouse abuse on children of battered women. *Violence Update* August, **1**, 9–11

Inter-University Consortium for Political and Social Research (1981) *National Sample. 1973–1979*. Ann Arbor, Michigan: Inter-University Consortium for Political and Social Research

Jacobson, A. and Richardson, B. (1987) Assault experience of 100 psychiatric inpatients: evidence of need for routine inquiry. *Am J Psychiatry* **144**, 908–13

Lent, B. (Ed.) (1991) *Reports on Wife Assault*. Ontario: Ontario Medical Association Committee on Wife Assault

Mandt, A.K. (1993) The curriculum revolution in action: nursing and crisis intervention for victims of family violence. *J Nurs Educ* **32**, 44–6

McLeer, S.V. and Anwar, R. (1989) A study of battered women presenting in an emergency department. *Am J Public Health* **79**, 65–6

Morley, R. (1993) 'Recent responses to domestic violence against women: a feminist critique' in R. Page and J. Baldock (Eds) *Social Policy Review 5*, pp.177–206. London: Social Policy Association

Mullender, A. (1996) *Rethinking Domestic Violence*. London and New York: Routledge

National Inter-Agency Working Party (1992) *Report of a National Inter-Agency Working Party on Domestic Violence*. London: Victim Support

Pahl, J. (1995) 'Health professionals and violence against women' in P. Kingston and B. Penhale (Eds) *Family Violence and the Caring Professions*, pp.127–48. London: Macmillan

Smith, S., Baker, B., Buchan, A. and Bodiwala, G. (1992) Adult domestic violence. *Health Trends* **24**, 97–9

Stark, E. and Flitcraft, A. (1985) 'Woman-battering, child abuse and social heredity: what is the relationship?' in N. Johnson (Ed.) *Marital Violence*. London: Routledge and Kegan Paul

Stark, E. and Flitcraft, A. (1996) *Women at Risk*. London: Sage

Stark, E., Flitcraft, A. and Frazier, W. (1979) Medicine and patriarchal violence: the social construction of a 'private' event. *Int J Health Serv* **9**, 461–93

Warshaw, C. (1989) Limitations of the medical model in the care of battered women. *Gender and Society* **3**, 506–7

Chapter 18

How can we help? – the role of general practice

Jo Richardson and Gene Feder

INTRODUCTION

Domestic violence against women is a world-wide problem with extensive health and social consequences. Population studies in a number of developed countries indicate that about 20–25 per cent of adult women have experienced domestic violence from a male intimate (Stark and Flitcraft 1991). Women may also experience violence from other family members and acquaintances, and from strangers – but this is much less common. These related issues are outside the scope of this chapter which focuses on violence against women by male partners or ex-partners.

Domestic violence is a complex area in which to undertake research (Richardson and Feder 1996). Studies use a wide range of methods and often focus on selected populations, making comparison difficult. Well-designed, methodologically rigorous studies are notably absent. Definitions of domestic violence vary considerably, including different personal relationships and different degrees or types of violence (physical, sexual, emotional, etc.); this particularly affects the results of prevalence studies. The evidence base from which to recommend good practice is therefore unreliable.

PREVALENCE

Despite its wide-reaching effects, much domestic violence goes unreported or undocumented in health-care and other settings. The results obtained from prevalence studies are thus dependent on data collection methods. For example retrospective studies of medical records will generally indicate a lower prevalence of domestic violence than community-based questionnaire surveys where participants are asked specifically about their experience of domestic violence. Whether or not data are collected face to face and by whom also affects results of research in an area as sensitive as domestic violence.

Research in American primary care shows a wide range of prevalence of domestic violence against women, from under 10 per cent to over 40 per cent (McFarlane *et al.* 1991; Elliott and Johnson 1995). No studies of the prevalence of domestic violence amongst women presenting to general practice in the UK have been undertaken. Experience of domestic violence amongst women attending for antenatal care may be greater than amongst other groups of women as pregnancy is a high-risk time. Studies report a wide range of prevalence of abuse during pregnancy from 0.9 per cent to over 20 per cent, according to the study methodology (Gazmararian *et al.* 1996), which compares with a figure of 5.5 per cent in the previous 12 months in one recent primary-care based prevalence study in the USA (McCauley *et al.* 1995). Abuse may increase during pregnancy and in one informal questionnaire study of pregnant American teenagers, 26 per cent were being battered, with 40–60 per cent reporting that battering had begun or escalated since becoming pregnant (McFarlane 1991). One study of a selected group of women (Stewart 1994) found the number of incidents of abuse to be highest in the three months after delivery.

OBSTETRIC AND GYNAECOLOGICAL PROBLEMS

Studies of pregnant women who have experienced domestic violence and the effect that this has on pregnancy outcomes are beset by a range of methodological problems (Newberger *et al.* 1992). Nevertheless, there appear to be a number of associations. Injury to the abdomen, breasts and genital area is common during pregnancy in abused women (Bullock *et al.* 1989). Miscarriage is more common amongst women who have experienced violence (Stark *et al.* 1979) and low birth-weight babies have been reported as more common (Bullock and McFarlane 1989). The aetiology of this may operate through direct mechanisms or through intermediate paths including the effects of psychological stress and behavioural risks, such as smoking, alcohol or illicit drug use. In the USA, abused women are more likely to enter antenatal care in the third trimester and abuse during pregnancy is a significant risk for smoking and use of alcohol or drugs as well as low birth weight, infections and anaemia (Parker *et al.* 1994).

In one Norwegian study (Schei and Bakketeig 1989), women who had experienced sexual and/or physical abuse by a partner or ex-partner were much more likely to experience sexual problems and were more likely to have gynaecological symptoms at the time of interview. A family-practice based prevalence study showed that women who had experienced domestic violence within the previous 12 months were more likely to have vaginal discharge or pain in the pelvis or genital area (McCauley *et al.* 1995).

THE CURRENT POSITION

Before moving on to discuss the role of general practice in the identification and care of women experiencing domestic violence, it may be useful to consider what is known about the current situation and the barriers which exist to providing good care.

Doctors and women experiencing domestic violence

Attitudes held by doctors may affect how frequently women experiencing domestic violence are identified; one influence on this is the medical model of care (Warshaw 1993). Standard medical language and an emphasis on objective findings such as physical trauma, may result in the true cause of the woman's symptoms being obscured. In one study (Warshaw 1989) which looked at emergency-room medical records of women who were deliberately injured by another person, the problem of ongoing domestic violence was mentioned in the discharge diagnosis in only one out of 52 cases where abuse was explicit or strongly indicated. In 75 per cent of cases, the physician failed to record the relationship of the assailant to the woman.

Other studies have explicitly investigated the attitudes and responses of doctors to women who may be experiencing domestic violence. Time pressures are frequently highlighted. Fears that domestic violence disclosure may be time consuming were expressed by general practitioners in one small study (McWilliams and McKiernan 1993). Lack of time was also seen as a barrier to identification in a survey of a selected group of American primary-care physicians (Sugg and Inui 1992), with a fear of 'opening a Pandora's box' were they to ask about violence in the home. Worries about offending the woman and jeopardising the doctor–patient relationship, feelings of powerlessness in the face of a situation the physician cannot 'fix', loss of control when attempts at intervention are useless and identifying too closely with patients from a similar background may also impede identification. Other problems raised in a study of 32 Canadian family doctors (Brown *et al.* 1993) included lack of medical school training about 'wife abuse' and lack of knowledge about community resources. Fears were expressed about possible threats to the doctor from the perpetrator of the violence. In another Canadian study of family physicians, nearly 75 per cent of respondents believed that they identified fewer than half of women who had experienced partner violence (Ferris and Tudiver 1992).

Despite ambivalence towards disclosure and its consequences, in one American study of 27 primary-care physicians (Friedman *et al.* 1992), most thought that they would be able to assist patients with problems arising from physical abuse. Australian general practitioners perceived themselves as capable of playing a preventive role through vigilance for indicators of violence (Easteal and Easteal 1992). Women may hold more sympathetic attitudes to victims than men: one study looking at physicians and nurses found that gender was more important in this respect than profession (Rose and Saunders 1986).

Women's views of doctors

A number of studies have explored the responses women receive when seeking help. In a study in one refuge, Pahl (1979) found that 32 out of 50 women had talked to their general practitioner about the violent behaviour of the man with whom they were living. Over half had found their GP's response helpful, characterised by listening, being sympathetic and offering appropriate advice. 'Unhelpful' GPs were said frequently to prescribe anti-depressants and tranquillisers. A later study (Hopayian *et al.* 1983) found that 89 per cent of women in refuges had consulted their GPs in the previous year but nearly half of these had concealed that they were being battered, mostly because they were ashamed or were afraid their partner would find out, but also because of the hurried, unsympathetic or hostile attitude of their GP. Other studies (Smith 1989) have reported similar findings with women not revealing that they had been beaten. According to women interviewed in Northern Ireland (McWilliams and McKiernan 1993), GPs apparently did not see obvious signs of injury and did not ask directly about the cause of injuries.

IDENTIFYING (OR MISSING) DOMESTIC VIOLENCE

In many cases the woman's GP may be the first person outside family and friends to be informed of domestic violence (Pahl 1995). However, for reasons reviewed above, the woman may not disclose that she is being abused, and the doctor may not ask. There are a number of health and other social factors associated with domestic violence which should raise suspicion of its occurrence but most features are so common that they are not specific indicators.

One American study based on a medical chart review (Saunders *et al.* 1993) found that a combination of all variables analysed in the study could only predict lifetime injury in about 50 per cent of cases and violence in the past year in about 20 per cent. However, the presence of certain features in the woman's past history raises the likelihood of her experiencing domestic violence. A detailed review of risk markers in husband–to–wife violence found that only witnessing violence in the wife's family of origin as a child or adolescent was consistently associated with being victimised by violence (Hotaling and Sugarman 1986). Other studies show that early and repeat sexual abuse in the family of origin may be associated with later domestic violence (Plichta 1992).

Sometimes women may present acutely with injuries to general practice and the pattern of injuries may indicate possible domestic violence. Women injured as a result of domestic violence are more likely to have injuries on the breast, chest and abdomen (Stark and Flitcraft 1991) and also in the genital area if pregnant. Multiple injuries, injuries in different locations and injuries located on the face, head and neck are highly indicative of abuse (Plichta 1992). Bruising may be in different stages of healing; abuse is typically ongoing and repeated (Stark and Flitcraft 1991; Pahl 1995). Be-havioural aspects such as an injured woman appearing nervous if her partner is present or an inconsistent account of the cause of an injury may raise suspicion of violence.

Women who have experienced domestic violence are at increased risk of drug and alcohol abuse. Rates of substance abuse rise considerably after the first battering episode has presented and this seems to be largely a consequence of domestic violence (Stark and Flitcraft 1991; Plichta 1992).

There is little doubt that psychiatric illness, particularly depression and anxiety and post-traumatic stress disorder, is greater amongst women who have experienced domestic violence (Richardson 1997). Suicide attempts are more common and seem to be a consequence of domestic violence; the increased rate is not noted prior to the first reported episode of abuse (Stark and Flitcraft 1991). A study in New Zealand of a randomly-selected group of women found that those who identified themselves as victims of physical abuse as an adult were significantly more likely to be identified as psychiatric cases than non-abused women. All had been abused by a male partner (Mullen *et al.* 1988). In a study of American psychiatric inpatients, 64 per cent of women disclosed a history of physical abuse as an adult and 38 per cent gave a history of sexual abuse as an adult, with the two tending to occur together (Jacobson and Richardson 1987).

Some studies suggest a high risk of child abuse amongst the children of women who have experienced domestic violence (Plichta 1992). In a review of the notes of mothers whose children were suspected of being abused or neglected, 45 per cent of the women had a trauma history that indicated battering (Stark and Flitcraft 1988). Children may suffer in other ways when their mother is being abused, with psychological and behavioural problems being common (Stark and Flitcraft 1991; Plichta 1992).

Most demographic features are not useful aids to identifying women experiencing domestic violence as they are not specific. Only younger age and being divorced or separated are consistent risk factors (Plichta 1992).

IMPROVING IDENTIFICATION: GUIDELINES

Guidelines and protocols for the care of women experiencing domestic violence were used in health-care settings in the USA from the late 1970s (Sheridan and Taylor 1993). In 1992, the Royal College of General Practitioners published guidelines (Heath 1992) but these are rarely implemented. One of the key recommendations in many guidelines relates to 'screening' for domestic violence. The American Medical Association (AMA) guidelines and others state that the physician should routinely ask all women direct, specific questions about abuse (American Medical Association 1992). This recommendation amounts to universal screening and emerges from the failure to detect women at risk from consideration of other factors.

In one questionnaire survey in primary care (Friedman *et al.* 1992), 75 per cent of American women interviewed favoured being asked routinely about any history of physical abuse and 97 per cent of male and female respondents stated that they would answer truthfully if asked directly. Only 7 per cent stated that they had ever been asked about a history of physical abuse. In another American survey (Rath and Jarrett 1990), women stated that physicians are responsible for making the diagnosis of abuse. Two-thirds of a group of women questioned in Northern Ireland thought that doctors should ask directly about violence (McWilliams and McKiernan 1993). Asking may increase the rate of identification around five fold in comparison with historic controls (McLeer *et al.* 1989).

CARE IN GENERAL PRACTICE

Those working in general practice and, in particular, general practitioners, often provide continuing care to patients over many years. They are in a unique position which can facilitate the development of an ongoing and supportive relationship with a woman who is experiencing violence before, during and after disclosure.

Women usually have direct access to other members of the primary health-care team, such as health visitors and practice nurses. Doctors often lack training and information about domestic violence whilst other health professionals, particularly health visitors, may have greater expertise and specific training. The sharing of information about women at risk of, or experiencing, domestic violence within the team may facilitate better care but, other than in exceptional circumstances, this should be with the consent of the woman.

Women experiencing violence seem quite clear about what they want from their doctors: recognition of their plight and immediate advice and information about what they can do and where they can go (McWilliams and McKiernan 1993). Identification is the first step towards achieving this. When initiating discussion about domestic violence, an initial supportive statement may be helpful, for example: 'Because abuse and violence are so common in women's lives I've begun to ask about it routinely.' The AMA guidelines (and others) list a number of questions which can routinely be asked to assess whether the woman has experienced domestic violence, including the following:

Are you in a relationship in which you have been physically hurt or threatened by your partner? Have you ever been in such a relationship?

Are you (or have you ever been) in a relationship in which you were treated badly? In what ways?

Has your partner ever destroyed things that you cared about?

Has your partner ever threatened or abused your children?

Has your partner ever forced you to have sex when you didn't want to?

Do you ever feel afraid of your partner?

Has your partner ever prevented you from leaving the house, seeing friends, getting a job or continuing your education?

These questions can be asked by doctors, practice nurses or others and could be incorporated into the new patient check, as well as being used in specific circumstances where abuse seems likely. Posters and information sheets prominently displayed in the surgery may help the woman to feel she can disclose a history of domestic violence in a supportive environment.

Doctors and others can then offer help to a woman who has disclosed domestic violence in three main ways: these are presented in more detail in most guidelines.

1.   Respect and validation

The woman's account of what has happened to her should be respected and taken seriously. It is likely to be difficult and distressing for her to recount her experiences. Many women will have met disbelief or encountered negative stereotypes (for example, that women ask for and deserve the violence they experience) and, therefore, a non-judgmental and supportive approach is particularly important. GPs and others need to make it clear to the woman that the abuser's behaviour is unacceptable and may be illegal.

2.   Assessment

At the time of disclosure, there may be obvious physical problems that need urgent attention, including possible referral to secondary care, such as injuries or acute mental health problems. The woman's immediate safety and that of her children need assessment to ensure she receives all relevant information and that any child-protection issues are addressed. Consultations should be carefully documented and any injuries recorded on body maps: these may provide vital evidence subsequently for any legal actions.

3.   Information giving

General practitioners should be able to provide the woman with basic information about where to get help: this might include the local Women's Aid service or police Domestic Violence Unit. Women's Aid provide refuge places and may have outreach workers who can offer support, counselling and advocacy in relation to police, social services, housing departments, solicitors, health-care professionals and so on. There are also a number of local and national helplines. GPs fear the time implications of supporting a woman experiencing domestic violence. Specialist agencies may have a greater capacity to spend time with the woman and may have more information about local resources than the GP.

Referral for couple counselling or family therapy may not be helpful. Although there will inevitably be problems in the relationship, the key difficulty which needs to be addressed is the man's violence. Focusing on the relationship rather than the man may leave the woman feeling guilty and responsible, removing the responsibility from the man himself. The role of anger or violence management groups for male abusers is contentious.

General practitioners need to be aware that women in abusive relationships may find it very difficult to make changes and that such changes may occur over a long period of time or not at all. Leaving a relationship may carry large social and economic costs, including homelessness, poverty and disruption of social networks for the woman and her children. The philosophy of the Women's Aid movement is to empower women to bring about change when and if it is right for them. An understanding of these concepts may help GPs to have realistic expectations of the situation and their ongoing relationship with the patient.

This ongoing relationship between patient and primary care team member, especially the GP, is one of the most important characteristics of general practice. The GP is in a position to offer continuing support to the woman and to be alert to the possibility of health consequences associated with domestic violence, such as depression, where specific types of intervention or drug treatment may be helpful.

ANTENATAL AND WELL-WOMAN CARE

The guidance outlined so far can be applied to general-practice consultations overall but there are also specific contexts where domestic violence needs to be addressed, such as consultations for maternity and well-woman care.

Although the organisation of antenatal care may differ from area to area, most antenatal care now takes place within primary care, with the GP in a central role (Royal College of General Practitioners 1995). Most women having their first baby will never have had contact with a midwife but many will be well known to their GP. The GP may therefore hold significant information, for example, about a woman's experience of domestic violence. Sharing this information with the woman's named midwife may be important so that those involved are alerted to her being at risk of violence and the possibility of associated problems such as depression, injury, low birth weight or substance abuse. Some women may find it difficult to attend for antenatal care if their partner controls and restricts their activities. As in the other contexts discussed above, other than in very exceptional circumstances, information sharing should only take place with the woman's consent (British Medical Association 1993). Since pregnancy and postpartum is a high-risk time for domestic violence, the argument for direct questioning of women about violence is even stronger than for other consultations. Arguably, such a question should be part of routine antenatal history taking. The six-week postnatal check, usually performed by the GP, is also an important opportunity to ask about domestic violence. Abuse may be even more likely during the postpartum period than during pregnancy.

Much routine gynaecological care in general practice is provided by practice nurses, including cervical smears and family planning. Nurses and GPs need to be sensitive to women who may reveal sexual difficulties during pelvic examination and ask further questions about abuse, if this seems appropriate. Nurses may receive more education about domestic violence during their training than medical students and may be able to provide help and support to women experiencing domestic violence. Given its extent and significance, there may be a case for nurses routinely asking about domestic violence during family planning or well-woman consultations, as well as during new patient health checks.

MALE ABUSERS

It is quite likely that the woman's abusing partner or ex-partner may also be registered with the same practice. The general principles of confidentiality which guide all patient contacts will apply and the doctor will have the usual duty of care. However, there may be situations in which it is possible to challenge the abuser's behaviour (for example, if it is raised by the patient) and let him know that it is unacceptable. A surgery environment in which information and posters about domestic violence are prominent will not only help in supporting women who are being abused but may encourage men to realise that their behaviour is unacceptable.

RESEARCH ISSUES

Research is needed to establish the prevalence of domestic violence in women presenting to general practice, including those who are pregnant. Little is known about how the problem is currently addressed from within general practice, for example, with respect to identification and provision of care or how effective such care is. The effectiveness and appropriateness of universal 'screening' and the form this should take needs further investigation. Answering these questions could be linked to the more widespread introduction and audit of guidelines on good practice in domestic violence, with training and educational input at all levels, and for the whole team.

General practice has a clear role to play in providing care for women experiencing domestic violence primarily through identification, support and information giving. However, progress in reducing domestic violence will require a fundamental change in attitudes of men towards women at all levels in society.

REFERENCES

American Medical Association (1992) American Medical Association diagnostic and treatment guidelines on domestic violence. *Arch Fam Med* 1, 39–47

British Medical Association (1993) *Medical Ethics Today: Its Practice and Philosophy.* London: BMA

Brown, J.B., Lent, B. and Sas, G. (1993) Identifying and treating wife abuse. *J Fam Pract* **36**, 185–91

Bullock, L.F. and McFarlane, J. (1989) The birth-weight/battering connection. *Am J Nurs* **89**, 1153–5

Bullock, L.F., McFarlane, J., Bateman, L.H. and Miller, V. (1989) The prevalence and characteristics of battered women in a primary care setting. *Nurse Pract* **14**, 47–56

Easteal, P.W. and Easteal, S. (1992) Attitudes and practices of doctors toward spouse assault victims: an Australian study. *Violence Vict* **7**, 217–28

Elliott, B.A. and Johnson, M.M. (1995) Domestic violence in a primary care setting. Patterns and prevalence. *Arch Fam Med* **4**, 113–19

Ferris, L.E. and Tudiver, F. (1992) Family physicians' approach to wife abuse: a study of Ontario, Canada, practices. *Fam Med* **24**, 276–82

Friedman, L.S., Samet, J.H., Roberts, M.S., Hudlin, M. and Hans, P. (1992) Inquiry about victimization experiences. A survey of patient preferences and physician practices. *Arch Intern Med* **152**, 1186–90

Gazmararian, J.A., Lazorick, S., Spitz, A.M., Ballard, T.J., Saltzman, L.E. and Marks, J.S. (1996) Prevalence of violence against pregnant women. *JAMA* **275**, 1915–20

Heath, I. (1992) 'Domestic violence: the general practitioner's role' in *Royal College of General Practitioners Members' Reference Book*, pp. 283–5. London: Sabrecrown

Hopayian, K., Horrocks, G., Garner, P. and Levitt, A. (1983) Battered women presenting in general practice. *Journal of the Royal College of General Practitioners* **33**, 506–7

Hotaling, G.T. and Sugarman, D.B. (1986) An analysis of risk markers in husband to wife violence: the current state of knowledge. *Violence Vict* **1**, 101–24

Jacobson, A. and Richardson, B. (1987) Assault experiences of 100 psychiatric inpatients: evidence of the need for routine inquiry. *Am J Psychiatry* **144**, 908–13

McCauley, J., Kern, D.E., Kolodner, K. *et al.* (1995) The Battering Syndrome':prevalence and clinical characteristics of domestic violence in primary care internal medicine practices. *Ann Int Med* **123**, 737–46

McFarlane, J. (1991) 'Violence during teen pregnancy: health consequences for mother and child' in B. Levy (Ed.) *Dating Violence – Young Women in Danger*, pp.136–41. Seattle: Seal Press

McFarlane, J., Christoffel, K., Bateman, L., Miller, V. and Bullock, L. (1991) Assessing for abuse: self report versus nurse interview. *Public Health Nurs* **8**, 245–50

McLeer, S.V., Anwar, R.A.H., Herman, S. and Maquiling, K. (1989) Education is not enough: a systems failure in protecting battered women. *Ann Emerg Med* **18**, 651–3

McWilliams, M. and McKiernan, J. (1993) *Bringing it Out in the Open: Domestic Violence in Northern Ireland.* Belfast: HMSO

Mullen, P.E., Romans-Clarkson, S.E., Walton, V.A. and Herbison, G.P. (1988) Impact of sexual and physical abuse on women's mental health. *Lancet* **1**, 841–5

Newberger, E.H., Barkan, S.E., Lieberman, E.S. *et al.* (1992) Abuse of pregnant women and adverse birth outcome. *JAMA* **267**, 2370–2

Pahl, J. (1979) The general practitioner and the problems of battered women. *J Med Ethics* **5**, 117–23

Pahl, J. (1995) 'Health professionals and violence against women' in P. Kingston and B. Penhale (Eds) *Family Violence and the Caring Professions*, pp.127–48. London: Macmillan

Parker, B., McFarlane, J. and Soeken, K. (1994) Abuse during pregnancy: effects on maternal complications and birth weight in adult and teenage women. *Obstet Gynecol* **84**, 323–8

Plichta, S. (1992) The effects of woman abuse on health care utilisation and health status: a literature review. *Women's Health Issues* **2**, 154–63

Rath, G.D. and Jarrett, L.G. (1990) Battered wife syndrome: overview and presentation in the office setting. *S D J Med* **43**, 19–25

Richardson, J. (1997) Women and domestic violence. *CML-Psychiatry* **7**, 87–91

Richardson, J. and Feder, G. (1996) Domestic violence: a hidden problem for general practice. *Br J Gen Pract* **46**, 239–42

Rose, K. and Saunders, D.G. (1986) Nurses and physicians' attitudes about women abuse: the effects of gender and professional role. *Health Care for Women International* **7**, 427–38

Royal College of General Practitioners (1995) *The Role of General Practice in Maternity Care*. Occasional Paper 72. London: RCGP

Saunders, D.G., Hamberger, L.K. and Hovey, M. (1993) Indicators of woman abuse based on a chart review at a family practice centre. *Arch Fam Med* **2**, 537–43

Schei, B. and Bakketeig, L.S. (1989) Gynaecological impact of sexual and physical abuse by spouse. A study of a random sample of Norwegian women. *Br J Obstet Gynaecol* **96**, 1379–83

Sheridan, D.J. and Taylor, W.K. (1993) Developing hospital-based domestic violence programs, protocols, policies and procedures. *AWHONN'S-Clin-Issues-Perinat-Womens-Health-Nurs* **4**, 471–82

Smith, L.J.F. (1989) *Domestic Violence: An Overview of the Literature* (Home Office Research Study No. 107). London: HMSO

Stark, E. and Flitcraft, A.H. (1988) Women and children at risk: a feminist perspective on child abuse. *Int J Health Serv* **18**, 97–118

Stark, E. and Flitcraft, A.H.(1991) 'Spouse abuse' in M. Rosenberg and J. Mercy (Eds) *Violence in America: a Public Health Approach*, pp. 123–57. New York: Oxford University Press

Stark, E., Flitcraft, A. and Frazier, W. (1979) Medicine and patriarchal violence: the social construction of a 'private' event. *Int J Health Serv* **9**, 461–93

Stewart, D.E. (1994) Incidence of postpartum abuse in women with a history of abuse during pregnancy. *Can Med Assoc J* **151**, 1601–4

Sugg, N.K. and Inui, T. (1992) Primary care physicians' response to domestic violence. Opening Pandora's box. *JAMA* **267**, 3157–60

Warshaw, C. (1989) Limitations of the medical model in the care of battered women. *Gender and Society* **3**, 506–17

Warshaw, C. (1993) Domestic violence: challenges to medical practice. *Journal of Women's Health* **2**, 73–80

Chapter 19

The role of the accident and emergency department

K. Lindsey H. Stevens

The recognition of domestic violence as an issue which should be addressed by emergency medicine has been growing steadily through recent years. From being viewed largely as a peripheral concern a decade ago, a session at the 1996 International Conference of Accident and Emergency Medicine was devoted to discussion of the topic. Guidelines on domestic violence (see Appendix I) were issued to each accident and emergency (A&E) department in the UK in 1994 (British Association of Accident and Emergency Medicine 1994). In the USA the Joint Commission on Accreditation of Healthcare Organisations requires that emergency departments have written policies and procedures on domestic violence (Joint Commission on Accreditation of Healthcare Organisations 1992) and an objective of the US public health initiative 'Healthy People 2000' is that 90 per cent of emergency departments should have domestic violence protocols by the year 2000 (Public Health Service 1991).

Hand-in-hand with this recognition has developed awareness of the multiple difficulties inherent in a service which was designed as generalist, reactive and 'quick fix', taking on a proactive, supportive and advisory role focused on a single patient group.

A&E departments in the UK have been facing rising patient attendances with dwindling hospital and community resources, increasingly demanding throughput, time, standards and staff shortages.

There is little doubt, however, that the specialty is failing domestic violence survivors at present. As well as low rates of identification, there is poor documentation when abuse has been identified (Bergman and Brismar 1990; Easley 1996) and the patients themselves have described their experience of emergency medicine care as negative (Campbell *et al.* 1994). Co-ordination with other medical, social or voluntary agencies is often poor (Bergman and Brismar 1990).

In this context, the specialty needs robust planning data on the scale and type of demands, convincing that A&E department involvement is appropriate and successful and the design of systems to address the needs of domestic violence survivors which can operate within the constraints of time, unpredictable patient load, a variable knowledge base and rapid staff turnover.

THE SCALE AND TYPE OF DEMANDS

There have been several studies of the attendance rate of adult domestic violence survivors at emergency departments. The majority of studies are from the USA and a few from the Antipodes; there is little work from the UK. Some are based on case-note review, some on questionnaire and some on interview. Some studied trauma patients exclusively. Some were conducted only in social hours, some excluded women when the partner would not leave, some stopped when the department was busy. They measure different types of rate: attendance due to abuse, one-year history of abuse and lifetime history of abuse. The types of study and results are summarised in Table 19.1.

Abbott *et al.* (1995) defined domestic violence as including intimidation as well as injury or the threat of injury, and held domestic violence to be the direct cause of attendance in those cases where abuse was a contributing factor to physical or mental illness. Those studies which were confined to female trauma found correspondingly higher rates of domestic violence than the general studies. Stark and Flitcraft's study (Stark *et al.* 1979) was based on chart review and not verified by reference to the patients. In that sense it is a 'best-guess' estimate.

The other research papers summarised are broadly similar, giving an adult life-time prevalence of around 25 per cent and a 'cause-of-visit' rate of around 2 per cent. This may be an underestimate. de Vries Robbe *et al.* (1996) comment that, 'evidence for under-reporting was found: 4 per cent of females and 6.3 per cent of males who did not report being victims revealed experiences of abuse on nine measures of types of violence.'

The low 'cause-of-visit' rate fits with Campbell's study of the use of emergency departments by shelter residents which found that 63.2 per cent did not attend immediately after the attack on them (Campbell *et al.* 1994) and with Bates' finding that 68 per cent of the women suffering domestic violence did not seek help at the time of their injuries (Bates *et al.* 1995).

Two conclusions arise from these studies: firstly, that at least a quarter of women attending A&E departments have experienced domestic violence at some stage in their adult life and, secondly, that it may be that the emphasis that has been placed on emergency department staff identifying when a patient has attended with acute injuries from domestic violence is mistaken. Whilst it is vital that such identification be made, the evidence is that the specialty would have a much greater impact, on both primary and secondary prevention, by routinely screening for abuse.

It has been established that abused people make greater use of inpatient, outpatient, psychiatric and emergency services than average, attending with ill-defined illnesses, anxiety, depression, sleeping difficulties, eating disorders,

Table 19.1.   Summary of studies of the incidence and prevalence of domestic violence amongst patients attending accident and emergency departments

Author	Year	Patient cohort	DV defined as	Type of study	DV caused visit (%)	DV in last year (%)	DV as adult (%)	Comment
Goldberg and Tomlanovich	1984	M/F General	Physical abuse	SAQ CR	—	—	22%	5% of DV recorded on notes as such
Roberts et al.	1993	M/F General	Physical abuse Threat	SAQ	1.2%	—	23.9% F 8.5% M	Patients attended mainly 5 pm–8 am
McFarlane et al.	1995	F Vaginal bleeding	Physical and sexual abuse	IAQ	0%	23%	38%	—
Bates et al.	1995	F General	Physical abuse	Int	1.7%	—	25%	Not conducted 12 am–8 am
Abbott et al.	1995	F General	Physical abuse Intimidation	SAQ	11.7% Injury Stress Illness	11.9%	54.2%	Research Assistant present during SAQ
Roberts et al.	1993	M/F General	Physical abuse	SAQ	1.1%	—	14.1% (M/F)	Most acute DV victims attended out-of-hours
de Vries Robbe et al.	1996	M/F General	Physical abuse	SAQ	—	—	19.3% F 8.5% M	—
McLeer and Anwar	1989	F Trauma	Physical abuse	Int	30%	—	—	5.6% detected before screening protocol introduced
Stark et al.	1979	F Trauma	Physical abuse	CR	25%	—	—	6.4% 'definite' DV; rest 'probable' or 'possible' 4% of DV noted

M = male; F = female; DV = domestic violence; SAQ = self-administered questionnaire; IAQ = interviewer-administered questionnaire; CR = casenote review; Int = interview.

irritable bowel syndrome, headache, abdominal and pelvic pain, chest pain, dyspnoea, sexual dysfunction and musculoskeletal pain (Bergman and Brismar 1990; Koss *et al.* 1991). They are several times more likely to deliberately self-harm or misuse alcohol or drugs than the norm – common causes of attendance at emergency departments (Bergman and Brismar 1991; Ratner 1993). Abused people are probably highly represented amongst 'frequent attenders' (Council on Scientific Affairs, American Medical Association 1992). A simplistic approach based on selected groups (e.g. trauma patients) is clearly inappropriate and this further supports routine screening.

It may also be more comfortable for the survivor to discuss her situation, resources available and safety planning at a time other than immediately after the acute episode and it may jeopardise her safety less as the abuser will have lower expectation of domestic violence being discussed during a consultation for an apparently unrelated matter.

SCREENING

A number of well-validated scales have been used when screening for domestic violence. These include the Conflicts Tactic Scale, the Danger Assessment Scale, the Abuse Assessment Screen and the Index of Spouse Abuse, as well as locally-designed protocols.

Norton *et al.* (1995) compared a group of patients interviewed along standard social service lines with a group who had the five-question Abuse Assessment Screen added to the interview. The lifetime prevalence rate identified rose from 4 per cent to 41 per cent, and the incidence of recent abuse from 3 per cent to 15 per cent. Grunfeld *et al.* (1994) used a single screening question at triage; 6 per cent of women attending their emergency department were identified as suffering domestic violence. The study was limited by the location of the triage booth which was not completely private and by the exclusion of women who were accompanied to triage by a relative. Olson *et al.* (1996) used a printed question on the emergency department casenotes to prompt staff to enquire about domestic violence; the rate of abuse identified rose from 2.0 per cent to 3.4 per cent by this manoeuvre. McFarlane *et al.* (1995) used two questions from the Abuse Assessment Screen together with the Danger Assessment Scale in their study which found a lifetime prevalence of 38 per cent.

Hoff (1989) and Waller *et al.* (1996) both recommend a two-stage assessment to accommodate the need to keep triage interviews brief. Hoff suggests that all clients with symptoms without a clear organic basis or in 'emotional pain' be assessed at 'Level 1' by a five-point scale aimed at identifying the risk to the life of the client or another. This should be followed for those at risk by a 'Level 2' assessment using the Comprehensive Mental Health Assessment Tool. However, Hoff and Rosenbaum (1994) describe an interrater reliability of 77 per cent for Level 1 assessment in domestic violence

Table 19.2.   Indicators of possible abuse at Stage 1 assessment

Delay in presentation
Inappropriate history
The attitude of patient or accompanying person
Type of injury
Site of injury
Substance abuse
Deliberate self-harm
Miscarriage, attempted self-termination of pregnancy
Frequent attender
Sleeping or eating disorders
Single car crash
Dried blood or semen

when a group of 60 experienced health professionals were given nine case scenarios to evaluate.

In Waller's study, as the triage point was in a semi-public area, Stage 1 assessment was conducted without direct questions about abuse, the suspicion of domestic violence being raised by characteristics of the history, illness or injury (see Table 19.2). If the Stage 1 screen was positive, the Stage 2 screen was conducted once the patient was within the department by the nurse allocated to her case. Stage 2 included further direct questioning about the possibility of abuse, examination of the patient's options and safety planning (Waller *et al.* 1996).

The study was conducted over two weeks, during which time 595 women attended. However, screening was performed on only 114. The suspicion of abuse was raised at Stage 1 in eight cases, two of which were confirmed at Stage 2. Two further cases were identified at Stage 2, giving an overall identification rate of domestic violence of 3.5 per cent. The researchers described the study as limited by staff numbers, time, lack of privacy for interview and examination, previous experience of difficulties in contacting community services (both hospital social work and local domestic violence agency cover were part-time), throughput standards, and a lack of commitment among staff evidenced by poor attendance at training sessions by the local domestic violence agency. All these are problems common to many A&E departments.

The authors point out that most research into domestic violence in emergency departments has been conducted by additional personnel and comment that 'a protocol' is only paper and ink unless it can be successfully implemented in the actual emergency department setting. Emergency department staff must believe in its utility and must be willing and able to use it as part of their normal routine of providing patient care. Changing the culture of an emergency department is not easy or straightforward. To address this important issue, we must take a long-term approach to the problem. Progress must be reinforced at every step.

McLeer and Anwar (1989), having found that the use of a screening protocol raised the detection rate of domestic violence from 5.6 per cent to 30 per cent, revisited the department eight years later to find the protocol in abeyance and the detection rate fallen to 7.7. per cent, despite raised staff awareness. They concluded that assessment for abuse must be institutionalised.

This varying commitment to tackling the issue of domestic violence within emergency departments is echoed by the finding of a survey in Massachusetts that, despite the requirements of the Joint Commission on Accreditation of Healthcare Organisations and 'Healthy People 2000' (Public Health Service 1991), only 20 per cent of departments responding had protocols in place (Isaac and Sanchez 1994). A similar study of Californian emergency departments found that 46 per cent had no protocol (MMWR 1993). This reflects doubt amongst emergency department staff about the acceptability, utility and practicality of such protocols.

Is screening acceptable?

Patients attending a family practice were asked whether they considered it acceptable for physicians to enquire about physical and sexual abuse. Of the total asked, 78 per cent thought it was acceptable to be asked about physical abuse and 68 per cent about sexual abuse (Friedman *et al.* 1992). Grunfeld *et al.* (1994) found that few women were displeased by being asked about violence at triage, and many appreciated the concern; a poll of women patients leaving the department showed that 96 per cent of respondents supported the screening programme

Is screening useful?

In one study (Friedman *et al.* 1992), 90 per cent of the patients believed that physicians could intervene positively in cases of physical and sexual abuse. Emergency department staff, by contrast, develop the impression that their intervention has little effect as, by definition, they see those individuals who have returned to an abusive relationship and been hurt again, and they have no access to information about the long-term progress of patients they have seen. There is a despair about positively intervening in the lives of certain categories of patients – alcoholics, substance abusers, people who attend recurrently with deliberate self-harm, frequent attenders – which leads to frustration and dismissiveness on the part of staff (Stockwell 1984).

The nature of domestic violence itself means that health professionals assist in a process of empowerment and self-management by the woman of her situation, and that it may be some considerable time before she reaches the point in that process where she is ready to take definitive action.

It must be reinforced that an apparently unsuccessful interaction with an abused patient may, firstly, have been more successful than supposed and, secondly, is not a reason to withhold support from the next comer. It is not foreign to A&E thinking that, despite the situation appearing hopeless for the vast majority of a particular patient group, one should still try to one's utmost on the chance that an individual patient can be helped. This is the philosophy behind attempting to resuscitate out-of-hospital cardiac arrests – a practice that few emergency medicine practitioners would abandon!

Any programme must include ongoing information of the progress of individuals entered by the emergency department staff to reinforce the utility of the department's involvement. One advocacy agency's evaluation of their work with emergency departments, hospital and community services is that: 'our long-term follow-up has shown us that, *with support and information*, battered women *do* make changes and take the action necessary to protect themselves and eliminate the violence in their lives' (Hadley 1992).

There is also an important primary prevention role in the message given to the public by routine screening that domestic violence is not acceptable behaviour, that the health services are concerned about it and that there is support available should it occur.

Is screening practical?

A practical screening protocol must have a high level of detection and be workable within the constraints of time and personnel of the average A&E department. It must be backed by robust health service and community provision for supporting those patients who are found to be abused.

McFarlane *et al.* (1991) emphasise that a screening assessment should be based on interview rather than self-administered questionnaire. In their study one group of women were given self-report questionnaires, which identified a one-month rate of domestic violence of 7.3 per cent. A second group of women were then interviewed by a nurse, and the identification rate rose to 29.3 per cent. Asking more than one screening question increases detection rates (Smith 1987).

The evidence seems to be that a modification of the Abuse Assessment Screen would be as effective an initial screening tool as the longer questionnaires such as the Conflict Tactics Scale. One possible modification is suggested in Table 19.3. A positive finding on this initial screen would have to be followed up by a more detailed interview covering an assessment of the danger to the woman and her children, an exploration of her options and safety planning. It is not workable, and perhaps not desirable, for this to be undertaken on a consistent basis by members of the general A&E staff. Hadley (1992) describes a model for working with battered women in the emergency department which seems practical. Hadley's initiative, Woman-Kind, is an organisation of paid and volunteer staff, funded by the local hospitals and donations, which provides free, 24-hours a day, seven days a week, services to local hospitals and the surrounding community. Woman-Kind provides advocacy for the woman, inservice training for the staff and assistance with documentation in the emergency department. The advocate

Table 19.3. Abuse assessment screen (modified)

1. Have you ever been emotionally or physically abused by your partner or someone important to you	Yes	No
2. Are you here today because you have been hit, slapped, or otherwise physically hurt by someone	Yes	No
If yes, by whom		
3. Are you here today because you have been emotionally abused by someone?	Yes	No
If yes, by whom		
4. Have you ever been forced to have sexual activities?	Yes	No
If yes, by whom		
When was the last time?		
5. Are you afraid of your partner or anyone you have listed above?	Yes	No

comes to the emergency department within half-an-hour of being called, stays with the patient during medical procedures and assists her in sorting options, setting priorities, making decisions and contacting community resources. WomanKind provides a link to existing community services such as shelters, mental health services, job counselling programmes, etc. but does not duplicate these. It also runs a support group for women who have been, or are being, battered, and is involved in the education programme of the local police force.

EDUCATING ACCIDENT AND EMERGENCY STAFF

The uptake of any educational programme depends on how relevant to the individual's practice it is seen to be, how informative it is and how well it is presented. A domestic violence training programme would be most effective if it accompanied a comprehensive protocol for the care of survivors and used trainers actively involved in the delivery of the care protocol.

A significant increase was seen in the willingness of health-care professionals to assess and intervene with battered, pregnant women after an educational programme (Helton *et al.* 1987). Emergency nurses changed their attitudes after attending a 60-minute presentation based on the 'cycle of violence' theory (Bokunewicz and Copel 1992).

Hadley's inservice training input consisted of a two-hour session within the orientation programme of new hospital nursing staff, the regular discussion of selected topics with emergency department staff and inservice training for other hospital departments on request (Hadley 1992). The programme was reinforced by the frequent presence of WomanKind staff or volunteers in the hospital and their incorporation as part of the emergency department team.

BUILDING THE TEAM

The suggested system of brief triage by A&E staff, followed by an advocate from a dedicated domestic violence team, who in turn hands on to hospital and community statutory and voluntary organisations, requires well-cemented links between all the agencies concerned. The first stage must be a working group to plan as comprehensive a system as possible for the reception and support of domestic violence survivors attending the emergency department, and the facilitation of the next stages in their progress to safety. This group should include representatives of the emergency department, social services, Women's Aid, alcohol/substance abuse unit, hospital security, police, paediatric department and general practice.

In the course of planning the system it may become clear that, between them, the different agencies do not have sufficient resources to provide a water-tight service; in this case the Health Authority and/or hospital should be asked to fund the advocate system. There is a robust case for asking them to do so – in human, legal and financial terms. Legally, the Health Authority will have failed in its duty of care if it does not provide a means of addressing the needs of a patient who is known to be at acute risk.

Financially, the National Crime Survey of 1973–1979 estimated the cost of domestic violence to the USA health-care system at $44 million, incurred in 28,700 emergency visits, 39,000 physician visits, 21,000 hospitalisations, and 99,800 bed days (Inter-University Consortium for Political and Social Research 1981). This is probably a gross underestimate. Such studies as have been performed of the prevalence of domestic violence in the UK (Social Services Inspectorate 1995) suggest that it is probably as common as in Australia or America, and the health costs would be correspondingly high.

SUMMARY

One in four women experience domestic violence at some stage in their adult life. Whilst they generally do not turn to hospital services in the immediate period after abuse, they are highly represented amongst A&E department users. There are moral, financial and legal imperatives for the detection of domestic violence survivors when they attend the emergency department. Such detection, and subsequent assistance given the survivors, must fit within the normal working practices and constraints of emergency medicine. A protocol of brief screening by A&E staff, who hand over to a dedicated domestic violence team member who in turns acts as the survivor's advocate and link to community and hospital services, seems the most likely to fit within these parameters. The protocol must be planned and funded to be consistently deliverable around the clock, every day of the year. It must be backed by an educational programme, preferably taught by members of the dedicated domestic violence team who are already viewed as part of the emergency department 'club'.

Setting up such a system will take time and effort but will result in a deliverable, effective service to those in jeopardy from domestic violence.

REFERENCES

Abbott, J., Johnson, R., Koziol-McLain, J. and Lowenstein, S.R. (1995) Domestic violence against women. Incidence and prevalence in an emergency department population. *JAMA* **273**, 1763–7

Bates, L., Redman, S., Brown, W. and Hancock, L. (1995) Domestic violence experienced by women attending an accident and emergency department. *Aust J Public Health* **19**, 293–9

Bergman, B. and Brismar, B. (1990) Battered wives – measures by the social and medical services. *Postgrad Med J* **66**, 28–33

Bergman, B. and Brismar, B. (1991) Suicide attempts by battered wives. *Acta Psychiatr Scand* **83**, 380–4

Bokunewicz, B. and Copel, L.C. (1992) Attitudes of emergency nurses before and after a 60-minute educational presentation on partner abuse. *Journal of Emergency Nursing* **18**, 24–7

British Association of Accident and Emergency Medicine (1994) *Domestic Violence: Recognition and Management in Accident and Emergency.* London: Royal College of Surgeons

Campbell, J.C., Pliska, M.J., Taylor, W. and Sheridan, D. (1994) Battered women's experiences in the emergency department. *Journal of Emergency Nursing* **20**, 280–8

Council on Scientific Affairs, American Medical Association (1992) Violence against women: relevance for medical practitioners. *JAMA* **267**, 3184–9

de Vries Robbe, M., March, L., Vinen, J., Horner, D. and Roberts, G. (1996) Prevalence of domestic violence among patients attending a hospital emergency department. *Australian and New Zealand Journal of Public Health* **20**, 364–8

Easley, M. (1996) Domestic violence. *Ann Emerg Med* **27**, 762–3

Friedman, L.S., Samet, J.H., Roberts, M.S., Hudlin, M. and Hans, P. (1992) Inquiry about victimisation experiences. A survey of patient preferences and physician practices. *Arch Intern Med* **152**, 1186–90

Goldberg, W.G. and Tomlanovich, M.C. (1984) Domestic violence victims in the emergency department. *JAMA* **251**, 3259–64

Grunfeld, A.F., Ritmiller, S., Mackay, K., Cowan, L. and Hotch, D. (1994) Detecting domestic violence in the emergency department: a nursing triage model. *Journal of Emergency Nursing* **20**, 271–4

Hadley, S.M. (1992) Working with battered women in the emergency department: a model program. *Journal of Emergency Nursing* **18**, 18–23

Helton, A, McFarlane, J. and Anderson, E. (1987) Prevention of battering during pregnancy: focus on behavioural change. *Public Health Nurs* **4**, 166–74

Hoff, L.A. (1989) *People in Crisis* 3rd ed. Redwood City: Addison-Wesley.

Hoff, L.A. and Rosenbaum, L. (1994) A victimization assessment tool: instrument development and clinical implications. *J Adv Nurs* **20**, 627–34

Inter-University Consortium for Political and Social Research (1981) National crime surveys: national sample 1973–79. Ann Arbor, Michigan: Inter-University Consortium for Political and Social Research

Isaac, N.E. and Sanchez, R.L. (1994) Emergency department response to battered women in Massachusetts. *Ann Emerg Med* **23**, 855–8

Joint Commission on Accreditation of Healthcare Organisations (1992) *Accreditation Manual for Hospitals*. Oakbrook Terrace, Illinois: 1992 Emergency Services

Koss, M.P., Koss, P.G. and Woodruff, W.J. (1991) Deleterious effects of criminal victimization on women's health and medical utilization. *Arch Intern Med* **151**, 342–7

McFarlane, J., Christoffel, K., Bateman, L., Miller, V. and Bullock, L. (1991) Assessing for abuse: self-report versus nurse interview. *Public Health Nurs* **8**, 245–50

McFarlane, J., Greenberg, L., Weltge, A. and Watson, M. (1995) Identification of abuse in emergency departments: effectiveness of a two-question screening tool. *Journal of Emergency Nursing* **21**, 391–4

McLeer, S.V. and Anwar, R.A. (1989) A study of battered women presenting in an emergency department. *Am J Public Health* **79**, 65–6

McLeer, S.V., Anwar, R.A., Herman, S. and Maquiling, K. (1989) Education is not enough: a systems failure in protecting battered women. *Ann Emerg Med* **18**, 651–3

MMWR (1993) Emergency department response to domestic violence – California, 1992. *MMWR* **42**, 617–20

Norton, L.B., Peipert, J.F., Zierler, S., Lima, B. and Hume, L. (1995) Battering in pregnancy: an assessment of two screening methods. *Obstet Gynecol* **85**, 321–5

Olson, L., Anctil, C., Fullerton, L., Brillman, J., Arbuckle, J. and Sklar, D. (1996) Increasing emergency physician recognition of domestic violence. *Ann Emerg Med* **27**, 741–6

Public Health Service (1991) Healthy People 2000: national health promotion and disease prevention objectives. DHHS publication no. (PHS)91-50212. Washington DC: US Department of Health and Human Services, Public Health Service

Ratner, P.A. (1993) The incidence of wife abuse and mental health status in abused wives in Edmonton, Alberta. *Can J Public Health* **84**, 246–9

Roberts, G.L., O'Toole, B.I., Lawrence, J.M. and Raphael, B. (1993) Domestic violence victims in a hospital emergency department. *Med J Aust* **159**, 307–10

Roberts, G.L., O'Toole, B.I., Raphael, B., Lawrence, J.M. and Ashby, R. (1996) Prevalence study of domestic violence victims in an emergency department. *Ann Emerg Med* **27**, 747–53

Social Services Inspectorate (1995) Domestic Violence and Social Care: A report on two conferences held by the Social Services Inspectorate. London: Department of Health

Smith, M.D. (1987) The incidence and prevalence of woman abuse in Toronto. *Violence Vict* **2**, 173–87

Stark, E., Flitcraft, A. and Frazier, W. (1979) Medicine and patriarchal violence: the social construction of a 'private' event. *Int J Health Serv* **9**, 461–93

Stockwell, F. (1984) *The Unpopular Patient*. London: CroomHelm

Waller, A.E., Hohenhaus, S.M., Shah, P.J. and Stern, E.A. (1996) Development and validation of an emergency department screening and referral protocol for victims of domestic violence. *Ann Emerg Med* **27**, 754–60

Chapter 20

The health professionals

Discussion

Friend: Lindsey Stevens raised the question of screening for domestic violence. We chose general practice, accident and emergency and our own specialty of obstetrics and gynaecology, as areas where abused women might present.

Lewis: One of the initiatives of the government may be to review *Health of the Nation*. Those of you who are health professionals will know that this sets outcome targets for a variety of illnesses. These are due to end soon and our new administration may wish to review the use of *Health of the Nation* targets. In your recommendations you may wish to consider such things as setting targets for guidelines being present in 90 per cent of accident and emergency (A&E) departments by the year 2000, or similar process targets for other professions. We would generally prefer to see outcome targets but process targets as a proxy would do, bearing in mind that you need to monitor their use.

My difficult point is the use of the word 'screening'. I wear both a public and a Department of Health hat. Screening, as currently defined, is not what you are discussing. Many of you will know the old 1994 Wilson criteria. Sitting on the National Screening Committee, I can tell you that we might be revising them. However, this does not fulfil the criteria of what we would expect to be able to support as a screening programme.

I am trying very hard to think of other words for this, such as 'opportunistic identification'. For example, the issue which might come to the Antenatal Screening Committee very shortly and the use of the word 'screening' could be turned down because it does not have an effective outcome.

Langley: Jo Richardson made the point that within GP surgeries there is a team, and it may be that practice nurses and health visitors have more involvement with, and more understanding of, domestic violence. If this is not too dangerous a question, I would like to ask about issues around status, and the difficulties around status within healthcare, particularly within GP surgeries. Are health visitors and practice nurses – particularly health visitors

– able to deal with, or discuss with GPs, issues around domestic violence in a way which allows them to be heard?

Richardson: That is an interesting question. There is always the potential for a team not to work as well as it should. The way general practice is set up at the moment, most people have direct access to a practice nurse or to a health visitor if that is what they wish. They are health professionals of first contact in the same way that GPs are.

I would make two points. The first is related to resources. Health visitors, in particular, are very over-stretched in dealing with the statutory issues with under-fives. To provide extra support for women may be more, in some areas, than health visitors have the resources to do.

The second point is about practice nurses. Practice nurses, and nurses generally, are very interested and much more open to exploring issues of violence than doctors, but a training and education input is definitely required, as it is for GPs.

Gwyneth Lewis raised the idea of asking women routinely about domestic violence. The problem is that we do not have the evidence to know whether it could be effective screening. We know that it is an opportunity and that women want to be given information. I do not know what outcomes we can look at beyond that. This does not mean that asking is not beneficial, or something we should not do. There clearly is need for research as to how best to ask, and what sort of outcomes we should measure.

Walker: I would like the group to come to a consensus about where they feel the primary responsibility for 'screening', or 'case finding', whatever we choose as the word, lies. I am quite convinced now that there is a specific role for obstetricians and gynaecologists but there is a danger, if everyone thinks everyone else will take the initiative, that no one does. Am I very wide of the mark when I say it should be a standard part of general practice and in the acute phase in A&E. Do people here believe, as I do, that the prime responsibility lies with the primary healthcare team? They are the only group which could not be excused from looking for it.

Friend: Presumably you wish to identify the group which is more likely to pick up the higher incidence, which means the people who will be involved more. That is why we chose experts from A&E and general practice, as well as obstetrics and gynaecology.

Within each specialty framework, who should be doing the asking? Is it easier to disclose to a nurse or a health visitor than to someone who wears a white coat? I do not know.

Walker: It would seem to me that all healthcare professionals have a responsibility to identify this very important phenomenon and it should be part of undergraduate training programmes. We must remember that there are many more patient contacts in general practice and in A&E than there are in gynaecology.

If the Royal College of General Practitioners is content for us to appear to take the major initiative, and mention general practice in passing, then I have a personal sympathy towards saying that all doctors have a responsibility, and all healthcare professionals have a responsibility, and obstetricians and gynaecologists have a particular interest because of their responsibility for the reproductive care of women, but there are other important areas, principally the primary healthcare team and A&E.

Edwards: In relation to training, we have heard that there is a need, a recommendation perhaps, that health professionals must take on training. We have heard about training or education within A&E departments. I am concerned that during yesterday and today we have not discussed the need for training of obstetricians and gynaecologists and what kind of training. We have not had the opportunity to consider how we challenge the kinds of myths and stereotypes that surround the whole area of domestic violence. It is interesting that, over the last 15 years, the police in this country have undergone training in which many of the authors of this book have taken part. Training has been provided not only for those officers within domestic violence units, but for some of the rank and file police officers, because it is recognised that, however professional you might be, your attitudes to women, femininity, sexuality and domestic violence all impinge on each other. There seems to be a presumption that obstetricians, gynaecologists and GPs, in the absence of training, will know how to respond, and will know what sense to make of the questions they ask. Perhaps we should address what kind of training should be given, not merely procedural or referral, but what sense we make of the information.

I want to ask Helene Langley and Lindsey Stevens how important it is for obstetricians and gynaecologists to have a conference? Will it be enough for them to receive this book? Will they read it? Do we need a conference to look at all these issues, and undergo the process of self-scrutiny?

Friend: It is true that we need to get into the whole process of training. You require training before you can ever begin to do any form of 'screening'.

Stevens: You have to institutionalise an ideology. In the sense of saying that there is a problem and we ought to be identifying it and doing something about it, we are stating an ideology. We are not really stating an action.

We brought out the guidelines in 1993–4 and have very much the same experience as the United States. It is not enough to set an objective. You also have to set up the shop floor systems to make that happen. That is partly why I was re-emphasising that the domestic violence team I am talking about are outsiders coming in, but they are people known to the department who come frequently and reinforce, reinforce, reinforce. Quite a number of A&E departments now have alcohol liaison nurses, and these have made a huge difference to any commitment to trying to pick up alcohol abuse. You have to put the two together.

We do some very brief training with undergraduates attached to the A&E department in relation to history taking. Even that is quite shocking for them, and it makes them think about something they have never previously considered. I hope that even these little things change the culture, little by little, but they need to be backed up by something very concrete in the system.

Langley: The point Susan Edwards was trying to make was that, somehow, training often seems to be 'out there'. It is about training in the information, in how to ask questions, in something about the subject. Much of the training I do starts with the practitioners, be it social workers, health visitors or whatever. It is about looking at themselves, their own expectations of their role and job, and their own understanding about the myths. How do they feel? What happens to them when they come into contact with issues around domestic violence? Do they feel they are failing if they do not somehow save a woman? Do they feel they have problems because it impinges on issues to do with them and their own experience?

Training is not just about 'out there', and what domestic violence is and how we deal with it. It is actually about how we, as people working with women who have experienced violence, feel about domestic violence ourselves, and how it impacts on us at a personal as well as professional level.

Mezey: I have a quick point about status. Helene Langley was right earlier. We have to face the reality that doctors are in a very prestigious position in terms of their voices being heard. Chris Bewley has been working in this area for a long time, and it takes the Royal College of Obstetricians and Gynaecologists to host a conference and formally recognise it. That is extremely important, but this is now coming onto the agenda because doctors, as a body, have said they think it is important for healthcare, even though women's groups and nursing staff have been talking about this for a long time.

We have to be very careful that the responsibility for asking these questions is not somehow simply located with the nursing staff. There may be reasons why we say that the nursing staff are better placed to do this: because more of them are female; they do not wear a white coat; there is less formality in the relationship and perhaps because they have more time. It is nevertheless very important that doctors do not simply wash their hands of responsibility for asking questions and intervening and recognising this as an issue, using the excuse that they do not do it as well.

There is a risk that this issue could be relegated, in the way that Stephanie Yearnshire talked about yesterday. In the police force, traditionally it was a Cinderella specialty. Domestic and child abuse were the areas people went into because nobody else wanted to and women did it. We have to be very careful not to replicate that kind of dynamic in terms of our own recommendations and practice.

Harwin: I have absolutely no idea what the medical definition of screening is. It is, however, important to find a term which works in the multi-agency context. In the past year, when we have been working on the Family Law Act 1996 and its implementation in relation to divorce and the relationship breakdown process, the term 'screening' was used. It was used frequently in relation to legal aid personnel or mediation personnel when making assessments about whether a woman ought to be required to have mediation with her potentially abusive partner.

Lindsey Stevens made a point about the problems of domestic violence for A&E staff. This is actually not just a problem for A&E staff, but right across the board with social workers and housing officers experiencing it. It is, 'Why doesn't this woman take any action? Why has she still gone back? Why is she here again?' As you rightly said, active intervention will make a difference in the end. But I am rather concerned about the idea of staff having access to information about previous outcomes. This relates to an issue about keeping records, confidentiality and safety – and we have not touched on this at all so far. How do you access information on hospital databases? I am quite worried. In the refuge movement we have already experienced in the last 25 years a number of problems in the way that computerisation and correlation of information across a range of fields has actually meant it is much easier for abusive men to find women who have tried to get away. I would like to put that as an issue on the agenda.

Stevens: I was not envisaging that we would give each senior house officer (SHO) a piece of paper with names, addresses and everything to chase up, to phone or pop round and see how they are getting on. They will not do it anyway. They do not even do that with blood results!

I would see it as a function in very broad terms for this link worker, who is vital to making progress in A&E. It is either an outcome analysis every six months, saying that we have had so many patients referred from you, and of that group, X have left, Y are attending our group, and unfortunately Z have lost contact with us. It would give staff some idea that they are doing something useful, because that is exactly what we do not see every day. We see the opposite, which can be very demoralising. It is not just in domestic violence, it is in all the groups where we try to do anything on the social front, with frequent attenders and everybody else. We have very little feedback. Actually, there is a message for obstetrics and gynaecology too. We do not have any feedback from our normal ward referrals either.

Cameron: I support what Lindsey Stevens said about feedback. Recently we have been receiving feedback from the forensic science laboratories about specimens that we sent, and what the results were. It does help to encourage, and is very important.

Second, with regard to teaching medical staff, as Susan Edwards says, it is very important to make sure that the staff are trained. Curricula changes take a long time. Take bereavement counselling or how to convey bad news, for example, these are now part of the curricula in medical schools, but it takes a long time for these to evolve.

Supporting what Lindsey Stevens said about frequent attenders, Richard Jones mentioned pelvic pain yesterday. In each department, in primary care, in A&E departments and in gynaecology outpatients there are frequent attenders. I remember a patient who attended the early pregnancy assessment unit with a threatened miscarriage with no evidence of bleeding whatsoever and it was a cry for help. She was a frequent attender and, although she was actually booked with me, I eventually saw her as a rape case some time later. Frequent attenders are a particular group which we should regard as a high risk category.

Jones: Would John Friend supply the group with the mission statement of the Royal College, if there is one? It might be interesting to see what you say about your mission in terms of providing healthcare for women. How do you express that? It would be interesting to see whether you are fulfilling that mission, or whether this group might suggest some changes.

Cameron: Or write it!

Jones: My other comment is that physicians are very much in the habit of defining what they think their patients should want. Perhaps we should think a little about what patients think they want. It would be interesting to know, for example, if the women around this table think that their obstetrician or gynaecologist should know about this issue and should ask about this issue. We discussed this at dinner last night, and views differ somewhat on different sides of the Atlantic. I feel passionately that obstetricians and gynaecologists must ask about this issue.

Patrick Walker has different views. I think he believes this is a legitimate issue for us, but he is not certain that it is his role in a primary way. That is his view, but what do our patients expect of us? It may be different on different sides of the Atlantic. I, clearly, am a primary care physician for the majority of my patients. Most women I see do not see any other physician. It is different over here, and I understand that. However, apparently, obstetricians and gynaecologists here do have private patients who do not see anybody else. If that is the case, then you are a primary care physician for that woman. If you do not see any women like that, then perhaps you can say it is somebody else's responsibility, but I would be interested to know what the perception of patients here is, because it may not be congruent with the physician's view.

Kerr-Wilson: Overlapping that, and coming back to the screening problem, it is quite important that we decide what we are trying to do. If you call it screening, and you take the analogy of cervical screening, for instance, we are screening the whole population and it is the duty of both primary care physicians and the obstetricians and gynaecologists to check that the patient is having cervical smears. Are we saying that we should screen, if you like to use that word, or identify every single woman? Richard Jones suggests that we should be asking *every single woman* we see. Or are we saying we should identify a sub-population?

Friend: It is the same argument as the prenatal diagnosis exactly: should you find that you have an indication for asking the questions, or should you screen everyone?

Kerr-Wilson: It goes back to Patrick Walker's point. Whose duty is it? If you say it is a sub-population, then what is the sub-population, or should we ask everybody?

Friend: This is an important point, because if we are making recommendations, we need a consensus. Is the general feeling that, if we are talking specifically about obstetricians and gynaecologists, that there should be some person within their department, whether it is the doctor or someone else, who according to whether they are in gynaecology, outpatients, the antenatal clinic or any other place, should be trained and have the means to ask these questions of every single patient?

Jones: I would be interested to know whether the women around this table expect that an obstetrician or gynaecologist will understand the basics of this issue, and know something about what to do about it.

Spence: In an ideal world I would have that expectation, but there is another important issue. In what people are saying, there is a sense that this is a once-and-for-all issue. Once it is asked and checked out, then it is clear what happens after that. It is not a once-and-for-all thing.

If we just turn our minds to some of what was said yesterday about what it feels like to be a woman who is abused by her partner, then she is in a constant process of staying, perhaps leaving, perhaps returning. She may not have fully identified herself as a woman who is abused. It is a very dangerous territory for her to give herself that label, because all sorts of issues come along with that.

There are also very important issues which Helene Langley has flagged up about the way training is conducted. Remember, the people we are talking about training, including ourselves, all have our own lives. It may be that doctors, health visitors or midwives are in abusive relationships now, or will be in them in the future. That comes into play too, and is not a once-and-for-all issue either.

We heard yesterday that one of the things which prompts a woman to seek help outside of her friendship network or her family network is the threat to her children, whether born or unborn. Along with that come childcare issues, social work intervention, child protection and another whole set of statutory implements and fears for the woman. None of this is a once-and-for-all-thing, but something which needs to happen in different ways and with different degrees of subtlety and explicitness in all the contexts we are talking about.

Friend: I understand Richard Jones's passion, and he is absolutely right to have that. Perhaps it is too early in the development of this in our particular specialty, within this context, to make those definitive decisions. It will, of course, come up within the training package. If, as I hope, we get a training pack in this College for our specialty registrars, within that package it will indicate very clearly not only how but when these things should be put in place.

Lewis: I hope your training package will go to consultants too. I would like to tidy up the screening business. Listening to the conversation has underlined the difficulty with the use of the word 'screening' – screening is available to all, and so on.

For the purposes of this paper, the compromise I might offer is that you adopt the word screening with a caveat before you use it at the beginning, which is that we are using the term because it is the easiest one to use. You have to accept that you are, in that case, looking at asking all women who come in. That is part of screening – whether it is by GPs, obstetricians, and whenever. I personally would not mind being asked by an obstetrician every time I saw them. If you insert a caveat about the use of the word, then you will get through the difficulties I am placing as a pedantic public health doctor.

S. Bewley: Perhaps I can explain why we are a little concerned about the word 'screening'. The official medical line is that screening is a thing you do to everybody, which then leads on to some further diagnostic test with some specific intervention that improves outcome. So you take a totally well group of people, do something to them, and it has some benefit. In that sense, we do not have proof that asking about violence can actually make things better. We all believe it, and you tell us that people appreciate it and feeling cared for is an outcome in itself. However, if, along the way, there are costs because of diminished safety, breaches of confidentiality, occasional increases in danger, or if it has no effect at all, then actually it is a waste of much time, effort and money. I cannot believe it will be, but in that sense, Gwyneth Lewis's problem is that we are talking about spending money and time on something which has not been proven to be effective.

We know it in our hearts, as does Richard Jones, but that is my caution. The ability routinely to question, identify and be comfortable about it, is screening in an opportunistic way. To recognise that violence is behind many presentations is important. We will be doing our jobs badly as doctors if somebody complains of feeling suicidal and we do not pick up that there is something in her life causing that. But to go around screening all the population all the time, thinking we are doing good when we are not, is leaping too far too soon. We do not even have the tools just to ask the right questions in the right situations. A woman says 'I've had a fall' and we do not even ask then. Full screening would be going a little too far at this stage.

Stevens: In some ways, I take the opposite line. Speaking personally, in the last eight years I have seen my GP about myself once and that is also in the context of two consultations about my children in a grand total of six minutes. I have gone to an A&E department once, and I have had three children. That gives you an idea of the relative importance in my life of my obstetric consultations against every other form of care. On the whole, that is fairly typical. In this country we are not as good as they are in the US about turning up to our family doctor for routine blood pressure screening and so on. You have a relatively fit group of relatively young women for whom you may be the only point of contact taking longer than about ten seconds. In that sense, there is a screening issue.

We have the same problem in A&E. The people who come to us do not go to other people a lot of the time. I should not say it in this particular company, but if you glance through Table 19.1 you will gather that about nine per cent of the men attending A&E departments are also abused. One of the resistances to moving forward in A&E, being still a largely male specialty, is that they are deeply resentful of the concentration on women. They say they are seeing battered men as well. So we have been quite careful to broaden the issue and that was the sense in which I was using screening. Given the multiplicity of presentations in A&E, and the unpredictability of who is at risk within those groups, I do not see how I am capable of dictating to which group I should be talking and even which sex.

In triage, we theoretically have a private opportunity to ask brief questions. My question to John Friend would be, do you ask routinely about smoking? Do you ask routinely about alcohol? Do you ask routinely about allergies? Yes, you do. Even in A&E, we do when we remember. I do not see it as fundamentally different, if you have a back-up to get rid of the problem quickly. If we are completely honest, the main limitation for most of us is that we need to be able to make it somebody else's problem as fast as we can. That is the real drag on people wanting to become involved.

S. Bewley: Should we actually call it routine history taking? We do not think that taking the smoking history is a screening intervention, but doctors ask and then advise against it. If we called it routine history taking, we would get around the 'screening' semantics.

Edwards: Let me make two very brief points. A caveat and the need for training and sensitivity must underscore this.

One case example comes from a gynaecologist at Manchester in the seventies, examining a woman with pelvic pain, with the medical students present. Whilst he is examining her abdomen, he says, 'Do you have difficulty with orgasm?' Obviously, somewhere along the line, some decision has been taken and there is some knowledge that there is a relationship between pelvic inflammatory disease and orgasm. So in goes our chap, and asks this inappropriate question, on the ward, to the patient. It is the warning.

The second warning takes us to the police professional. We are in Duluth, Minnesota. The police have their instamatic cameras and go to the scene. A woman has had her head smashed into a car by her aggressor, and the aggressor has also kicked and smashed the car to bits. The policeman comes back with his camera, with 27 photographs. Twenty-five photographs are of the car. He has been told, along the line, that this is what you do in evidence gathering. What I wish to emphasise is that we have to go back to training and sensitivity. It is relevant all to professionals. It is not enough to say, 'you will screen', but it is how that professional does it and relates to the patient. If the professional thinks, 'I have got to get this in somewhere. Oh, God, I had better do it now. This is not really the right opportunity but I have to ask this domestic violence question', in that way one could finish everything you tried to achieve.

SECTION 6

THE OBSTETRIC CONSULTATION

Chapter 21

Domestic violence in pregnancy

Gillian C. Mezey

INTRODUCTION

Domestic violence affects many women and families. It is used by the perpetrator to acquire power and control, through instilling feelings of fear and insecurity. It has harmful effects on the physical and psychological health of the victim, whilst at the same time producing short-term gains for the perpetrator. During pregnancy women are most vulnerable and least able to defend themselves or take evasive action. Repeated violent assault has a detrimental effect on maternal and fetal health and physical development, in extreme cases leading to prematurity, miscarriage or fetal death (Mezey and Bewley 1997). It is likely that the idealised image of pregnancy and the nuclear family interferes with detection and appropriate intervention by health professionals.

BACKGROUND

For the purposes of this chapter the victim will be assumed to be the pregnant woman, although it is recognised that children are also affected by domestic violence, both as direct victims and as witnesses to the assaults on their mother. Around one in four women in England and Wales are affected by domestic violence (Andrews and Brown 1988; Mooney 1993). Domestic violence refers to the intentional and repeated infliction of physical violence or restraint on a spouse or family member. Sexual abuse and assault and sexually degrading acts are also commonly reported (Campbell 1986). Psychological abuse, a common accompaniment, serves to reduce the victim's sense of certainty about, and control over, what is happening. Acts of brutality are frequently followed by expressions of contrition and remorse by the perpetrator; he promises to change, never to hit her again, tells her how much he loves her and begs her not to leave. The victim alternates between feeling totally powerless and believing that his very survival depends on her remaining with him, that he only hits her because he loves her. She is further subjected over a period of time to restrictions over her movements and social contacts. The victim becomes gradually isolated from friends, family and social contacts, who might provide a means of escape. The victim becomes increasingly dependent on her partner as a reference point and, as the degrading and critical comments and jealous accusations increase, she begins to see the world and herself through the eyes of her abuser. She starts to accept his view of her as inadequate, incompetent and ugly. She loses her sense of pride and self-esteem and may even begin to accept the notion that, because of her failure, her beatings are a consequence of her own shortcomings and therefore deserved. In order to avoid further beatings the woman adopts strategies that she hopes will minimise her partner's displeasure: she attempts to manipulate the environment to appease or distract him and avoids situations that are likely to provoke him (such as threatening to leave). Unfortunately, in many relationships the violence becomes less and less dependent on outside triggers and appears to take on a life of its own. The battered woman thus becomes less able to predict or control the violence. She lives in an altered reality, in which her perception of the world, herself and potential options for escape are the product of his projections.

High rates of psychiatric and social problems have been noted in women who have experienced domestic violence including alcohol and drug abuse, suicide attempts, depression and post-traumatic stress disorder, homelessness and divorce (Bergman *et al.* 1988; Amaro *et al.* 1990; West *et al.* 1990; Bergman and Brismar 1991; Malos and Hague 1993; Campbell *et al.* 1995; Scott-Gliba *et al.* 1995). Battered woman syndrome (BWS) was described in the 1970s as a characteristic pattern of psychological, emotional and behavioural deficits, consequent on repeated chronic violence (Walker 1979). Although the concept of BWS has recently met with criticism, Walker's work has, nevertheless, been tremendously influential in raising awareness of domestic violence, directing research efforts and in forensic work. A central feature of BWS is 'learned helplessness', which might better be described as an adaptive, and even life-preserving, reaction. Contrary to expectation, battered women tend to develop intense attachments to their abusers, similar to that described in abused children (Kempe *et al.* 1962), hostages and prisoners of war (Herman 1992). The combination of 'active inaction' and apparent loss of volition and autonomy makes it extremely difficult for outsiders to offer effective solutions. It is not that the woman wishes to remain within a dangerous situation, rather that the alternative may appear even more dangerous and unpredictable. She will go when she believes that the moment is right, when the risks of staying outweigh the risks of leaving and when she has a chance of surviving physically, psychologically and financially.

PREVALENCE IN PREGNANCY

Estimates of violence in clinic attendees are likely to underestimate the problem as women are generally reluctant to disclose such experiences for fear of retaliation. Very often the male partner will accompany her to the casualty department or antenatal clinic, his presence acting as a deterrent both for the health professional to make the necessary enquiries and for the woman to admit to her partner's violence. It would appear that domestic violence is more common than major obstetric complications such as pre-eclampsia, placenta praevia, twins or gestational diabetes for which the population is routinely screened. Helton and colleagues (1987) assessed 290 healthy pregnant women in antenatal clinics of whom eight per cent reported battering during, and another 15 per cent before, the current pregnancy (23 per cent total). None had been questioned by health care providers about abuse. Amaro and colleagues (1990) interviewing 1,243 pregnant women attending a prenatal clinic, found that seven per cent reported physical or sexual violence during pregnancy. Hillard (1985) reported that 10.9 per cent of women attending an obstetrics and gynaecology clinic reported abuse at some point in the past (one in five of these women were still living with the abusive partner) and 3.9 per cent reported abuse during the current pregnancy. Gielen and colleagues (1994) examined the frequency and severity of domestic violence in 275 women through repeat interviews during the pregnancy and at six months postpartum. Their findings suggested an increased rate and severity of violence in the postpartum period (19 per cent antenatal, 25 per cent postnatal). Using a simple three-question assessment screen in a population of 691 pregnant women, McFarlane and colleagues (1992) detected a 17 per cent prevalence of physical or sexual abuse during pregnancy, largely recurrent. It is likely that domestic violence is fatal for some women and their babies; trauma is a leading cause of maternal deaths, although neither the national Confidential Enquiry into Maternal Deaths (CEMD), nor the Confidential Enquiry into Still Births and Deaths in Infancy (CESDI) allow for death due to accidental or 'non-human cause' to be differentiated from death secondary to interpersonal violence.

CHARACTERISTICS AND PRESENTATION OF DOMESTIC VIOLENCE DURING PREGNANCY

Campbell (1993) has proposed four different categories of domestic violence in pregnancy:

(1) Jealousy towards the unborn child;

(2) Anger towards the unborn child;

(3) Pregnancy-specific violence; and

(4) 'Business as usual'.

Most research suggests that domestic violence may commence or escalate during pregnancy (Gelles 1975; Stark *et al.* 1979; Bowker 1983; Hillard 1985; Surgeon General 1986; Bohn 1990), although some women report a decrease in violence (Hilberman and Munson 1978). Women attending casualty with physical injuries due to domestic violence are more likely to be pregnant than women attending with accidental injuries (Stark *et al.* 1979; Berrios and Grady 1991). In addition, the pattern of violence alters: pregnant women are more likely to have multiple sites of injury, including the breasts and pregnant abdomen (Helton and Snodgrass 1987; Hilberman and Munson 1978; Stark *et al.* 1979; Hillard 1985). This would imply that the fetus, as well as the woman herself, is the focus of the man's anger, hatred and envy.

Women assaulted during pregnancy are more likely to be divorced or separated and to be of greater parity (Hillard 1985). They are more likely to have had psychiatric problems, to have attempted suicide and to report a higher consumption of tobacco and alcohol (Hillard 1985; Webster *et al.* 1996). Higher rates have been found in teenagers, later bookers, and women with unwanted or mistimed pregnancies (Gazmararian 1995). No consistent relationship has been found between risk of intimate violence and employment status or income (Hillard 1985; Gielen *et al.* 1994). Protective factors for the woman include being older, having a confidante, and available social support from friends (Gielen 1994). The risk of domestic violence in pregnancy is correlated with the male partner's use of injectable drugs (Gielen *et al.* 1994). Domestic violence during pregnancy also appears to be a risk factor for the eventual homicide of the woman (Browne 1987). Feticide is a crime and third parties responsible for the criminal or negligent destruction of fetuses are criminally liable. Civil courts can bring claims for injuries inflicted before birth if the child survives and is born alive, but these are rarely brought. In Britain, until recently, a charge of murder or manslaughter could not be brought in such cases as the victim was not 'a person in being' at the time of the act leading to injury. A recent Court of Appeal judgement has reversed this view, ruling that for the purposes of the Homicide Act 1957 a fetus should be regarded as an extension of the mother. Thus a man who had been convicted of the manslaughter of his pregnant wife, should also have been charged with the killing of the baby, who was born alive, but died a short while later (Attorney General 1995).

UNDERSTANDING DOMESTIC VIOLENCE IN PREGNANCY

Domestic violence is, in part, an attack on the woman's sexuality: injuries are often located around the breasts and, in pregnancy, around the abdomen and genitalia. The fetus is as much the target of the man's anger, hatred and envy, as the woman. Pregnant women are less physically mobile and therefore more vulnerable to physical assault; they may be less able to avoid oncoming blows and more likely to sustain injuries. However, the pregnancy symbolises the woman's independence from her partner, and is about the only thing in the relationship that belongs to the woman alone and that she can control. The pregnancy and anticipation of the baby's birth may be the necessary trigger for the woman to break away or leave (Mezey and Eastman 1997). It is interesting to note how often the male batterer attempts to control the woman's reproductive powers, through rationing her contraception, insisting on terminations, often in the context of jealous delusions and oversolicitous and intrusive attendance during each obstetric or gynaecological consultation.

In order to understand why a woman might be at greater risk of assault by her partner during pregnancy, it is important to understand the characteristics of men who batter. Perpetrators of domestic violence are described as insecure, inadequate and dependent men (see Chapter 4). Control is achieved not only by the use of physical violence, threats and intimidation, but through psychological abuse which undermines the woman's confidence and assertiveness, binds her to him and engenders feelings of loyalty, pity, fear and dependence. Victims of domestic violence tend not to disclose their injuries to health professionals but, if detected, often fabricate explanations. These explanations are often accepted at face value, out of respect for the woman's autonomy, as a 'choice' about whether to discuss her private affairs with her doctor, and because the health professional often feels impotent in intervening and offering a solution to the problem. Women may not get away with providing implausible explanations for their injuries during pregnancy. The woman is subject to repeated physical examinations, which make bruising or injuries more difficult to hide, particularly injuries to the abdomen, breasts or genitalia. Moreover, health professionals are more likely to be concerned about potential risk or injury to the unborn child. This sets up a dilemma for the woman: should she risk her partner's anger and the probability of more beatings by disclosing the violence, or should she lie, and risk being labelled as evasive, unreliable and possibly even an unsafe and unsuitable mother?

The woman's pregnancy and impending birth of a child alters the family dynamic and, more crucially, alters the balance of power between the adult players. In addition, it creates a potential for the the family to be exposed to outside scrutiny. Friends and family members may wish to be involved in the arrival of the new baby, which further increases the risk of the violence being recognised. The intrusion of outsiders threatens the perpetrator's position of power and the rewards that the perpetrator derives through his actions. He feels more insecure, less able to control the situation and is thus liable to retaliate against the woman and the child she is carrying.

Many men's conception of self-worth centres on possessiveness with regard to women as partners and wives (Horder 1997). Dobash and Dobash (1984) questioned battered women about the sources of the conflicts leading to violent episodes with their partners. In 45 per cent of cases the women cited possessiveness or sexual jealousy. A further 16 per cent of cases centred on expectations about domestic work. Male batterers are likely to feel intensely threatened by their partner's pregnancy. The intrusion of a third party, such as the fetus, undermines the man's possession, power and control over his partner and represents competition for the woman's attention, labour, presence and love on demand. The pregnancy may, in a concrete way, block the man's free access to his wife's body, creating further grounds for dispute and resentment. The pregnant woman is also likely to be preoccupied with her baby and the changes in her body and less emotionally available to her partner. She is more likely to require support from her husband than respond to his needs.

The woman's pregnancy may trigger accusations of infidelity and suspicions about the child's paternity in these very jealous men. A new baby puts a financial strain on most households. Within violent relationships, it is frequently the man who has control of the money and these demands may provoke violence. A potential deterrent to a pregnant woman seeking help is her concern that being a victim of domestic violence might reflect on her mental stability and suitability as a mother. Women who have been beaten and abused over a number of years, told they are useless and labelled 'mad' by their partners, tend to internalise these projections. They lose the sense of being able to be a good mother and may fear that it will be their behaviour, rather than their partner's, that will come under critical scrutiny. In extreme cases they may fear that their baby could be taken away from them.

EFFECTS OF DOMESTIC VIOLENCE IN PREGNANCY

Many of the effects of domestic violence also represent complications which place the health of the mother, as well as the unborn fetus, at risk. Domestic violence has been associated with miscarriages, premature birth and low birth weight, fetal injury and fetal death (Hilberman and Munson 1978; Stark et al. 1979; Bullock and McFarlane 1989; Bohn 1990), premature labour and chorioamnionitis (Berenson et al. 1994). How much poor obstetric outcome is due to violence itself or other adverse co-factors, such as poverty, drug abuse and smoking, is difficult to ascertain (Hillard 1985; Amaro 1990). Poor maternal health, including depression, suicide attempts and increased tobacco and alcohol use, are also risk factors during pregnancy (Stark et al. 1979; Hillard 1985; Helton 1986; Wiemann 1995). Even after the child is born it is at risk, as battered women are more likely to report child abuse, or fear of it (Stark et al. 1979). Violence during pregnancy is also associated with late booking, sporadic attendance at antenatal appointments and the pregnancy being described as 'unwanted'.

CONCLUSIONS

Far from offering protection, pregnancy appears to increase the risk of violence against women by their partners. Repeated assault affects the woman's physical and mental health and causes both direct and indirect harm to the developing fetus. It is crucial that health professionals involved in the care of women during pregnancy are alert to the existence of domestic violence and its presentation and that they manage such cases with particular care.

REFERENCES

Amaro, H., Fried, L.E., Cabral, H. and Zucherman, B. (1990) Violence during pregnancy and substance use. *Am J Public Health* **80**, 575–9

Andrews, B. and Brown, G.W. (1988) Marital violence in the community: a biographical approach. *Br J Psych* **153**, 305–12

Attorney General (1995) Death after antenatal injury can be murder. *TLR* 48–49

Berenson, A.B., Wiemann, C.M., Wilkinson, G.S., Jones, W.A. and Anderson, G.D. (1994) Perinatal morbidity associated with violence experienced by pregnant women. *Am J Obstet Gynecol* **170**, 1760–9

Bergman, B. and Brismar, B. (1991) Suicide attempts by battered wives. *Acta Psychiatr Scand* **83**, 380–4

Bergman, B., Larsson, G., Brismar, B. and Klang, M. (1988) Aetiological and precipitating factors in wife battering. *Acta Psychiatr Scand* **77**, 338–45

Berrios, D.C. and Grady, D. (1991) Domestic violence: risk factors and outcomes. *West J Medicine* **155**, 133–5

Bohn, D.K. (1990) Domestic violence and pregnancy. Implications for practice. *J Nurse-Midwifery* **35**, 86–98

Bowker, L.H. (1983) *Beating wife beating.* Lexington, MA: Lexington

Browne, A. (1987) *When battered women kill.* London: Collier Macmillan

Bullock, L.F. and McFarlane, J. (1989) The birth-weight/battering connection. *Am J Nursing* **89**, 1153–5

Campbell, J.C. (1986) Nursing assessment for risk of homicide with battered women. *Advances in Nursing Science* **8**, 36–51

Campbell, J.C. (1993) Why battering during pregnancy? *Clinical Issues in Women's Health Nursing* **4**, 343–9

Campbell, R., Sullivan, C.M. and Davidson, W.S. (1995) Women who use domestic violence shelters: changes in depression over time. *Psychology of Women Quarterly* **19**, 237–55

Dobash, R.E. and Dobash, R.P. (1984) The nature and antecedents of violent events. *Br J Criminology* **24**, 269

Gazmararian, J.A., Adams, M.M., Saltzman. L.E. *et al.* (1995) The relationship between pregnancy intendedness and physical violence in mothers of newborns. *Obstet Gynecol* **85**, 1031–8

Gelles, R.J. (1975) Violence and pregnancy: a note on the extent of the problem and needed services. *The Family Coordinator* **24**, 81–6

Gielen, A.C., O'Campo, P.J., Faden, R.R., Kass, N.E. and Xue, X. (1994) Interpersonal conflict and physical violence during the childbearing year. *Social Science Medicine* **39**, 781–7

Helton, A. (1986) Battering during pregnancy. *Am J Nursing* **86**, 910–13

Helton, A.S. and Snodgrass, S.C. (1987) Battering during pregnancy; intervention strategies. *Birth* **14**, 142–7

Helton, A.S., McFarlane, J. and Anderson E.T. (1987) Battered and pregnant: a prevalence study. *Am Journal Public Health* **77**, 1337–9

Herman, J.L. (1992) *Trauma and Recovery: from domestic abuse to political terror.* London: Pandora

Hilberman, E. and Munson, K. (1978) Sixty battered women. *Victimology* **2**, 460–70

Hillard, P.J.A. (1985) Physical abuse in pregnancy. *Obstet Gynecol* **66**, 185–90

Horder, J. (1997) *Provocation and Responsibility.* Oxford: Clarendon Press

Kempe, C.H., Silverman, F.N., Steele, B.S., Droegemueller, W. and Silver, H.K. (1962) The battered child syndrome. *JAMA* **181**, 17–24

Malos, E. and Hague, G. (1993) *Domestic Violence and Housing: Local Authority Responses to Women and Children Escaping Violence in the Home*. Bristol: Women's Aid Federation England and School of Applied Social Studies, University of Bristol.

McFarlane, J., Parker, B., Soeken, K. and Bullock, L. (1992) Assessing for abuse during pregnancy. *JAMA* **267**, 3176–8

Mezey, G.C. and Bewley, S. (1997) Domestic violence and pregnancy. *BMJ* **314**, 1295

Mezey, G.C. and Eastman, N.L.G. (1997) Characteristics of women who kill. *J Forensic Psychiatry* (Submitted)

Mooney, J. (1993) *The Hidden Figure: Domestic Violence In North London – The Findings Of A Survey Conducted On Domestic Violence In The North London Borough of Islington*. London: Centre for Criminology, Middlesex University

Scott-Gliba, E., Minne, C. and Mezey, G.C. (1995) The psychological, behavioural and emotional impact of surviving an abusive relationship. *The Journal of Forensic Psychiatry* **6**, 343–58

Stark, E., Flitcraft, A. and Frazier, W. (1979) Medicine and patriarchal violence: The social construction of a "private" event. *International Journal of Health Services* **9**, 461–93

Surgeon General's Workshop on Violence (1986) Recommendations of spouse abuse. *Response* **9**, 19–21

Walker, L.E. (1979) *The battered woman*. New York: Harper and Row

Webster, J., Chandler, J. and Battistutta, D. (1996) Pregnancy outcomes and health care use – effects of abuse. *Am J Obstet Gynecol* **174**, 760–7

West, C.G., Fernandez, A., Hillard, J.R., Schoof, M., and Parks, J. (1990) Psychiatric disorders of abused women at a shelter. *Psychiatric Quarterly* **61**, 295–301

Wieman, C.M., Berenson, A.B. and Landwehr, B.M. (1995) Racial and ethnic correlates of tobacco, alcohol and illicit drug use in a pregnant population. *J Reprod Med* **40**, 571–8

Chapter 22

The role of the midwife

Chris Bewley and Andy Gibbs

INTRODUCTION

Domestic violence constitutes a corruption of women's physical and emotional health and is morally and socially unacceptable (Bewley and Gibbs 1994). The abuse of women and their children by a current or former male partner results in a total experience of physical injury, abject depression, low esteem and helplessness. When perpetrated against a vulnerable, pregnant woman, it is particularly reprehensible. The sense of injustice on behalf of abused women engendered by our first article for midwives (Bewley and Gibbs 1991) was captured in the words of the editor of *Midwifery*:

> When this article first arrived on my desk I read it with incredible sadness. Re-reading it makes me more and more angry and I am now at the stage where I have extreme difficulty in expressing my anger at this further indignity inflicted on some women – words fail me! (Thomson 1991, p. 101)

This chapter concentrates on the prevalence and effects of domestic violence on pregnant women, and reviews positive steps taken by midwives to address the issue of domestic violence and pregnancy. The authors draw on their experiences of awareness raising with midwives and other groups since 1990 to highlight areas of good practice and make recommendations for the role of midwives in an interdisciplinary approach to domestic violence.

DOMESTIC VIOLENCE AND PREGNANCY

Research provides overwhelming evidence that domestic violence may begin or escalate during pregnancy, resulting in an adverse pregnancy outcome and physical and emotional harm to women. Miscarriage, placental abruption, stillbirth, preterm labour, chorioamnionitis, low birth weight babies and injury to fetal limbs and organs are more common in abused women (Bohn 1990; Norton *et al.* 1995). Pregnancy may be affected directly as a result of abdominal injury or rape (Norton *et al.* 1995), or indirectly, by self-harming practices such as smoking, alcohol or drug abuse, which may alleviate the woman's day-to-day stress but compromise the pregnancy (Newton and Hunt 1984). Suicide and depression are also more common in abused women (Pahl 1995). It is difficult to obtain accurate assessments of the numbers of pregnant women affected; in the USA, a review of studies into prevalence rates revealed figures between 0.9 per cent and 20.1 per cent. The highest detection rates were found in studies using screening tests administered by trained personnel more than once during the pregnancy (Gazmararian *et al.* 1996).

Additionally, between 27 per cent and 70 per cent of men who abuse their partners will also abuse their children (NCH Action for Children 1994; Johnson 1995). Therefore, pregnant women and their children are at physical and emotional risk if they live in a climate of domestic violence. One of the aims of midwifery care is to ensure the safety of mothers and babies, and domestic violence clearly constitutes a threat to the physical and psychological welfare of both. Since most pregnant women present for health care, and will see a midwife during their pregnancy, it would seem that there is a clear role for midwives to be alert for signs of domestic violence.

THE ROLE OF THE MIDWIFE

Midwives provide evidence-based care for pregnant women and their families throughout the antenatal, intrapartum and postnatal period, taking account of physical, social, cultural and spiritual needs (United Kingdom Central Council for Nursing, Health Visiting and Midwifery 1995). Midwives also contribute to preparing couples for their role as parents. They visit women in their own homes and although they have no legal right of entry, they are rarely refused access. As well as talking to women, they examine them at every visit, so they are easily able to see any signs of abuse, particularly as the focus for physical abuse in pregnancy is the breasts, genitals and abdomen (Chez 1988; Bohn 1990). During initial antenatal interviews they are able to assess risk markers associated with domestic violence from the woman's history such as: previous miscarriages; preterm labour; low birth weight babies; and a previous history of depression or psychiatric illness.

In this position midwives are well placed to observe and discuss family circumstances, including domestic violence. They are also well placed to detect signs of stress and clinical depression which are often exhibited by abused women (Bewley and Gibbs 1991). Given the clear evidence for domestic violence beginning or escalating during pregnancy and its wide-spread adverse effects on pregnancy outcome, it is alarming that major studies into various agency responses to domestic violence have not included midwives (Smith 1989; Tayside Women and Violence Working Group 1994; Pahl 1995). Thus it seems that while midwives are well-placed to help abused women, their possible contribution has not yet been fully utilised.

INTERVENTION AND SCREENING

Nurses and nurse-midwives in North America have been closely involved in interdisciplinary work on domestic violence in pregnancy and have used screening and intervention strategies for some time (McFarlane *et al.* 1992). Whilst the wholesale adoption of other countries' strategies is not always appropriate, some of the interventions developed merit attention.

The American Surgeon General recommends that all pregnant women who present for health care be screened for abuse (Young and McFarlane 1991). Studies in North America have consistently shown that a process of systematic questioning by trained and sensitive personnel leads to high levels of disclosure of domestic violence (Gazmararian *et al.* 1996). Nurse-midwives have been encouraged to undertake training which equips them to administer written screening tests, and to document evidence of abuse which may be used in the future, such as photographs or body maps (Helton 1987; Young and McFarlane 1991).

In the United Kingdom, there is a divided view on whether it is appropriate for midwives to ask directly about domestic violence. One paper suggests that although evidence of abuse may be obvious, midwives may inadvertently collude with women to keep the violence secret by choosing not to notice it (Kent 1987). This attitude contributes to victim-blaming, in which the woman is held responsible for remaining in a violent situation, when, in fact, the practical and psychological risks associated with leaving are enormous. Kent also suggests that asking the question 'Does he hit you?' is not appropriate unless the woman and midwife know each other well; it may also be discriminatory and fail to address the plight of women who are not visibly injured. A spokesperson from Scottish Women's Aid cautions against active screening, asserting that it would do more harm than good, although she does not say why (Cochrane 1997). It is clearly an area which requires careful consideration and, more importantly, must be underpinned by a programme of referral; it would be unethical to encourage disclosure without providing appropriate support for abused women and, indeed, for the midwives who work with them (Bewley and Gibbs 1994).

Studies in the US advocate education of women about the nature and effects of domestic violence, stressing that violence is likely to continue and worsen in frequency and severity (Helton 1987). Education of women and health professionals is a key strategy for raising awareness about domestic violence and its effects on pregnancy (Young and McFarlane 1991).

RAISING AWARENESS

The impact of domestic abuse on pregnancy and the lives of abused women and their children requires the establishment of a legitimate role for midwives. The lack of an articulated role for midwives, together with a complete disregard for their potential in helping abused women, led to extensive work by the authors in raising awareness.

Table 22.1. Myths about domestic violence

Domestic violence is a private matter between the couple concerned
Women cause their own beatings
Women enjoy violence – it contributes to their sexual experiences
Abused women won't leave their violent partners so it is pointless trying to
help
Most abused women are of low socio-economic status and are poorly
educated

Our initial work with midwives in the United Kingdom began in 1990 with local and national study days. Using sociological research into the nature and reasons for domestic abuse (Binney 1981; Dobash and Dobash 1987; Andrews and Brown 1988), the days aimed to show how violence against women arose from socially-constructed, stereotypical, gender expectations. The main reasons for conflict in a relationship are sexual jealousy and possessiveness by the male partner, his expectations concerning the woman's domestic work and disputes over money (Dobash and Dobash 1987). We explored the potential for pregnancy to increase conflict in all those areas (Bewley and Gibbs 1991), resulting in domestic violence. Speakers from the Home Office, Police Domestic Violence Units and from Women's Aid contributed to morning sessions designed to give a sound background to the subject before moving on to the effects of domestic abuse on pregnancy and the role of the midwife. The afternoon sessions were devoted to workshops in which midwives were able to examine their own attitudes to domestic violence, explore some of the myths surrounding abuse (Table 22.1) and formulate strategies for addressing domestic violence during pregnancy. Both authors have counselling backgrounds and are experienced in small group facilitation, which encouraged participants to raise sensitive issues in a non-judgemental setting.

Although individual midwives responded well in recognising the need for midwifery intervention, responses from the organisations they returned to following the study days were less positive. During the early years, management responses from NHS Trusts clearly indicated an unwillingness to address domestic violence, arising partly from disbelief that there was such a problem, and partly from a fear that any intervention strategies would be expensive and belonged in a social rather than a health sphere. Additionally, individual attitudes of some midwifery managers, midwifery teachers and obstetricians revealed that belief in the myths surrounding domestic violence (Table 22.1) was as prevalent in health professionals as in the general public. Research and promotion of the topic of domestic violence as significant in maternity care at that time was hampered by prejudice and the lack of a medically sanctioned opinion.

As change was not going to occur rapidly a 'softly, softly' approach to continued awareness raising was adopted (Kennedy 1996). Study days and further publications have continued to promote the issue as relevant to midwives and other health professionals (Bewley and Gibbs 1992, 1994). On a wider scale, campaigns by various organisations in the public sphere such as 'Zero Tolerance' have further highlighted the issue of domestic abuse and changes in attitudes and responses are occurring. Many initial midwifery education programmes now incorporate sessions on domestic abuse; midwives are organising their own local study days and writing on domestic abuse and pregnancy (James-Hannan and Long 1994). The authors now receive regular requests for information and advice from individuals which suggests an increasing readiness to act.

However, despite these positive signs in study days and workshops, midwives identify clear barriers to providing care for abused women. It seems, therefore, that there is a discrepancy between individual responses and collective, professionally-supported, midwifery responses for intervention.

Midwifery practice strives to provide holistic care through therapeutic relationships with women and continuity of care and carer. However there may be a conflict in the midwife's perception of who her client is. Is it the mother or the baby? Increasingly, interventions are seen to be acceptable when the fetus is compromised, whereas the abused woman is deserving of help in her own right, not just in her capacity as a reproductive agent. Thus, while the question of active screening needs further investigation, the issue of asking an individual woman if she is being abused is more complex. McFarlane (1993) suggests that in pregnancy, a 'window of opportunity' arises for an abused woman to discuss the issue with a midwife. If that opportunity is lost because the midwife does not know how and when to broach the subject, the woman may lose her one chance of a hearing.

Nevertheless, there are clear and valid reasons why midwives find intervention difficult.

BARRIERS TO MIDWIFERY INTERVENTION

Little work has been carried out into midwives' views on their role in domestic violence. A small, unpublished study of 90 midwives in North London (Tucker 1995) received a 30 per cent response rate to a postal questionnaire seeking views on a potential role for midwives dealing with domestic violence. Although it would be inappropriate to base practice on the results of such a small piece of research, Tucker's findings are borne out time and time again by midwives involved in our domestic violence study days. These areas of concern, which we explore in depth further on, relate to:

(1) Lack of awareness;

(2) Fear of making things worse and fear for own personal safety;

(3) Lack of guidelines at national and local levels;

(4) Fear of breaching confidentiality versus possibility of child abuse;

(5) Pressure of other work and economic constraints;

(6) Lack of interdisciplinary approach.

Two midwives in the study were of the firm opinion that domestic violence is a private matter and does not belong in the midwife's remit, and although occasionally we have found this in our work with raising awareness, most midwives are keen to learn more about how they can detect or prevent domestic violence.

A review of abused women's experiences with health workers (Sadler 1994) confirmed that many of the midwives' concerns with their own practice were areas of concern for abused women, such as: a lack of understanding of women's feelings, not enough time, insufficient training in awareness, and inability to provide information and refer to other agencies.

These are valid concerns, but do not present barriers which are in-surmountable, as the following sections show.

Lack of awareness

Lack of awareness can be dealt with in a number of ways; posters, leaflets, and booklets on domestic violence are available from Women's Aid and Police Domestic Violence Units and can be displayed in hospitals, clinics and educational settings for health professionals and clients. Educational programmes must address domestic violence at undergraduate and post-graduate levels. Nursing students on a course dealing specifically with crisis intervention in family violence reported that their skills in communicating effectively with victims increased notably after the course (Mandt 1993). Domestic violence educational progammes for nurses and nurse-midwives in the USA increased the participants' ability to identify abused women and to assess their risk of further harm. They were also able to help women formulate their own plans for remaining in the relationship or for escaping (Helton 1987).

Issues relating to the incidence and consequences of domestic violence can also be dealt with by education programmes, by presenting research in which the overwhelming evidence of the prevalence of domestic violence can be reviewed.

Fear of making things worse and fear for own personal safety

Most midwives are women and most perpetrators of violence are men. Kent (1987) reports an incident where a health visitor remonstrated with a man for ill-treating his wife; he then banged his wife's head against a wall to illustrate that he was undeterred by censure and to inspire fear in the health visitor. This incident highlights how the interference made things worse for the woman and jeopardised the health visitor's own safety. Midwives attending study days confirmed that in some cases they were afraid of the partners of women they cared for.

Midwives must remember that the person responsible for making things worse is not the woman, the midwife or anyone else except the violent man. Considering that 48 per cent of all women who are murdered are killed by a partner or former partner (Victim Support 1992), lack of intervention could lead to murder or to many more years of brutalisation.

However, to minimise further danger to the woman and the midwife, any discussions about violence should take place away from the partner. This is difficult in some cases because midwives have made such strenuous efforts in the past to encourage men to become involved in the pregnancy. Men attend antenatal clinics, parenting classes and accompany women to labour wards. Open visiting postnatally means that men are able to be with their partners almost all the time. It is sometimes difficult to know whether a man who is overly solicitous and constantly stays by his partner's side is genuinely supportive or fearful that she might talk about him abusing her. However, there are ways of seeing women alone, perhaps visiting when the man is out, or, in the clinic setting, accompanying women to the ultrasound scanning department or laboratory. In ward areas, one room should be set aside for women only.

As far as personal safety is concerned, midwives' views reflect a general fear of violence in the community. Midwives are entitled to go about their work without threat of violence. Violence is a criminal offence, and in any situation where the midwife feels threatened, she should call for hospital security or the police. The United Kingdom Central Council for Nursing, Health Visiting and Midwifery (UKCC) Guidelines (1995) are clear that all health professionals should be protected by their employers, although this is obviously more easily said than done. Midwives who have to visit homes should be issued with mobile telephones or radios and personal alarms. They should also leave details of where they are, and when they are expected back at base. If there is a perceived threat of violence, then midwives should not visit the home alone.

Guidelines and policies

Midwifery practice is regulated by the UKCC and guidance for the scope of midwifery practice is contained in a series of codes (United Kingdom Central Council for Nursing, Health Visiting and Midwifery 1993), most recently summarised in Guidelines for Professional Practice (United Kingdom Central Council for Nursing, Health Visiting and Midwifery 1996). In addition, all midwives are subject to a process of supervision, under which each midwife is allocated a supervisor whose function, amongst other things, is to provide advice in difficult cases and to monitor the continuing professional development of the midwife.

Midwives facing dilemmas or problems in practice would consult the UKCC Guidelines, their supervisor, or professional body, usually the Royal College of Midwives. In response to a rising number of enquiries from members about domestic abuse, the Royal College of Midwives, in conjunction with the authors, is currently drawing up guidelines for safe and appropriate midwifery practice.

In addition to professional bodies, midwifery practice is influenced by National Health Service (NHS) Trust local policies and guidelines, by consumer pressure groups and by local, interdisciplinary groups such as audit committees. Thus, while each midwife is professionally and legally accountable for her own practice, local and professional frameworks can act to support midwives or exercise constraints on individual midwives' actions.

Midwives are concerned that although they may suspect domestic violence, they are unsure of their own role and, in the absence of a referral process, are unsure how to proceed in a supported way. This is not to suggest that no interventions are made by midwives, rather that there is no systematic approach (Bewley and Gibbs 1991). Our work suggests that midwives need guidelines from professional bodies and at local levels which would support intervention, but not be prescriptive or mandatory. Any guidelines must arise from an interdisciplinary perspective which does not leave responsibility for the woman to one professional group. Guidelines should reflect the local organisation and the agencies available in the local community, and should involve women who have been abused. There is a tendency for midwives to think only of the social worker when considering referral, but for some women, this may not always be appropriate. When considering referral, midwives must be made aware that work by Pahl (1995) and Lloyd (1995) reveals that the only single agency which women consistently reported as being helpful was Women's Aid.

Where physical injury is present, midwives must refer women to a GP or obstetrician, and records should be kept of injuries, with photographs if possible. These records must be kept separate from the woman's own personal notes.

Whatever guidelines are formulated, the woman must remain in control; no referral should be made without her knowledge and permission, and if she chooses to remain in a violent relationship, or to return to a violent partner, the role of the midwife is to support and not judge.

However, for some midwives, issues other than the well-being of the mother may arise, as the next section shows.

Confidentiality and child abuse

Midwives take the issue of maintaining confidentiality very seriously, yet understand the requirement for confidentiality to be breached where there is a risk of child abuse. The Children Act of 1989 makes clear the need for children at risk of violence to be protected. A study of 108 women living in a refuge found that 27 per cent of them reported that their children had also been abused (NCH Action for Children 1994). Midwives see families in their own homes and are alert to the possibility of child abuse. Midwives, however, spoke of their dilemma when a woman discloses that she is being abused and the midwife has concerns about child safety. They felt that their loyalty to the woman was compromised by their need to ensure protection for the child. Provided the midwife is aware of the links between domestic violence and child abuse, she should discuss these with the woman. NCH Action for Children (1994) recommends that all children living in violent households be considered 'children in need' and be supported by a social worker and other local agencies.

Economic constraints and pressure of work

The volume of work undertaken by midwives has dramatically increased over the last three years, particularly since the implementation of the re-commendations of the Second Expert Maternity Group (Department of Health 1993). This, coupled with moves to reduce junior doctors' hours, has led to pressure on midwives' time and energy which may result in midwives experiencing 'burn-out' and leaving the profession (Hunt and Symonds 1996). Of all maternity units, 78 per cent are currently experiencing staff shortages and only 36,000 of 97,000 registered midwives are currently practising (Walker 1997). Systems designed to facilitate continuity of carer have not been adequately funded and have resulted in many midwives working excessively long hours (Walker 1997). The philosophy of *Changing Childbirth* (Department of Health 1993) with its emphasis on continuity of carer, may have led to unrealistic expectations for midwives and mothers about quality of available midwifery care (Warwick 1995).

The issue of midwives actively confronting the issue of domestic violence, therefore, raises real problems for midwives' workload, which then raises economic considerations if additional staffing is needed. However, as Ingram (1993) points out, the consequences of interpersonal violence are themselves expensive in terms of treatment of physical and mental problems. There are minimal strategies which can be achieved without extra cost. Displaying posters, incorporating details of local provision for abused women into hospital pregnancy books and displaying cards showing telephone numbers of Women's Aid and local police domestic violence units, can all be done without significant additional use of midwifery time.

Lack of interdisciplinary approach

Studies show overwhelmingly that an interdisciplinary, multi-agency ap-proach is essential in dealing with domestic violence. Until now, midwives have not been included in that approach, and have not perhaps been aware that such an approach is effective. Midwives on our study days revealed that where they had come across women in violent relationships, they felt as though they were working alone to overcome an insurmountable problem, even when they enlisted the help of their supervisor. The adoption of an interdisciplinary approach would reduce feelings of personal responsibility and secure better support for abused women.

RECOMMENDATIONS

It is clear that midwives have a role in the detection and prevention of domestic violence during pregnancy; however, the professional and organisational support for their involvement has not yet been clearly articulated. The production of professional guidelines from the Royal College of Midwives may contribute to a clearer role for midwives.

In the meantime, we would recommend that midwives receive further education and training on the subject of domestic violence. Ideally this should take place in an interdisciplinary setting, so that professional groups can identify each other's strengths and learn from good practice, while appreciating areas where some groups would find intervention difficult and cross-referral would be advantageous.

The following action plan (Bewley and Gibbs 1991), provides a starting point for midwives, but it is equally applicable to any allied professions involved in an interdisciplinary approach to domestic violence and pregnancy:

(1) Examine your own attitudes to domestic violence – most midwives are women and by the widespread nature of domestic violence, some of them must have experienced it in their own lives. Similarly, midwives will have absorbed the same myths (Table 22.1) about domestic violence which are prevalent in society. They need to talk through their beliefs in an open and non-judgemental way, which draws on research to support or refute their views;

(2) Build up a picture of your local area – records should be kept of women who are known to be abused so that data can be collected; however, active screening of women is inappropriate where midwives have not received training, and where referral mechanisms have not been set up. Find out what is available to support abused women in your local area, e.g. police domestic violence units, local women's offices and neighbourhood centres, Women's Aid etc. Women need this information if they want to take action;

(3) Vulnerable groups – all abused women are vulnerable, but those in same sex relationships, the disabled and those who do not speak English have particular needs. When building up the local picture, bear in mind what may be helpful to these groups;

(4) Display posters in clinics – this has a two-fold effect. It gives women information about where to get help, and gives out the message that there is an awareness of domestic violence. Posters should also be

displayed for men who abuse their partners and who want help to stop;

(5) Develop appropriate guidelines – liaising with obstetricians, social workers, GPs, health visitors and consumer groups should enable the production of local guidelines which are not restrictive or prescriptive, but supportive;

(6) Create non-judgemental settings – women need to know they are safe to talk about their experiences without being blamed or judged;

(7) Act on instincts – if a woman shows signs of injury or exhibits behavioural signs consistent with domestic violence, ask her if she is being hit or hurt. Contrary to assumptions, women are not offended when asked about domestic violence, and many are relieved to find someone to talk to (Mooney 1993). However, any discussion must take place away from the man, and midwives should not act as go-betweens;

(8) Observe couple interactions – is the overly concerned and solicitous man or the one who is constantly belittling his partner in public beating her in private?

(9) Follow up non-attenders to clinics – bear in mind that the woman may not attend because she has a visible injury;

(10) Actively support the view that violence is not acceptable – avoid collusion to keep violence secret, and counter statements which perpetuate the myths about domestic violence.

CONCLUSION

Domestic violence is a significant factor in maternal and perinatal mortality and morbidity. Although midwives are ideally placed to identify abuse, their role is poorly articulated and lacks professional and local support (Bewley and Gibbs 1994). Nevertheless, midwives are responding with concern and must be included in a collaborative approach to addressing domestic violence.

REFERENCES

Andrews, B. and Brown, G.W. (1988) Marital violence in the community: a biographical approach. *Br J Psych* **153**, 305–12

Bewley, C.A. and Gibbs, A. (1991) Violence in pregnancy. *Midwifery* **7**, 107–12

Bewley, C.A. and Gibbs, A. (1992) Abusing the pregnant woman: a crime against the future? *Modern Midwife* **2**, 15–18

Bewley, C.A. and Gibbs, A. (1994) Coping with domestic violence in pregnancy. *Nursing Standard* **8**, 25–8

Binney, D. (1981) 'Domestic violence – battered women in Britain in the 1970s in Cambridge' in Women's Group (Eds) *Women in Society*. London: Virago

Bohn, D.K. (1990) Domestic violence in pregnancy: implications for practice *J Nurs Midwifery* **35**, 86–98

Chez, R.A. (1988) Woman battering, *Am J Obstet Gynecol* **158**, 1–4

Cochrane, L. (1997) Mothers to be face increased risk of violence. *Scotsman*, 3 May, p.2

Department of Health (1993) *Report of the Second Expert Maternity Group – Changing Childbirth*. London: HMSO

Dobash, R. and Dobash, R. (1987) 'Violence towards wives' in J. Orford (Ed.) *Coping with disorder in the family*. London: Croom Helm

Gazmararian, J., Lazorick, S., Sptiz, A., Ballard, T., Saltzman, L. and Marks, J. (1996) Prevalence of violence against pregnant women. *JAMA* **275**, 1915–19

Helton, A. (1987) *A Protocol Of Care For The Battered Woman*. New York: March of Dimes Birth Defects Federation

Hunt, S. and Symonds, A. (1996) *The Midwife And Society*. London: Macmillan

Ingram, R. (1993) Violence from known men. *Open Mind* **66**, 18–19

James-Hannan, D. and Long, L. (1994) Crime prevention: an issue for midwives. *British Journal of Midwifery* **2**, 29–32

Johnson, N. (1995) 'Domestic violence: an overview' in P. Kingston, and B. Penhale, (Eds) *Family Violence And The Caring Professions*, pp. 101–26. London: Macmillan

Kennedy, D. (1996) Pregnant women face biggest risk of domestic violence, *The Times*, 12 November, p.7

Kent, A. (1987) Home is where the fear is. *Nursing Times* **85**, 16–17

Lloyd, S. (1995) 'Social work and domestic violence' in P. Kingston and B. Penhale (Eds) *Family Violence And The Caring Professions*. London: Macmillan

Mandt, A. (1993) The curriculum revolution in action: nursing and crisis intervention for victims of family violence. *J Nurs Educ* **32**, 44–6

McFarlane, J., Parker, B., Soeken, K. and Bullock, L. (1992) Assessing for abuse during pregnancy. *JAMA* **267**, 3176–8

Mooney, J. (1993) *The Hidden Figure: The North London Domestic Violence Survey*. Middlesex: Middlesex University Centre for Criminology.

NCH Action for Children (1994) *The Hidden Victims: Children and Domestic Violence*. London: NCH Action for Children

Newton, R.W. and Hunt, L.P. (1984) Psychosocial stress in pregnancy and its relation to low birthweight. *BMJ* **288**, 1191–4

Norton, L.B., Peipert, J.F. and Zierler, S. (1995) Battering in pregnancy: an assessment of two screening methods *Obstet Gynecol* **85**, 321–5

Pahl, J. (1995) 'Health professionals and violence against women' in P. Kingston and B. Penhale (Eds) *Family Violence and the Caring Professions*. London: Macmillan

Sadler, C. (1994) Hidden from help. *Health Visitor* **67**, 185–7

Smith, L.J.F. (1989) *Domestic Violence: An Overview Of The Literature. Home Office Research Study no 107*. London: HMSO

Tayside Women and Violence Working Group (1994) *Hit Or Miss: An Exploratory Study Of The Provision for Women Subjected To Domestic Violence In Tayside Region*. Tayside: Equal Opportunities Unit, Tayside Regional Council

Thomson, A. (1991) Editorial: Indignities suffered by women. *Midwifery* **7**, 101

Tucker, A. (1995) *The Role Of Midwives In Preventing Domestic Violence*. Unpublished research project, North London College of Health Studies

United Kingdom Central Council for Nursing, Health Visiting and Midwifery (1993) *Midwives Code of Practice*. London: UKCC

United Kingdom Central Council for Nursing, Health Visiting and Midwifery (1995) *Midwives Rules*. London: UKCC

United Kingdom Central Council for Nursing Health, Visiting and Midwifery (1996) *Guidelines for Professionals*. London: UKCC

Victim Support (1992) *Domestic Violence: Report Of A National Inter-agency Working Party*. London: Victim Support

Walker, L. (1997) Return to practice midwifery: does it have a future? *MIDIRS Midwifery Digest*. **7**, 19–21

Warwick, C. (1995) Tensions in the system. *Br J Mid* **3**, 358–9

Young, A. and McFarlane, J. (1991) Preventing abuse during pregnancy: a national educational model for health providers. *J Nurs Educ* **30**, 202–6

Chapter 23

The role of the obstetrician

Susan Bewley

INTRODUCTION

Pregnancy is always a time of change and thus of opportunity. Whilst for many the imminent child and new family are matters of joy and a welcomed development, for others they are sources of threat, fear, disappointment and loss. All pregnant women have contact with health services and thus obstetricians have an opportunity to identify and help women exposed to the hazards of violence.

BACKGROUND

As explored in more detail in other chapters, domestic violence is a common lifetime experience for women, associated with significant psychological and social sequelae. Contrary to both intuition and the taboo on harming pregnant women, most research has found that violence may begin or escalate in pregnancy (Gelles 1975; Hilberman and Munson 1978; Stark *et al.* 1979; Bowker 1983; Hillard 1985; Surgeon General 1986; Bohn 1990) and increases again post-partum (Gielen *et al.* 1994). This suggests that the woman is not the only focus (as outwith pregnancy) but that the pregnancy and unborn baby are also objects of the attack. This may reflect a response on behalf of the perpetrator to changing relationships, threats to his prior exclusive attention and the normal maternal preoccupation with the newborn. Domestic violence carries direct and indirect risks to the mother as well as to the unborn fetus. Suicide attempts and increased tobacco and alcohol use are additional hazards. Ultimately, domestic violence can lead to death (see Cases 1 and 2). Present anecdotal estimates of violence are likely to grossly underestimate the problem as women are generally reluctant to spontaneously disclose such experiences, particularly if there is a justified fear of retaliation. Very often the male partner will accompany a woman to the casualty department or antenatal clinic, his presence acting as a deterrent, both for the health professional to make the necessary enquiries and for the woman to admit to violence. The prevalence of violence in the British population is unknown but relevant literature suggests recurrent physical and sexual violence occur in 15 per cent of the population before (Helton *et al.* 1987), 7–9 per cent during (Helton *et al.* 1987; Amaro *et al.* 1990; McFarlane *et al.* 1992; Gielen *et al.* 1994) and 25 per cent after pregnancy (Gielen *et al.* 1994). Thus there would be much medical, let alone social, gain if violence were identified and an effective intervention applied.

Case 1

A 25-year-old mother of two children by different fathers was found dead at the bottom of a staircase at 32 weeks of pregnancy with head injuries thought initially to be the result of a fall. She had attended clinics irregularly and was not well known to the three different health professionals who had seen her. The post-mortem revealed death secondary to a blow to the head with a hammer. The present partner was arrested, charged and found guilty of murder.

Case 2

A 32-year-old married woman with two children and no other relevant history booked at 28 weeks' and repeatedly missed appointments. She was brought in dead by an ambulance, having been found by her husband at home drowned in the bath at 38 weeks' gestation. The husband had a prior conviction for grievous bodily harm. Although the GP had been treating her for depression and the couple had separated on several occasions there was nothing else suspicious noted in the background. The husband was questioned by police but his brother gave a solid and unwavering alibi. The coroner's post-mortem was inconclusive and an open verdict was reached.

WHAT IS THE ROLE OF THE OBSTETRICIAN WITH RESPECT TO ANY PREGNANT WOMAN?

Increasingly, in the last decade, the role of the obstetrician has been questioned; whether it is necessary at all for the majority of women or even possibly harmful through over-investigation or over-intervention. Through *Changing Childbirth* (Department of Health 1994), the emergence of maternal-fetal medicine specialists and greater teamwork in medicine generally, the role is being clarified as that of:

(1) Being the key professional in women with, or at high risk of, complications; and

(2) Being a member of a team delivering care to all pregnant women in a population (and thus having a justified interest in the services and

screening of normal healthy pregnant women, even if not actively involved).

As we have seen, domestic violence is present in many women's lives and may lead directly and indirectly to pregnancy complications. There is therefore a justification, if not an imperative, for obstetricians to have an interest. There are two main levels at which identification may occur:

(1) Through investigating or direct questioning in a suspicious circumstance;

 or

(2) Through screening for violence.

IDENTIFICATION OF VIOLENCE

It is a maxim in medicine that 'if you don't look, you don't find'. If a practitioner claims never to have seen a case of domestic violence, it is very likely that he or she is asking the wrong questions or asking them in the wrong way. A high index of suspicion is required as only a minority will present straightforwardly and openly as a direct result of assault. There are many situations in medicine where an underlying problem of family disharmony, violence, poverty, depression, mental illness or drug or alcohol abuse is highly relevant to an understanding of an individual's situation and to the likely or available responses. If the right questions are not asked, or if they are not asked sensitively, the background will remain hidden and doctors and patients alike become frustrated by poor communication and lack of progress. We know some of the risk factors associated with domestic violence: divorce, separation and high parity (Hillard 1985), teenagers, late bookers and women with unwanted or mistimed pregnancies (Gazmararian 1995), past psychiatric problems or attempted suicide and high use of tobacco and alcohol (Hillard 1985; Webster 1996). Certain clinical presentations can raise suspicion (see Cases 3 and 4 and Table 23.1).

These are obviously common situations with many other important medical differential diagnoses or simple social explanations. Some are quite non-specific. They may also overlap with presentations of depression, drug or alcohol abuse. Nevertheless, the key point is to think 'is there anything else going on?' and to have an ability to open the discussion with the pregnant woman if she is ready and willing to engage in conversation with the doctor.

Case 3

A 37-year-old GP's wife in her second pregnancy was noted to have black-eyes at a routine antenatal check at 30 weeks' gestation. On questioning, she said she had slipped and fallen down the stairs. No other enquiry was made and nothing else was noted or done. Five years later, after a drink-driving conviction, several Family Health Service Authority complaints and a break-up of the GP partnership, her husband was referred to the General Medical Council professional conduct committee and onto the Sick Doctors scheme. They built up debts and had to move to a smaller house. The family stayed together while she became the main breadwinner.

Case 4

A 27-year-old married Catholic woman in her third pregnancy requested termination at 12 weeks' but was very ambivalent. She explained that her husband was a soldier serving in Northern Ireland who maltreated her, kept her very short of money and beat her during frequent rows when home on leave. The pregnancy was a result of non-consensual intercourse during one of these short periods of leave. She had no family support or close friends, felt her finances were too precarious to bring up another child and that her present children were at risk from him. She was reluctant to approach army medical or social services. Having seen a counsellor she decided to proceed but unfortunately suffered a perforation of the uterus that required laparotomy and oversewing of the uterus and a damaged segment of bowel. She made a full medical recovery but sustained a prolonged and very severe depression.

Table 23.1.   Presentations that may be associated with domestic violence

Unplanned, unwanted pregnancy, late or refused request for termination of
 pregnancy
Past history of IUD/prematurity/injuries
Late booking, high non-attendance rate
Fall, unexplained injuries
Abdominal pain
Vaginal bleeding or possible abruption
Multiple non-specific admissions
Alcohol or drug abuse
Depression
Known family disharmony, separation during pregnancy
Bizarre behaviour, evasive, cowed or aggressive attitudes
Overbearing or over-solicitous partner
Disquiet or unease in health professional (nurse, midwife, junior doctor)

HOW DOES ONE APPROACH A DIFFICULT TOPIC?

The first requirement of any sensitive conversation is the context in which it takes place, and the most important requirement is that of confidentiality.

Confidentiality

A woman's concerns may be 'Are we alone? Can we be overheard? Can I trust this doctor?' Doctors start with a certain advantage in that it is common knowledge that they have a duty of confidentiality to patients. However, we all know how easy it is for confidentiality to be threatened or broken, and that many people have an innate distrust of any, or all, authority figures. Thus obstetricians have to make a special effort to think about how confidences are elicited, what barriers may exist and how they might be protected once obtained. The on-call senior house officer (SHO) is unlikely to obtain any valuable or sensitive information if interviewing in a public ward or in an antenatal bed separated by curtains from the next patient and her visitors!

Ideally, for *any* and *every* medical consultation one should have a private one-to-one conversation in a soundproof room, and if an interpreter is required, a professional is preferable to a friend, relative or partner. The traditions of the medical consultation have gradually become eroded, partly as pregnancy and birth are social events and as male partners have been welcomed over the years into the consultation, labour and delivery rooms. With our modern enthusiasm to encourage men to enter and participate in this traditional female sphere has come the cost of becoming distanced from our vulnerable female patients. Thus, instead of privacy being an everyday feature we can take for granted, it has to be actively created.

Obstetricians have to be very alert to tiny signals of discomfort and the need to create privacy. Doctors are usually in a strong position to conduct the consultation in their own fashion as they are authority figures and largely operating on their own territory. For a midwife in the home environment to demand privacy may be much more difficult, though she may be able to find a plausible reason for referral to a GP or obstetrician if she is concerned. How does one keep or get a partner out of the room? Body language may say 'keep out', such as closing a door between the woman and her partner, as she comes into the room. Gently asking a partner 'Could you just step out for a moment while I examine her?' may work. Sometimes it may be achievable by moving room and saying 'I'll just speak to her alone first and then get you to join us in a minute'. Indeed, a partner's reaction, particularly if hostile or refusing to leave, may itself be informative (see Case 5). The gender of the doctor may also be relevant, or act as a barometer to the male-female dynamics of a relationship. Some hostile reactions, particularly to male doctors examining women, may be indicative of a proprietory attitude held by a jealous or controlling partner. One can try to diffuse tension with smiles or charm or 'it's our routine to talk to women alone first', 'we like to examine in privacy, and I can get a chaperone (or another female doctor)'. If a situation is becoming tense or inflamed it may not be possible or wise to persist. But, particularly if suspicions have been raised by other health workers, we can attempt to use our professional duties and advantages as doctors to good effect.

Case 5

A quiet, subdued 16-year-old with ruptured membranes presented to Labour Ward at 27 weeks' gestation with her boyfriend. When she was asked if she'd like him to leave the room for the speculum examination he became very aggressive; 'You f... ing doctors, you're all the f... ing same, you know f... all. Don't you tell me what to do or I'll f... ing kill you'. She said it was OK for him to stay and ruptured membranes were confirmed. She discharged herself against advice two days later and was readmitted with chorioamnionitis and premature labour at 28 weeks', delivering a baby that subsequently had a stormy course on the neonatal unit and died. Concern was expressed about the boyfriend, his hostility and threatening behaviour to neonatal staff but she was discharged with no medical, social service or police follow-up. Two years later a transformed, confident 18-year-old rebooked in her second pregnancy at the hospital having left the first partner and admitted to staff that she had been repeatedly beaten during and after the pregnancy. No charges were ever brought.

Questions, tone and language

The quality of the history is the responsibility of the doctor. If a doctor, in a white coat, leans over a woman lying prone in a bed and interrupts her narrative with a stereotype-filled question such as 'So, are you are a battered wife then?' it would be unlikely to produce any answer but 'No!'. It would be an example of 'victim-blaming' to claim 'but *she* never told me that!'

The doctor should look unhurried and allow her to talk. Sitting at a distance, but at the same level or below her may give a sense of equity and control. A sympathetic or relaxed listening manner and simple non-judgmental language is also helpful. As with other history taking, it is best to start with open questions and then follow with details or specifics. For example, 'Is there anything you are unhappy about?', 'Who is at home?', 'How are things at home?', 'Do you and your partner argue?', 'Do you ever fight?' or 'Do your arguments get physical?'. Women will observe the doctor's reactions closely before deciding what else to reveal if next asked 'Have you ever been hit?', 'Where are you hit?', 'How often?'. She needs to be reassured in advance that her story will not shock and that she will not be judged harshly.

The exact words and phrases women use must be listened to carefully. Sometimes there are clues or revelations in the choice of words, absence of comment or the gaps and silences between sentences. For example, 'How are things between you?' 'Not too bad'. Does that mean not too good? 'They're better now'. Does that mean they were worse before, and how much worse? 'Alright most of the time'. And what does that mean for some of the time? Or (as in Case 6), 'He just hit me too hard'. *Just*. Is she saying he hits her frequently but it is normally acceptable to her except that he made a mistake this time (for which she has forgiven him) in that he broke her jaw?

Obstetricians' reaction

The appropriate response should be of non-judgmental support and again, confidentiality is critical.

'Hand-held' notes are not safe or confidential and all maternity services should have a separate system of documentation. Any abuse reported must be systematically and carefully documented separately, including taking photographs of injuries. Even if women do not take prosecutions immediately, this may become evidence in later criminal cases. It can be explained as 'We do this as part of our professional job. It will be completely confidential, but available if you ever want it in the future for any police or legal action'.

The doctor should assess the woman's safety and believe her if she says 'he'd kill me if . . .'. At present a health professional may offer to inform the police, although he or she cannot do so without the woman's permission (Knight 1995; Morley 1995), and can also refer on to a women's shelter. Admission to hospital to relieve a crisis, even if the injuries themselves do not require treatment, might occasionally be appropriate, and can be justified in terms of monitoring the fetus.

If the woman is unable or unwilling to leave her partner, she should nevertheless always be provided with telephone numbers of refuges and assisted in identifying an exit plan; e.g. to keep a suitcase packed with essential items at home, to accumulate spare change, to obtain a spare set of keys and necessary documentation to allow her to register her children at another school etc. The woman will only be able to take this advice when she eventually feels mentally and physically ready. Although frustrating, it may not be within the power of health professionals to effect any immediate protection, and it is certainly possible to make matters worse. Being non-judgmental does not mean having to collude with a woman's vision of the world where violence is everyday, or justified, or even an expression of how intensely her partner cares for her. The doctor's role might be to focus or name the problem or voice a view, 'It sounds as though you are in a very difficult situation . . .', 'He's got a problem', 'One day you may have to get out in a hurry if your life's endangered'. It may be helpful to encourage an attitude of empowerment, 'If things get worse, I believe you can and will get out of this situation somehow'. Domestic violence is a difficult, chronic and complex problem whose resolution may only take place in small steps, but obstetricians are ideally placed to make interventions that break the cycle of violence for future generations (see Table 23.2).

Case 6

A 22-year-old primigravida came to antenatal clinic at 26 weeks' gestation to obtain a Maternity B1 and sick certificate and explained to the receptionist that she had been in a car accident. She was referred to the obstetrician who asked closely about the circumstances of this accident and she said that her boyfriend had hit her, 'just the once'. 'He didn't mean to do this, he just hit me too hard, that's all.' She was reluctant to say anything else. Her jaw was broken in two places and wired so that she was unable to eat solid food for a month. From the strange wording of the comment made, the obstetrician suspected repeated abuse and that she felt in some way that she deserved it (the boyfriend was entitled to hit her hard, but made a mistake on this occasion by hitting too hard). The obstetrician gave general advice, ostensibly accepting the presented story of a 'one-off'; 'I don't think it's ever right to lose your temper so badly that you break a jaw, even if he felt provoked', 'Sometimes a relationship gets better after an accident like this but sometimes things get worse in pregnancy or when the baby comes and women have to think or plan to get away', 'If that happens you can always tell us in confidence. If you want help there are places to go and we've got phone numbers and details of refuges on a poster outside if you ever need them. I'll write the number down for you just in case', 'Why don't I check you and the baby in a month when you'll be eating again and you can let me know how things are getting on.'

Table 23.2.   Obstetricians' aims

Provide sympathetic woman-centred services
Treat all women with kindness and respect
Provide confidentiality
Reassure women that help is available and their situation is understood
Encourage belief in their ability to change or get out when ready
Document history and injuries for a potential later legal action
Crisis action (e.g. admission)
Active liaison: local refuges, victim support schemes, GPs and community resources
Alert others with woman's agreement: e.g. family doctor, paediatric or social services, police
Improve identification of victims of domestic violence
Increase awareness of domestic violence

Inappropriate responses include shock, horror or disbelief. Directive advice to 'get out' may have the counterproductive effect of leaving the woman feeling that the doctor does not understand her trapped situation. It may even make her feel more worthless or drive her from care rather than face the unspoken accusation that 'she's asking for it'. She may pick up subtle clues that the doctor is fed up with her, and either not return or lie that things are better. Though understandable, astonishment that the women does not take obvious, logical and caring advice is also unhelpful. One just has to hope that she will, if and when she wishes and can.

Is stigma and shock appropriate? If doctors become able to talk casually about violence does that mean some kind of acceptance or that they are inured to the problem? It is possible to retain one's internal shock at a behaviour even if externally looking unshaken. It may be helpful to realise that there are different kinds of negative public stigma; those involving the perpetrator (which may act as a rein on violent behaviour), and those regarding the victim (that she must be a willing and passive participant in the violence as staying somehow indicates acceptance). Indeed, there may not be enough stigma; in many societies it is still acceptable to beat unruly wives with sticks, or, only a step away, to make jokes about hitting the wife to make her behave.

There are deep cultural notions of proper behaviour of men and women. It is possible that we hold powerful subconscious views about pregnancy that are shaken by the reality of domestic violence. These stereotypes might elicit unhelpful responses when a professional meets domestic violence. For example:

(1) The 'innocent fetus'. By contrast we have the not-so-innocent mother (who has been sexually active by definition) who chose her partner and has not left him;

(2) 'Bad mothers'. Those women who fail to protect their children or appear to expose them to harm;

(3) 'Battered women'. These are abused, tortured and degraded victims, pitiable women to whom we must be sympathetic. They seem quite unlike the rude women using bad language who turn up drunk late at night in casualty;

(4) 'Caring obstetricians'. These are active, intelligent, skilled diagnosticians and surgeons who make quick decisions and solve problems. Unfortunately the image of the 'white knight' who saves 'damsels in distress' is severely dented and frustrated by powerlessness in the face of chronic, nasty and brutish behaviour by perpetrators of domestic violence.

We should not be taken in by the above caricatures, but they have a degree of resonance and familiarity within them. Women who experience domestic violence are a heterogeneous group with no set pattern of presentation, behaviour or typical explanation. Any stereotyping (by doctor or patient) will lead to misunderstanding and muddled communication.

Another longer-term role of obstetricians is to be a public advocate for women and women's rights, during pregnancy in particular. In view of the medical risks, they must state that there is zero tolerance of violence against pregnant women. One unfortunate side-effect of the recent enforced caesarean section debate has been the public perception that obstetricians will act against pregnant women's wishes, and in a particularly violent way too! This is despite the RCOG guidelines to the contrary (Royal College of Obstetricians and Gynaecologists 1994, 1996) and now clarification (in *Re MB* 1997) that there is no authority for enforced caesareans without consent in the competent.

SCREENING

Should we actively screen for domestic violence?

If it is such a problem should we screen all women routinely, perhaps at booking? It could be argued that these pregnancies are high risk, and standard questions about violence should be included in the same way as questions eliciting risk factors such as diabetes, smoking and alcohol use (Surgeon General 1986). If a history of violence is not sought, it cannot be recognised and therefore the pregnancy will not be considered high-risk (Stark *et al.* 1979; Helton 1986).

Criteria for screening

However, before introducing widespread screening, a few further steps need to be taken. Firstly, we are ignorant of the prevalence. It is estimated that within a healthy population of female patients receiving antenatal care at least one in ten women, and maybe as many as one in four, could be expected to be a victim of domestic violence at some point in their life (Mezey and Bewley 1997). Research is needed to determine local prevalences of battering during pregnancy, as most work so far has been performed in urban areas in the USA and Scandinavia and may be affected by bias in either direction; towards higher rates, if studies have been performed in high-risk populations or centres, or lower rates due to under-reporting and under-recognition. Secondly, the point of screening is to institute effective intervention, and there is little work on this. If screening has not been shown to be beneficial, there remains the possibility that it could be positively harmful, either by wasting the woman's and health professional's time that would be better served on other effective care, or by exacerbating the social situation. If there were an effective intervention, there would still be a question of who was the most appropriate health professional to be undertaking screening. As this is usually a long-standing and social problem, it might be more appropriate to be performed by a member of the primary health care team (such as the GP or health visitor) rather than the less holistic and time-limited pregnancy professional (midwife or obstetrician). If pregnancy is viewed as a time of change and opportunity, then the midwifery booking interview would be an ideal time and place for screening. Clearly this is another urgent area for multi-disciplinary research.

How would we screen?

The use of simple structured questions for screening (Table 23.3) can increase the detection of violence several-fold (Norton *et al.* 1995). Although booking is an obvious time to enquire, questions may need to be asked repeatedly (as reporting increases with repeated enquiry) (McFarlane *et al.* 1992; Norton *et al.* 1995). It has not been shown whether continuity of carer

Table 23.3.   Nolan screening questionnaire

1. Have you ever been emotionally or physically abused by your partner or someone important to you?	YES/NO
2. Within the last year, have you been hit, slapped, kicked, or otherwise physically hurt by someone?	YES/NO
If yes, by whom? (circle all that apply) Husband/Ex-husband/Boyfriend/Stranger/Other/Multiple No. of times:	
3. Since you have been pregnant, have you been hit, slapped, kicked or otherwise physically hurt by someone?	YES/NO
If yes, by whom? (circle all that apply) Husband/Ex-husband/Boyfriend/Stranger/Other/Multiple No. of times: . . . . Mark area of injury on the body map	
1 = Threats of abuse, including use of a weapon 2 = Slapping, pushing; no injuries and/or lasting pain 3 = Punching, kicking, bruises, cuts and/or broken bones 4 = Beaten up, severe contusions, burns, broken bones 5 = Head, internal, and/or permanent injury 6 = Use of weapon, wound from weapon	
4. Within the past year, has anyone forced you to have sexual activities?	YES/NO
If yes, by whom? (circle all that apply) Husband/Ex-husband/Boyfriend/Stranger/Other/Multiple No. of times:	
5. Are you afraid of your partner or anyone you listed above?	YES/NO

is more or less likely to facilitate disclosure of violence. Reporting also reflects the practitioner's own attitudes and training. Training and education of health professionals can be successful in increasing their knowledge and willingness to screen pregnant women for abuse (McFarlane 1989). Lack of training has been cited as the most common barrier to obstetricians screening for violence, although some felt that it was not a problem with their patients, that they had a lack of time or were frustrated that they could not help the victim (Parsons *et al.* 1995). For any proposed screening to be successful, there needs to be increased awareness amongst health professionals that domestic violence occurs during pregnancy and training to enable health professionals to be able to ask the relevant questions without appearing insensitive or judgmental. Training must include information about available local community resources and about the scope and limitations of existing legal remedies.

Even if we do not screen pregnant women, we can provide them all with basic information in the form of cards, leaflets or posters. Telephone numbers of shelters can be placed in routine antenatal literature and prominently displayed posters in relevant local languages, without women having to openly admit abuse.

ETHICAL DIMENSIONS

The obstetrician-patient relationship is qualitatively different from the midwife-pregnant woman one in a variety of ways that may be relevant here. Whereas midwives have statutory duties to look after all pregnant women, obstetricians usually see women in the context of a referral to a clinic or hospital with some problem – that is why they, or their pregnancies, are being brought to our attention. The ethical and legal dimensions of the relationships are not identical and in an era of 'informed choices' the culture of *caring* for both mother and fetus within the context of their family and wider society may seem paternalistic and slightly old-fashioned (see quote below). If all women were truly free and autonomous and their lives filled with 'informed choices', then our understanding of violence might be that it is a woman's personal choice. Is it paternalistic to see some women as trapped victims with low self-esteem? Would women feel abandoned by a shrug or casual comment from their doctor that 'well, it's up to you, it's your choice'? Should we be developing an idea of 'neo-paternalism' or 'parentalism' where we care for women, but also try to empower them by giving hope, aspirations, ideas, information and small amounts of control where we can, e.g. in our consultations and negotiations? Violence is harmful to both the mother and unborn child, and the mother has to be the centre of our attention as we care for the fetus through her.

> A woman about to become a mother, or with her newborn infant upon her bosom, should be the object of trembling care and sympathy, wherever she bears her tender burden or stretches her aching limbs. God forbid that any member of the profession to which she trusts her life, doubly precious at this emotional period, should handle it negligently, inadvisedly or selfishly. (Oliver Wendall Holmes)

CONCLUSION

Although domestic violence has medical sequelae and associations, effective interventions by doctors may be limited. However, if we do not ask, we do not find out and we cannot help. If domestic violence is revealed we can do nothing, something helpful or something harmful. With 'first of all, do no harm' in mind, even nothing is better than harmful! Merely hearing a woman's story, validating her experience and treating her considerately may help if she feels cared for and sympathised with. Many other agencies can be involved. Pregnancy and birth are fundamental life events and there is a role for obstetricians to facilitate change in this common, chronic problem.

REFERENCES

Amaro, H., Fried, L.E., Cabral, H. and Sucherman, B. (1990) Violence during pregnancy and substance use. *Am J Public Health* **80**, 575–9

Bohn, D.K. (1990) Domestic violence and pregnancy. Implications for practice. *J Nurs Midwifery* **35**, 86–98

Bowker, L.H. (1983) *Beating Wife Beating*. Lexington MA: Lexington Books

Department of Health (1994) *Changing Childbirth*. I: Report of the Expert Maternity Group. London: HMSO

Gazmararian, J.A., Adams, M., Saltzman, L.E. *et al.* (1995) The relationship between pregnancy intendedness and physical violence in mothers of newborns. *Obstet Gynecol* **85**, 1031–8

Gelles, R.J. (1975) Violence and pregnancy: a note on the extent of the problem and needed services. *The Family Coordinator* **24**, 81–6

Gielen, A.C., O'Campo, P.J., Faden, R.R., Kass, N.E. and Xue, X. (1994) Interpersonal conflict and physical violence during the childbearing year. *Soc Sci Med* **39**, 781–7

Helton, A. (1986) Battering during pregnancy. *Am J Nurs* **86**, 910–13

Helton, A.S., McFarlane, J. and Anderson E.T. (1987) Battered and pregnant: a prevalence study. *Am J Public Health* **77**, 1337–9

Hilberman, E. and Munson, K. (1978) Sixty battered women. *Victimology* **2**, 460–70

Hillard, P.A. (1985) Physical abuse in pregnancy. *Obstet Gynecol* **66**, 185–90

Knight, M.A. (1995) The police surgeon's view. Medical paternalism is unacceptable. *BMJ* **311**, 1620–1

McFarlane, J. (1989) Battering during pregnancy: tip of an iceberg revealed. *Women Health* **15**, 69–84

McFarlane, J., Parker, B., Soeken, K. and Bullock, L. (1992) Assessing for abuse during pregnancy. *JAMA* **267**, 3176–8

Mezey, G. and Bewley, S. (1997) Domestic violence and pregnancy. *Br J Obstet Gynaecol* **104**, 528–31

Morley, R. (1995) Sociologist's view. More convictions won't help victims of domestic violence. *BMJ* **311**, 1618–9

Norton, L.B., Peipert, J.F., Zierler, S., Lima, B. and Hume, L. (1995) Battering in pregnancy: an assessment of two screening methods. *Obstet Gynecol* **85**, 321–5

Parsons, L.H., Zaccaro, D., Wells, B. and Stovall, T.G. (1995) Methods of and attitudes toward screening obstetrics and gynecology patients for domestic violence. *Am J Obstet Gynecol* **173**, 381–7

Re MB [1997] 8 Med LR 217

Royal College of Obstetricians and Gynaecologists (1994) *RCOG Guidelines, Ethics, No. 1. A consideration of the Law and Ethics in Relation to Court-authorised Obstetric Intervention*. London: Royal College of Obstetricians and Gynaecologists

Royal College of Obstetricians and Gynaecologists (1996) *RCOG Guidelines, Ethics, Supplement to No. 1. Supplement to A Consideration of the Law and Ethics in Relation to Court-authorised Obstetric Intervention*. London: Royal College of Obstetricians and Gynaecologists

Stark, E., Flitcraft, A. and Frazier,W. (1979) Medicine and patriarchal violence: the social construction of a 'private' event. *Int J Health Serv* **9**, 461–93

Surgeon General (1986) Surgeon General's workshop on violence: recommendations of spouse abuse. *Response* **9**, 19–21

Webster, J., Chandler, J. and Battistutta, D. (1996) Pregnancy outcomes and health care use – effects of abuse. *Am J Obstet Gynecol* **174**, 760–7

Chapter 24

The obstetric consultation

Discussion

Edwards: I was extremely encouraged by Susan Bewley because she put the specific issues of domestic violence in a much more global context. We have had one or two brief testimonials. Perhaps I could give you one of mine.

My image of obstetricians has been such that it has stopped me communicating at all. If I presented to my GP it would be because I had to do it. I would go straight in and say, 'I am far too busy to discuss anything to do with my pregnancy.' That is how I dealt with both of my pregnancies. The whole focus on image is critical. It is not just the image when talking with those who suffer from domestic violence, but it is the whole image to women generally.

What you have said in opening up that debate is on a much more global level: if you are going to communicate with women about domestic violence, you have to consider the plethora of articles on the sociology of health and illness, and the work sociologists have been doing about concepts of time in gynaecological practice. There are many studies about women's experiences of health professionals. I can see that we are taking it on board, and that is a step which is part of this if we are going to get to the specificities of relating to a patient over something so sensitive and difficult as domestic violence. We are opening up self-scrutiny here, and Susan Bewley's paper was absolutely superb and we need to take that further.

Crowley: It is time we gave women back the right to have obstetric consultations alone, without their partner, regardless of whether there is any suspicion of domestic violence. Every woman has the right to have some privacy about her reproductive health. She may have elements in her reproductive history that are unknown to her partner, and she is entitled to retain that privacy. We will never get these histories if women are not all guaranteed one session during their pregnancy where they attend alone and have their history taken, or, if it has already been taken, re-taken when they are alone.

Harwin: I completely support that. In a sense, it is a principle which needs to be applied again right across a range of disciplines. Women should have a right to speak, whether it is to a doctor or to a mediator or to a court welfare officer. So many women, between one in three and one in ten in the estimates, experience violence from a known intimate, and usually a partner. The principle of being able to speak to someone on their own first is really important. To be asked, 'Do you want your partner involved? Is there any reason why that would be difficult for you? Are there any reasons you would not be able to answer?' is important.

Secondly, the only problem I see with this screening questionnaire is that, in some ways, asking if you are afraid of your partner is perhaps the first question rather than the last. In terms of 'by whom?', one has to remember that women are also chastised and abused by other family members, particularly in extended family networks, and that should be included. They may be experiencing violence not just from their partner, but from his brother or the mother-in-law.

Yearnshire: On the questioning matter, I agree that women should be given the opportunity to disclose what is happening to them, but it is also important that questions are asked sensitively. They do not have to be bald. They can be put in a range of ways. In fact, if you say to the woman beforehand, 'I now need to talk to you about . . .', she is already mentally attuned to what you are going to ask.

Walker: What about the healthcare record? It concerns me that most women now carry their own healthcare records and therefore there will be no opportunity to record these questions and no opportunity to record the significant results. Will the College need to think about that?

Kerr-Wilson: I can only speak on a very practical basis. Certainly in our hospital, apart from the mother carrying her own notes, there is a separate hospital note kept in which such things can be recorded, which the mother does not see.

S. Bewley: The ideal person to conduct the private interview that Patricia Crowley was talking about is the midwife at the booking interview, when a range of sensitive questions are asked. A doctor's consultation should always be private, or at least part of it should be, and we should not just drop that. We certainly do not drop it in our gynaecological consultations or elsewhere in medicine. If there are pregnancies that do not involve doctors at all – it has to be part of the midwifery booking. It is very easy to say, 'I am now asking medically-sensitive questions. Can your partner make me a cup of tea and then we will have him back and we will talk about the birth and breast feeding' or whatever. It is not difficult to do, as I am sure Chris Bewley knows. As doctors, we should not abandon privacy at any point.

As for the confidential notes, what Richard Kerr-Wilson is saying is not universal. We supposedly have a ghost folder, but it is never there. When the juniors take histories, they just write in the notes. I am just amazed to read: 'Came in having been assaulted by her partner ...' and she will just walk out with the notes. The other day I opened some notes and under special features written by the midwife it said, 'violent partner', and he was leaning over me while I was reading it! I thought it was very odd, but when the woman was admitted to the ward, surprise surprise, it had been crossed out. Is this is the soap opera mentality – 'Oh, you have a violent partner?'

We had another dreadful case where a woman came in with repeated antepartum haemorrhages. She had many social problems and finally came in with vaginal injuries. We suspected the partner was doing something and then started thinking she might have a personality disorder and be putting knitting needles up herself. I asked for a consultant psychiatrist, emphasising it had to be confidential, but they sent a junior, who wrote all our suspicions over the notes. So the patient tore the notes up, threw the assessment in the bin, and then refused to come back to the hospital. So we really are failing at rather basic things sometimes. I am not confident that the hand-held notes and separate folders work, but I do not think we can buck a very fashionable trend and not have-hand held notes at all.

Wilson: There is a very good opportunity for this College to put in something about the way in which hand-held notes are used. By 24 October 1998, the Data Protection legislation in this country will have to change. If the Data Protection Registrar gets her way, it will change to be privacy legislation, which will be a big step forward. Whether she gets her way or not is another matter – it might just be amendments to the existing legislation.

It will, however, change significantly how medical records are held, who holds them, and the state in which they are held. That is quite important because as we move more and more into electronic records and encryption systems, it is quite possible that although the woman might physically hold the set of notes, only part of those notes will actually be physically readable. It will be possible to encrypt certain parts. This is happening in other European countries, and the opportunity will exist quite soon when the new legislation comes through.

Second, we have to be really careful how we treat the notion of confidentiality and where confidentiality butts onto autonomy and paternalism. I approach this from a different angle from everybody else. I am very wary of doctors leaping in and suddenly starting to handle information. The only way in which you can really encourage women to report the experience of violence is to assure them repeatedly that this is their information and that they can stop and direct where it goes.

I have not had a great deal of direct experience of dealing with how information about violence is handled. I have had a great deal of experience of how information about HIV status is handled. When patients think they are going to lose sight of who gets hold of their information, they just will not give it. We have to remember that. Perhaps it is very different for women who experience violence, but I would be hesitant to suggest that it is so different.

Hepburn: With regard to the hand-held notes, when we did a survey of women in my own surgery, most of them did not want to carry their own notes. Not only did they not want to carry them, but they did not want it to be optional. If it was perceived as optional, then their partner would want to know why they had turned down the option. Even making the offer to them in private, away from their partner, would not be enough because they said the partner would know that some other women carried their notes, and would therefore ask why they had not accepted the offer to carry theirs. We have a differential system. We have a complete set held in the hospital and we agree with the women what should be entered in that set. We also agree with them what is entered into the tiny little abridged version which they carry themselves. It is not always as simple as the question whether or not you give them – there are other ramifications beyond that.

C. Bewley: On the issue of confidentiality versus child abuse, where there is a suspicion that a violent partner may also be abusing, or be likely to abuse, the child, in my experience midwives find themselves in a great dilemma as to whether they should report their suspicions. If they do report them, to whom should they do so, and how could they justify their breach of confidentiality under the issue of being in the wider public interest. I would be very pleased to hear what others have to say about that, because it is a very real dilemma.

Wilson: I hope that one of the case studies I will go through in Chapter 30 will touch on that. I have one problem where it is suspected that a child will also be at risk. That is not to say that I will be able to give all the answers.

Richardson: I wanted to say two things. First, about seeing women on their own. That probably happens much more in primary care. It is very much the exception rather than the rule when I do an antenatal clinic that the partner accompanies and the same probably applies to midwives working in the practice. I suspect when the woman is accompanied up to the hospital, even by a non-abusive partner, it is more to do with the hospital being perceived as a threatening environment where the woman needs support. The opportunity for obtaining information about violence may be easier in primary care.

I think this would probably apply to all GPs. I think we always have separate notes as well as the hand-held record. We would always be entering significant things on our own records. Those records would be shared almost always with the midwife. Perhaps someone could tell me what the role is for verbal communication between the community midwives and the hospital midwives as to significant things which may not go into the woman's hand-held records.

C. Bewley: With many midwives now working in teams, it means that the different roles between community and hospital midwives are disappearing. Many midwives are working in both hospital and community settings. In some areas, that would not be an issue.

Yearnshire: On the issue of carrying paper-based notes, we have moved into the arena of allowing individuals to see their notes any time they wish, but we certainly do not hand them over. They can view them, see them, comment on them, criticise – but they do not carry them about with them.

S. Bewley: You are right about the hospital. I reckon that 70 per cent of women in the antenatal clinic and nearly 100 per cent when they arrive in casualty or labour ward, are accompanied by a partner, friend or relative. It is hugely difficult to create that privacy.

A second point about hand-held notes. It is politically incorrect to say that we want the notes in hospital and that the information is medically important. It belongs to the woman, and we are bad at trusting them.

With regard to HIV and stigma, you made quite an interesting analogy there. I am the link obstetrician for all our HIV-positive pregnant women. We negotiate with every woman what is written down. We say that it is actually important for other people to know. Can we use coded references such as, 'needs anti-virals in labour'? When you ask, you are surprised to find that up to one-third of women say, 'No, that is fine, put HIV-positive in my notes'.

We are also seeing a change over time. It is more common that people know other HIV-positive people and they are less stigmatised and more prepared to talk. One problem is that if we go round saying that this is very bad information and we want it hidden, then as health professionals we are saying that it *is* stigmatising. What is more, we are stigmatising them and we do not want to write it in the notes. The tension is with leading a social change, and saying that we are relaxed and happy about HIV, and it is very difficult. I am concerned that being too secretive adds to the stigma, but at the same time we must have confidentiality. The woman must be confident that we will not pass the information on.

Wilson: Perhaps I expressed myself wrongly. I am not in any sense saying that we should say that this is secret and thereby increase the stigma. In HIV cases I have found it was very important to empower patients, so that they would be able to stop someone else getting the information if they want to. That might be important here as well.

A woman could say she was quite happy, during the course of her pregnancy, for this information to be shared, but she could also say she would be very scared if a social worker found out. Would that make her a bad mother?

Would it be possible that someone might say that her children should be taken away from her? Women need to be reassured that, wherever possible, they will be able to stop where information is passed on. That has loads of caveats on it because, particularly where child abuse is involved, you have to balance risks.

O'Brien: Going back to the husband's presence in the clinic, it might already have been stated but I wonder whether the very presence of a husband, particularly in a gynaecology clinic, should be considered as a risk factor for identifying patients? I just feel that when a husband is there in a gynaecology clinic, on occasions I sense there is something unusual about that situation.

Walker: I think you have picked it up. It is how we would frame any guidance that would allow the woman to have the option of both without restricting her freedom in either sense. That is a difficult balance.

SECTION 7

MODELS OF SPECIALIST AND GYNAECOLOGICAL PRACTICE

Chapter 25

Domestic violence and reproductive health care in Glasgow

Mary Hepburn and Siobhan McCartney

INTRODUCTION

In Glasgow a strategic approach has been adopted as the basis for improving the health service response to the issue of domestic violence. This strategic approach has been developed under the auspices of the Glasgow Women's Health Policy and the Greater Glasgow Health Board's Health Gain Commissioning Team (HGCT) on domestic violence. It is based on an understanding that a policy framework is essential to ensure that existing good practice by individual services is not only consolidated but standardised across all services. The Glasgow Women's Reproductive Health Service (WRHS) is one such example of good practice, having developed a service which is both appropriate and sensitive to the needs of women who are experiencing domestic violence. This paper will:

(1) State its working definition of domestic violence;

(2) Outline the prevalence of domestic violence in Scotland;

(3) Outline the health effects of domestic violence in relation to pregnancy;

(4) Describe the work of the WRHS as an example of good practice;

(5) Explain Glasgow's policy framework and introduce the HGCT on domestic violence;

(6) Outline the work of the HGCT in Glasgow as a means of taking forward a strategic response to domestic violence.

Definition

It is important to define what is meant by the term 'domestic violence'. The definition used will determine both the extent of the problem and the subsequent action required to tackle the issue. The definition used to inform this paper is in line with that used by the Scottish Needs Assessment Programme (SNAP) Report (1997) and is as follows:

> Domestic violence is psychological, emotional and economic as well as physical and sexual abuse of women by male partners or ex-partners.

The SNAP Report adopts this definition in the recognition that domestic violence is part of a continuum of male violence which includes child sexual abuse, pornography, sexual harassment, sexual abuse and rape.

The extent of the problem

It is estimated that as many as 174,000 Scottish women may have experienced physical violence and 260,000 may have experienced mental cruelty over a twelve-month period (SNAP 1997). Research indicates that violence is likely to begin or escalate during pregnancy (Stark *et al.* 1979; Hillard 1985). Estimates of the numbers of pregnant women who are physically abused by their partners vary from 1-in-50 at best (Campbell 1986) to one in six at worst (McFarlane 1992).

The health effects in pregnancy

Domestic violence can adversely affect health in a number of ways. Women who experience domestic violence are more likely to suffer from poor health, chronic pain problems, depression, addictions, problem pregnancies and to attempt suicide (Plichta 1992). In the specific context of reproductive health they are also more likely to turn up late for antenatal care and to give birth to low birth-weight babies (Bullock and McFarlane 1989; Goodwin and Breen 1991; Newberger *et al.* 1992). Domestic violence can also cause severe physical injury to both mother and baby. Reported injuries include: maternal rupture of the uterus, spleen or liver; premature onset of labour; placental abruption; premature spontaneous rupture of the membranes; miscarriage or fetal death (James-Hanman and Long 1994).

Current clinical response

There is growing awareness within the UK of a need for action by the health service and health care professionals to tackle the issue of domestic violence (McIlwaine 1989; Heath 1992; Richardson and Feder 1995; Shepherd 1995). However this awareness has not yet been translated into effective action. Although they are often the first port of call for women experiencing domestic violence (Dobash and Dobash 1979, 1984; Walker 1979), health care professionals are failing to identify a large proportion of such women and even those women who are identified receive either no treatment or inappropriate treatment (Dobash and Dobash 1979, 1984; Borkowski *et al.*1983; Pahl 1985). This failure of detection may result from a lack of awareness but also from a fear of addressing an area which is perceived as time-consuming, where knowledge is lacking and in which they feel unable to 'fix' the problem (Warshaw 1993; Richardson and Feder 1995). In addition, women may not disclose violence, either from fear of a negative response or from lack of opportunity (McWilliams and McKiernan 1993; Pahl 1985).

Policy and practice initiatives

On an international level the United Nations General Assembly passed the Declaration on the Elimination of Violence against Women (United Nations General Assembly 1993) describing such violence as a historical manifestation of unequal power relationships between men and women. On a UK level the National Agenda for Action was drawn up following the United Nations Fourth World Conference on Women in Beijing. Zero Tolerance campaigns have been developed to raise awareness and challenge society's views of the problem and the Home Office Report (Smith 1989) made a series of recommendations for development within the NHS. In Scotland the SNAP Report has addressed the role of the health service in relation to domestic violence and made recommendations for action by both purchasers and providers. A small number of projects have been developed in an attempt to implement these various policy recommendations. In Scotland these include the development of a Multi-Agency Domestic Violence Strategy in central Scotland and a Glasgow project funded by the Health Education Board for Scotland (HEBS) which aims to investigate the primary health care response to domestic violence in one community and to establish a city-wide inter-agency strategy.

In addition, a number of specialised services have simultaneously but independently developed models of care reflecting recognition of domestic violence as a legitimate clinical concern. The WRHS is one such example.

THE GLASGOW WOMEN'S REPRODUCTIVE HEALTH SERVICE

The WRHS began with development of a pilot clinic in 1986 and was established as a city-wide service in 1990. It provides a full range of reproductive health care services for women with severe social problems or in need of additional support and for whom standard services are inappropriate or unacceptable. Women attend for reasons which include problem drug or alcohol use, mental health or learning difficulties, a history of statutory care for themselves or their children, previous child-care problems or simply failure to use standard services. While the majority of women come from backgrounds of socio-economic deprivation, some attend because they need support for reasons not associated with deprivation.

The service is based in Glasgow Royal Maternity Hospital with care delivered through community-based multidisciplinary clinics dealing with both medical and social problems. On first attendance a comprehensive medical and social history is taken by the obstetrician and/or midwife. As part of this history women are routinely asked if they have ever been subjected to any form of violence, past or present, whether from parents, other family members, partners or any other person. Those women who volunteer such a history are offered advice and information about available services or sources of help with the offer of either referral elsewhere or introduction to an appropriate individual arranged within the WRHS. Denial of such a history is not necessarily interpreted as indicating it does not exist and where the clinical suspicion exists the possibility is borne in mind and informs subsequent management of the woman.

Prevalence of violence

Attendance rates have steadily risen to a current level of more than 200 pregnant and a similar number of non-pregnant women per annum. While the entire ten-year database has yet to be analysed, a preliminary study was carried out on a sample of 98 women who delivered in the first six months of 1994. Of these 98 women 61 (62 per cent) had problems of substance abuse, 44 reporting drug use and 17 problem alcohol use. At booking, 29 women (30 per cent) gave a history of physical violence, nine past, 17 present and three both past and present. Twelve women reported violence by their parents, 11 by their partners and four by both parents and partners. Two women reported some form of violence or abuse while in statutory care. Two of the 29 women specifically reported previous sexual abuse.

The reporting of sexual abuse at booking by only a small number of women in this sample is typical of general experience in the service which also suggests that the true prevalence is higher than that reported at booking. The discrepancy is due either to women's initial reluctance to admit to sexual abuse or to their failure to perceive it as such. Such initial under-reporting also appears to apply, although possibly to a lesser extent, to other forms of violence. The level of reported violence at booking is therefore remarkable both for its absolute level and for its indication of women's willingness to volunteer such a history if routinely asked.

Staff attitudes

Staff in the unit as well as in the rest of the maternity hospital initially perceived violence and any form of abuse as being commoner among women from poorer socio-economic backgrounds and therefore likely to be more prevalent among women attending the WRHS. In addition, some women attend the service specifically because of a history of violence. Nevertheless, staff were initially extremely reluctant to ask about such a history, especially in the case of women who were not from deprived backgrounds.

This reluctance also applied to other aspects of the social history. Staff were afraid such questions might cause offence and felt they did not have the skills or knowledge to deal with a positive response. Considerable training and ongoing support were necessary to enable them to take a full social history without asking questions in a biased way which encouraged a negative response. The reluctance to ask about violence persisted beyond the point where they had acquired skills in dealing with problems such as drug use or even to deal with problems due to violence where these were volunteered. While experienced staff within the WRHS now have the confidence to ask such questions elsewhere in the hospital, only a limited social history is taken and, in particular, routine questions about violence are neither asked nor perceived as relevant or appropriate.

The WRHS is a specialist service which recognises the impact of social factors on health and was specifically developed to address this area of health care. Nevertheless, even in this service, informed by the social model of health, gaining recognition of violence against women as a legitimate, far less routine area of concern, has proved challenging. Furthermore, by being restricted to the WRHS, such questions can be stigmatising and the fact that similar questions are not routinely asked throughout the hospital is more often seen as a sin of commission by the WRHS rather than a sin of omission by the rest of the hospital! Thus while action by individual services is helpful and desirable, its potential is limited in isolation and indeed it will only achieve maximum effectiveness if developed in the context of a policy framework involving not only all health services: both purchasers and providers, but also other relevant statutory and voluntary agencies.

THE GLASGOW POLICY FRAMEWORK

In June 1992 the Women's Health Working Group of the Glasgow Healthy City Project launched the Glasgow Women's Health Policy with the overall aim of improving the health and well-being of the women in Glasgow. The policy was adopted by Greater Glasgow Health Board, Strathclyde Regional Council, Glasgow District Council and the other partner organisations of the Healthy City Project. The policy identified six priorities for action which included the issue of women's safety in their home and in the community. As part of its commitment to the implementation of the Women's Health Policy and in recognition that domestic violence is a large public health issue, Greater Glasgow Health Board set up a commissioning team to investigate the problem.

The HGCT on domestic violence

Remit of the HGCT on domestic violence

In order to explain the purpose and subsequent remit of the HGCT it may be helpful to define the terms 'commissioning' and 'health gain'. The purpose of NHS commissioning is to make the best use of available finance to improve health and prevent illness by influencing other organisations to contribute to these ends and by contracting health services (Ovretveit 1995). The concept of health gain helps to redefine the purpose of NHS commissioning as seeking improvements in health with contracting services as an intermediate aim. As a result the remit of the HGCT is to develop and evaluate effective methods of service delivery in an attempt to improve the health service response to women who are experiencing domestic violence. In addition, the group has to produce recommendations to inform the commissioning process.

Membership of the HGCT on domestic violence

Representation on the HGCT on domestic violence was established from a number of different health service settings and from a variety of disciplines. The group is chaired by the Women's Health Co-ordinator and presently includes a consultant obstetrician (who is also consultant in charge of the WRHS), a GP, a deputy clinical director of family planning and well woman services, a clinical psychologist, a health economist, a training worker from the Centre for Women's Health, a representative from the Women's Support Project and a senior health promotion officer. In addition the group has support from a health board researcher.

Selection of health service settings

Evidence suggests that women who are experiencing domestic violence use a variety of health service settings either as a direct result of the domestic violence or where it is a factor in their attendance. The HGCT selected health service settings for further work and investigation according to two main criteria. The first criteria was the available evidence from British research studies about women's comparative use and experiences of a variety of different health service settings. The second was that of opportunity and co-operation from various health care providers. Therefore in the first phase of work the HGCT agreed to conduct audits in an accident and emergency (A&E) setting and in a family planning setting. The second phase of work will involve an obstetrics and gynaecology setting and exploration of collaborative working with providers of primary health care.

Health service audits

The audits in A&E and family planning were designed with the intention of informing the Greater Glasgow Health Board's commissioning strategy and providing the participating departments with possible methods for improved detection and response to women who are experiencing domestic violence. The audit process was informed by the need to implement and evaluate the Home Office recommendations to introduce protocols or guidelines on domestic violence in conjunction with staff training within the health service.

The main aim of the audits was to determine whether the introduction of a standard protocol changes detection and/or alters the response of health service staff to women experiencing domestic violence. The audit process has involved a range of activities as follows:

(1) Establishing incidence rates of abused women attending a number of different health service settings to improve knowledge about users of services within the Greater Glasgow Health Board area;

(2) Establishing current methods of management of abused women within a number of health service settings to improve knowledge of current practice by health care providers;

(3) Developing good practice guidelines informed by Home Office recommendations (Smith 1989) and American Medical Association guidelines (Council of Scientific Affairs, American Medical Association 1992) and in consultation with local health care practitioners and women's groups;

(4) Developing training programmes to facilitate the introduction of good practice guidelines with the aim of improving patient care;

(5) Monitoring and analysing the effect of the introduction of good practice guidelines and staff training within different health service settings with the aim of ensuring a high quality of patient care.

Protocol on domestic violence

Considerable time was devoted to drawing up the protocols on domestic violence in conjunction with service providers and support agencies for women. The protocols were informed by the Home Office recommendations (Smith 1989) and American Medical Association guidelines (Council of Scientific Affairs, American Medical Association 1992) and were designed to:

(1) Describe how to identify domestic violence through routine screening and recognise clinical presentations;

(2) Provide examples of how to ask questions in ways that can elicit meaningful responses and help women explore their options and take action;

(3) Provide information about options and resources for women experiencing domestic violence;

(4) Describe how to ensure clear documentation of the abuse for the purposes of monitoring and prevention of further abuse.

Training

Both services presented a number of logistical and organisational problems which resulted in alternative scenarios being developed for training purposes. For example difficulties in releasing staff in the selected A&E department led to the development of an open learning pack. The pack relied on staff motivation, managerial support and the release of staff from duties for completion. The training programmes were designed to introduce the protocol on domestic violence and, drawing on staff's experience and expertise to:

(1) Improve their awareness and understanding of domestic violence;

(2) Improve their awareness and understanding of agencies which provide support for women experiencing domestic violence;

(3) Consider their attitudes to domestic violence;

(4) Acquire the tools to implement the protocol effectively and systematically in their work setting.

Results

The audits produced mixed results. In terms of detection there was little change in the percentage of acknowledged or detected cases of domestic violence before (A&E six per cent; family planning one per cent) and after (A&E five per cent; family planning two per cent) the introduction of protocols and staff training. Some change in attitudes and knowledge in relation to the issue was detected amongst A&E and family planning staff after the intervention. However it is not clear whether any change in attitudes and knowledge has led to a subsequent change in behaviour.

Discussion of audit results

In attempting to explain the mixed results produced by the audit process in the two selected settings it may be helpful to explore those factors which may have been forces against organisational change and those that were supportive of change. In both settings there were a number of logistical problems in accessing staff for training due to financial costs of covering staff, negotiating rotas and changing shifts for whole departments. Also staff in both pilot settings were overloaded with change which may have had an impact on their ability or willingness to implement what was perceived as yet another change. On a hospital or Trust-wide basis, as opposed to the individual departments involved in the pilots, there were no nominated 'responsible' officers who could have monitored progress from within the organisation. Finally there was also some resistance from the involved health care professionals in both settings over their role in relation to a perceived 'social issue'.

There were also factors which were supportive of the work. The context of the Glasgow Women's Health Policy as a strategic framework for action promoted support for the audits from both within Greater Glasgow Health Board and the involved hospital Trusts as part of their commitment to implement the Policy. There are also a growing number of other local and national initiatives in relation to the health service response to domestic violence which lent further weight to the pilots. In addition there was considerable commitment from within Greater Glasgow Health Board to provide support for the work by nominating the time of a health board researcher, covering the costs of releasing Trust staff for training and providing information resources. At a local level there were also good relationships with local Women's Aid groups and other women's services. This was important for two main reasons, firstly in terms of informing and implementing the protocol training programmes and secondly in terms of ensuring open communication and dialogue about the impact of referral to these agencies from health services as a result of protocol implementation.

Other progress made by the HGCT

In addition to the completed pilots in A&E and family planning, there have been a number of other areas of progress made by the HGCT. As a result of the audit in the A&E department of one acute hospital Trust, there was recognition by the Trust of implications at the corporate level for improving the A&E response to domestic violence. In order to maintain a quality response the Trust recognised that there should be Trust-wide guidelines on domestic violence and that the training implications of securing their implementation should be explored. As a result a small working group has been set up within the Trust to take these issues forward.

The HGCT recognised that primary health care was an important health service setting in relation to the issue of domestic violence. As a result, the HGCT has contributed to the West of Scotland Postgraduate Medical Education training sessions by hosting a seminar on the implications of domestic violence for primary care. Subsequently a pilot survey has been conducted of those GPs who attended the seminar, to explore their perceptions of the size of the problem and their role in relation to the issue of domestic violence. This group of GPs were also asked if they would be interested in collaborating on further work on the issue. A number of positive replies have been returned and negotiations are underway.

The local Dental Hospital Trust also approached the HGCT to host a seminar on the implications of the issue for their service. This proved a useful and stimulating collaboration and the Trust is now working to develop a more appropriate response to women who are experiencing domestic violence.

Finally the HGCT has hosted an information meeting for local voluntary groups who provide services for abused women. Its aim was to discuss the possibility of establishing a mechanism for ongoing consultation between the voluntary sector and the health board. This resulted from recognition of possible implications for voluntary organisations as a result of the ongoing work of the HGCT in relation to increased demand for services for women, information, leaflets and training for staff.

FUTURE DEVELOPMENTS

There are a number of future developments which the HGCT is planning to undertake over the next year. The first of these is to work with an obstetrics and gynaecology department to develop new approaches to improving the health service response to domestic violence in pregnancy. This work will draw on the experiences and lessons learnt from the first two pilots in A&E and family planning settings.

In addition the HGCT plans to engage with a small number of general practices to explore the implications for general practice of domestic violence. There are also plans to continue supporting the development of the corporate domestic violence strategy in the West Glasgow Hospitals University NHS Trust – one of the five Glasgow acute hospital trusts. The group will also continue to bring forward recommendations for the management of domestic violence in A&E departments. Finally, it will continue its ongoing work in setting strong links with the voluntary sector in order to ensure effective and appropriate health services for survivors of domestic violence.

THE WIDER PICTURE

The work of the HGCT has fed into a wider picture both at a local, national and international level. The ongoing work of the group is currently being complemented by the HEBS funded project which aims to investigate the primary health care response to domestic violence in one Glasgow community and establish a city-wide inter-agency strategy. The work has informed the SNAP Report on domestic violence (1997) and has been recognised as a model of good practice by the World Health Organisation who have requested consultancy support for a project on violence against women in central Asian states.

CONCLUSIONS

Domestic violence is a widespread problem with implications not only for reproductive health care but for all health services. The current health service response is based on a medical model of health. Consequently, while health care professionals are involved in the management of domestic violence this is largely limited to the treatment of presenting injuries. Neither the underlying factors nor the secondary health problems which they cause are recognised as part of the health service remit. Furthermore, health care professionals do not routinely receive appropriate training before or after qualification and, as a result, provide inadequate care to women who have experienced domestic violence. The secondary health problems, if dealt with at all, are usually inappropriately managed in isolation while the underlying factors are either not recognised or ignored.

Effective clinical management requires recognition of the impact of social factors on health. It also requires recognition that in this context social is not synonymous with low socio-economic status. Health care services thus informed by the social model of health would be able to provide an appropriate, systematic response in which participation by health care professionals would not be restricted to the treatment of presenting physical problems. Such services would also recognise their wider remit and responsibility. This would include sensitively taking an appropriate history, documenting this with the woman's permission, providing relevant information about support services, discussing options and arranging onward referral as appropriate. This type of systematic response requires appropriate training and consequently educational bodies must also embrace this philosophy.

While examples of this approach to service delivery do exist, they are often isolated and provided by specialist services. To maximise their potential, such initiatives must operate within the context of a strategic policy framework which aims to consolidate and standardise good practice throughout the health service. Furthermore, the health service cannot deal with the issue of domestic violence in isolation, but only as part of an inter-agency response to training, planning and service delivery. Domestic violence must be recognised at national level as an issue for health services and those responsible for the training of health care professionals.

REFERENCES

Borkowski, M., Murch, M. and Walker, V. (1983) *Marital violence: The Community Response*. London: Tavistock Publication

Bullock, L. and McFarlane, J. (1989) The birth-weight/battering connection. *Am J Nurs* **89**, 1153–5

Campbell, J. (1986) Nursing assessment for risk of homicide, with battered women. *Am J Nurs* **86**, 910–13

Council of Scientific Affairs, American Medical Association (1992) Violence against women: relevance for medical practitioners. *JAMA* **267**, 3184–9

Dobash, R.E. and Dobash, R.P. (1979) *Violence Against Wives*. New York: The Free Press

Dobash, R.E. and Dobash, R.P. (1984) The nature and antecedents of violent events. *British Journal of Criminology* **24**, 269–88

Goodwin, T.M. and Breen, M.T. (1991) Pregnancy and trauma. *Am J Obstet Gynecol* **162**, 665–71

Heath, I. (1992) *Domestic Violence: the General Practitioner's Role. Royal College of General Practitioners Members Reference Book 1992*. London: Sabrecrown.

Hillard, P.J.A. (1985) Physical abuse in pregnancy. *Obstet Gynecol* **66**, 185–90.

James-Hanman, D. and Long, L. (1994) Crime Prevention: an issue for midwives? *British Journal of Midwifery* **2**, 29–32

McFarlane, J. (1992) Assessing for abuse during pregnancy. *JAMA* **267**, 3176–8

McIlwaine, G. (1989) Women victims of domestic violence. *BMJ* **299**, 995–6

McWilliams, M. and McKiernan, J. (1993) *Bringing it Out in the Open: Domestic Violence in North Ireland*. Belfast: HMSO

Newberger, E.H., Barker, S.E., Lieberman, E.F. *et al.* (1992) Abuse of pregnant women and adverse birth outcomes. *JAMA* **267**, 2370–2

Ovretveit, J. (1995) *Purchasing for Health*. Buckingham: Open University Press

Pahl, J. (1985) *Private Violence and Public Policy*. London: Routledge

Plichta, S. (1992) The effects of woman abuse on health care utilisation and health status: A Literature Review. *WHI* **2**, 154–63

Richardson, J. and Feder, G. (1995) Domestic violence against women. Needs action from doctors and the health service. *BMJ* **311**, 964–5

Shepherd, J. (1995) Ethical debate. Should doctors be more proactive as advocates for victims of domestic violence? *BMJ* **311**, 1617–21

Smith, L.J.F. (1989) *Domestic violence: an overview of the literature. Home Office Research Study No. 107*. London: HMSO.

SNAP Report (in press) Scottish Forum for Public Health Medicine, 69 Oakfield Ave, Glasgow G12 8QQ

Stark, E., Flitcraft, A. and Frazier, W. Medicine and patriarchial violence. The social construction of a private event. *Int J Health Serv* **9**, 461–93

United Nations General Assembly (1993) *Declaration of the Elimination of Violence Against Women* (Vienna Declaration) (*unpublished policy statement*)

Walker, L.E. (1979) *The Battered Women*. New York: Harper and Row

Warshaw, C. (1993) Domestic violence: challenges to medical practice. *Journal of Women's Health* **2**, 73–80

Chapter 26

Rape – including history and examination

Helen Cameron

INTRODUCTION

There seems to be an 'escalating epidemic' of rape in the US with the annual incidence of sexual assault in 1990 being 80 per 100,000 women (Hampton 1995). The 'rape index' in Oslo, Norway, was 37 per 100,000 women in 1987, where the 'rape index' is the number of rape victims who apply for help per 100,000 inhabitants. It is felt that the vast majority of sexual assault cases are not reported to the police and domestic or spousal rape is even less commonly reported (Whatley 1993). In the US most States have laws requiring that hospitals report a sexual assault to the law enforcement agencies and knowledge of this fact may deter victims from seeking medical advice (Young 1992). In addition the majority of rape allegations do not proceed to court. In 1982–5 in Oslo, only 20 per cent of the reported cases went to court (Bang 1993), and the conviction rate as a percentage of complaints is approximately 10 per cent (Craven 1996). To achieve a successful conviction, corroborating evidence must be presented (Hockbaum 1987).

It is important that all the professionals involved with victims of sexual assault recognise that the assault may be followed by 'rape trauma syndrome' with two defined phases; short-term disbelief and shock and the longer-term reactions of anxiety and depression (Hampton 1995).

The examining doctor must take a precise and accurate enough history of the incident to ensure that an appropriate examination is undertaken and that the collection of forensic evidence is complete. It is, however, the police officer's role to obtain a detailed investigative history. The use of a Medical Record booklet, with a clear checklist of the historic facts and physical examination together with body diagrams to illustrate the clinical findings, provides invaluable assistance to the examining doctor, who is not infrequently called to a victim of sexual assault in the middle of the night. One of the principal aims of all those involved in the medical examination of sexual assault victims should be to minimise the mental and physical trauma to the woman, whilst endeavouring to collect the useful forensic evidence in as dignified and understanding manner as possible.

CONSENT TO THE MEDICAL EXAMINATION AND DISCLOSURE IN CONNECTION WITH JUDICIAL PROCEEDINGS

Consenting to a medical and forensic examination may be perceived as allowing the victim a sense of control over the examination (Hampton 1995). The General Medical Council (GMC) recently re-inforced the principles of confidentiality indicating that 'patients have a right to expect that you will not disclose information which you learnt during the course of your professional duties, unless they give permission' (General Medical Council 1995). Standard consent forms include a statement by the doctor saying that they have explained the investigations and such appropriate options as are available to the patient in terms that are suited to the understanding of the patient. Consent for forensic medical examination requires modification to accommodate details about disclosure of evidence to the police.

Before a forensic medical examination can be undertaken, consent must be obtained for:

(1) A medical examination – non-genital/genital;

(2) Collection of forensic evidence;

(3) Retention of relevant items of clothing for forensic examination;

(4) Disclosure of details of medical record to the police/Crown Prosecution Service (CPS).

It is usual practice to read the consent form to the victim, who is advised about the role of the medical examination, namely, that the principal reason is to record the findings for legal purposes and to collect intimate and non-intimate samples for forensic tests. Consent should also be sought for clothing taken at the time of examination to be sent to the forensic science laboratory and it should be made clear that clothing may be retained indefinitely or until the conclusion of the case. It is often the case that the woman is already in the acute phase of the 'rape trauma syndrome', exhibiting shock, disbelief, anger and possibly memory blocking. The examiner may question whether such a woman is able to give 'informed' consent to all aspects of the forensic medical examination. It may be appropriate, in this case, to complete the consent for examination and sample collection and defer the consent to disclosure of the medical details until a later date. It remains the doctor's responsibility to ensure that the patient understands what will be disclosed, the reason for disclosure and to whom the information is going to be revealed.

If the woman wishes the police to pursue investigations of the incident she should be made aware that the medical findings and results of laboratory tests will be disclosed to the police and may be released to the CPS or Crown Court for use as evidence. The victim may agree to a 'qualified consent', that is, to the release of information to the prosecution without allowing scrutiny by the defence. If the victim does not consent to release of the medical details then the examiner may be ordered to disclose information by a judge, in which case 'only as much as is relevant to the proceedings' should be disclosed (General Medical Council 1995). In the absence of a court order, a request for disclosure by a third party such as a solicitor or police officer is not sufficient justification for disclosure without the patient's consent. If the woman is a non-police referral or does not wish to involve the police initially, she should be informed that she can pursue a formal complaint subsequently. Under such circumstances the details about disclosure of medical evidence should be clarified for her and additional consent should be sought. Confidentiality must be respected and be seen to be respected if the woman does not wish all or part of the information to be passed to the police. The medical record should be completed in the same detailed way as if there was consent to disclosure and release of the statement, in case the woman decides to report the incident to the police at a later date, at which stage additional consent to disclosure should be sought. The woman should also be made aware that the examination can be discontinued at any stage if she wishes. The stage of the examination and the time at which she decides against further examination should be recorded. In addition to the victim's and the doctor's signatures, any witness, such as the police officer present at the interview, should also sign the consent form.

EXAMINATION OF THE FEMALE RAPE VICTIM

Who should undertake the examination?

In ideal circumstances the victim of sexual assault should be allowed to choose the gender of the examining doctor. The gender of the examining physician is not always felt to be a factor affecting the victim's response to the medical examination (Hockbaum 1987). In the Northumbria police force the rota for examinations of adult female victims is covered entirely by trained women doctors who provide support and supervision of new members undertaking their first examinations.

Training of specialist registrars in rape examination

To ensure optimal care for the victims of sexual assault a co-ordinated multi-disciplinary approach should be made to tackle the theoretical and practical training issues. The aim of the Royal College of Obstetricians and Gynaecologists Specialist Registrar (SpR) Main Log Book module on 'Rape' is that the trainee develops an understanding of the clinical, legal and ethical issues involved in rape examination. Thus, in cases of rape allegation the trainee is expected, ultimately, to be able to undertake the following procedures under direct supervision of a senior colleague:

(1) Assess the need for genital examination;

(2) Explain the need for an intimate examination;

(3) Examine appropriately;

(4) Recognise abnormalities.

It is proving very difficult to provide sufficient training opportunities for examination, especially by doctors of the opposite sex to the victim, and the approach to the subject of training must be handled with care and diplomacy by the trainer faced with an embarrassed and frightened victim. As more educational programmes are created at deanery level, it is hoped that trainees will have completed a theoretical component of the module on rape before observing clinical practice and subsequently undertaking supervised assessment of a rape victim.

Northumbria Police women doctors' scheme

In 1983 Northumbria Police initiated a scheme whereby a number of women doctors from a variety of professional backgrounds (gynaecology, general practice etc.) volunteered to undertake the examination of victims of sexual assault. Night time, weekend and bank holiday cover is provided on a rota system. There is no retainer payment but doctors receive a standard fee for each call-out and statement prepared. Elsewhere in England and Wales many police forces have specially designed and equipped centres, often on hospital sites but the 'on call' rota of the Northumbria Police women doctors' scheme is unique. (Wright *et al.* 1989).

The REACH project

The REACH (Rape examination, advice, counselling and help) Project was opened in 1991 to provide a service to women in the Northumbria region who have been sexually assaulted. The Rhona Cross Centre in Newcastle upon Tyne and the Ellis Fraser Centre in Sunderland offer a range of services within the same building. The services that REACH provides include:

(1) Experienced women doctors able to conduct the medical examination in the purpose-built suite;

(2) Confidential access to experienced counsellors regardless of whether the woman reports the assault to the police or not;

(3) Specially trained women police officers to conduct the interview and statement taking for those women who wish to involve the police.

Referral may be through the police, GP, hospital doctor or by self-referral.

THE ROLE OF THE POLICE OFFICER

The police officer has an important role in the rape victim's experiences and decision to further pursue legal prosecution. Northumbria police established a police liaison group in 1996 with at least one policewoman in each area command being nominated to maintain links with REACH. The representatives attend the scheme meetings and, having undertaken training themselves, are able to assist with the training of new recruits to the scheme. At the time of the examination, the trained woman police officer gives advice and information about the criminal justice process as well as taking the formal statement. In addition to the main role of the police officer in taking the detailed statement, the officer accompanies the victim to the REACH centre, ensuring that she takes a change of clothes. Prior to the doctor taking a history of the assault the officer provides a summary of the allegation for the doctor. During the examination the officer not only chaperones the examining doctor but assists in a discreet manner with the collection of significant items of clothing and also ensures that each forensic sample is correctly labelled and sealed. An additional responsibility of the police officer is to complete the documentation accurately using the sexual examination kit – samples reference form on which she records the time the examination commences and finishes and the time the blood alcohol sample is taken. Each sample is numbered in order of submission and referenced with the doctor's initials. Within the Northumbria Police Force the forensic samples are then sent to a central submissions unit for later dispatch of the appropriate samples to the scientific aids laboratory. The police officer is responsible for arranging the transport of the forensic specimens.

THE SEVERELY INJURED PATIENT

The medical needs of the victim must take priority over the need to achieve forensic samples and urgent medical advice should be sought where necessary in an appropriately equipped setting, such as the accident and emergency (A&E) department. The reason for delay in undertaking the forensic examination should be carefully documented in the medical record. Where possible, a police photographer (of the same gender) should be involved. A supply of special examination kits are available in the REACH centres and in addition to using these kits at outreach facilities they can be used to facilitate the examination of inpatient victims. The incidence of major non-genital injuries may be as high as five per cent of rape victims (Marchbanks 1990) and the majority of female victims (approximately 80 per cent) will have some form of physical injury, although most will be of a minor nature (Bowyer 1997). Interestingly, four per cent of 168 victims attending a medical rape trauma service in 1987 in Oslo, Norway, had been raped by their partner, and all had serious injuries (Bang 1993). Eighty per cent of these battered women endured many violent episodes before seeking medical treatment.

THE EXAMINING DOCTOR

The examining doctor must be objective and non-judgmental and must avoid giving even the smallest cues of suspicion or disbelief which may heighten the victim's anxiety and emotional trauma or cause a spiralling decline as her guilt and shame increase and her story is shaken (Dupré 1993). The examining doctor must be familiar with the appearance of the normal genitalia and anus of an adult woman. A record of the initial examination and forensic specimens should be kept. This record should contain contemporary notes and although it acts as an *aide memoire*, should the complainant wish to proceed with her allegation and has consented to disclosure of the evidence, the document effectively loses its confidential status and access may be granted to the police, the CPS or even relevant details to the plaintiff's legal representatives. The doctor may be called to submit a statement. It is a wise practice to complete a statement as soon as possible after the examination and include an interpretation and opinion at the end of the statement either using lay terms where possible or including a glossary of the medical terminology.

NORTHUMBRIA POLICE RECORD OF MEDICAL EXAMINATION

Since the Northumbria Police Record of Medical Examinations was first used in 1983 there have been many alterations to its style and content to accommodate changes in certain elements of the examination and also changes in forensic techniques. Other centres have also devised protocols. In the late 1980s the US Department of Justice sponsored a programme to establish protocols for forensic and medical examinations of victims of sexual assault and subsequently States such as New Hampshire and Michigan have developed their own protocols based on this national model (Hochbaum 1987; Young 1992).

NOTES ON HISTORY OF ASSAULT

The purpose of the history of assault from the medical perspective is that it allows the doctor to adapt the standard forensic examination according to the circumstances of the assault. It should not be an exhaustive account of the details of the crime, but should be limited to the information necessary to treat any possible injuries and collect appropriate specimens for evidence. Specific questions can be asked to clarify the details of the assault.

In the free text sections regarding the details of the assault and events that followed the record may be taken down verbatim. Many victims are unable

Table 26.1.   Patient details and medical history

Patient Details – General

Name	Address and telephone number
Date of birth	Age
GP	Officer in charge
Place of examination	Officer attending
Date of examination	Police station
Time of arrival	

Other persons present at examination and relationship to victim

Medical History
Date of menarche
Last menstrual period
Bruising tendency – Yes/No
Skin problems – Yes/No
Gynaecological problems – details (free text)
Sexually active? – Presently/previously/never
Last coitus
       Date
       Time
Genital problem – details (free text)
Sexually transmitted diseases – Yes/No
Pregnancy
       Previous – Yes/No
       Outcome
       Present – Yes/No
Present occupation
Serious medical/psychiatric problems

or unwilling to recall details of the assault and in these cases the doctor will not be able to limit the sample-taking to specific areas, lest significant forensic evidence is sacrificed (Table 26.1, 26.2).

NOTES ON MEDICAL EXAMINATION

The examination must be undertaken in a good light using ancillary lighting for the genital examination (Table 26.3). It is important to inspect every area of the victim's body including the inside of the mouth, especially where penile/oral assault has occurred, to exclude trauma to the frenulum or petechiae on the roof of the mouth. The medical record should contain a reference to any area that is omitted. A magnifying lens should be available for closer examination of any surface markings.

Table 26.2.   Details of assault

Details of assault

Date of assault	Time of assault
Time lapse	Relationship to victim
Name of assailant	

History of assault

Source	Events preceding the assault
Place of assault	Drugs/alcohol consumed by the victim
Details of assault (free text)	Damage or disruption to clothing
Site and mechanism of injuries	Weapon/implement used?
Defence used	Ejaculation – Yes/No

Exact nature of assault

Digital/vaginal – Yes/No	
Oral/vaginal – Yes/No	
Oral/penile – Yes/No	
Penile/vaginal – Yes/No	Ejaculation – Yes/No
Penile/anal – Yes/No	Ejaculation – Yes/No
Digital/anal – Yes/No	
Lubricant used?	
Condom used?	

Events following assault

Free text description
Victim's activities subsequent to the incident

Change of clothes – Yes/No	Bathed – Yes/No
Showered – Yes/No	Washed genital area – Yes/No
Cleaned teeth – Yes/No	Micturated – Yes/No
Washed hair – Yes/No	Defecated – Yes/No
Vomited – Yes/No	Eaten food/drank fluids – Yes/No

Medical treatment received since assault

MODIFICATIONS TO SAMPLING

Whilst it would seem reasonable only to take samples appropriate to the circumstances of the assault with a careful history of the exact nature of the assault to facilitate the collection of relevant samples being emphasised, the persistence of forensic evidence (such as spermatozoa in the vagina) is very variable. In addition, the patient may be unable to recall the details of the assault (possibly due to the influence of alcohol/drugs at the time of the assault or subsequently), she may be naturally reticent (as in the elderly

Table 26.3.   Northumbria police sexual assault – special examination kit

REACH Information Pack	A4 plain paper × 4 sheets
Paper bags – large	Clear bags for specimens
Sexual offence book	Sexual offence kit information sheet
Blue 'Record of medical examination'	Exhibit labels
Sheet of brown paper	Modesty gown
Combs × 2	Swabs
Cocktail sticks	Gloves (small, medium and large sizes)
Cotton wool	Tourniquet
Bottles for DNA; blood grouping and blood alcohol level	Butterfly needle
Monovette needles × 2	Monovette syringes × 2
20 ml syringes × 2	10 ml syringes × 2
Tampon × 1	Disposable speculum
Sachet of lubricating jelly	Disposable scissors

victim), or already suffering 'memory block' associated with 'rape trauma syndrome'. Hence it is safer practice to complete the full forensic sampling at this, usually the only, opportunity afforded to the doctor to collect forensic evidence.

DELAY IN REPORTING SEXUAL ASSAULT

A delay in the reporting of a sexual assault may affect the historical detail given by the victim, especially if she has begun to block any memory of the event. The examination findings may also be affected, especially with alteration to the emotional state together with the healing of minor injuries. The forensic evidence may be severely limited.

Spermatozoa persist for varying lengths of time after a sexual assault ranging from:

(1) Vaginal intercourse – up to ten days (Wilson 1982);

(2) On rectal swabs – up to 65 hours (Willott 1982);

(3) On anal swabs – up to 46 hours (Willott 1982);

(4) After oral intercourse – 12–14 hours (Willott 1986).

There is considerable variation between individuals with respect to the probability of detecting spermatozoa at different times after intercourse and this should be taken into consideration when deciding on the appropriateness of samples and evaluating the results (Davies 1974).

DESCRIPTION OF WOUNDS

The doctor examining a victim of sexual assault may experience difficulty with the nomenclature when describing wounds and may be daunted by the medico-legal significance of the lesions. Even more difficulty may be encountered when the doctor is asked to give an opinion as to how they may have been caused.

Crane recommended the following classification of wounds in 1996:

(1) Bruises;

(2) Abrasions – injury to the outer layers of skin;

(3) Lacerations – blunt force splitting full thickness of skin;

(4) Incisions – caused by sharp cutting instrument;

(5) Stab wounds.

Each individual mark and injury should be recorded on the body diagrams with a full description entered into the written notes. The length of the victim's fingernails should be recorded.

FORENSIC SAMPLES

The evidence collected during the examination is used to help prove three points:

(1) The occurrence of sexual contact;

(2) The lack of consent on the part of the victim;

(3) The identity of the assailant.

A sexual examination kit should be at hand with all necessary equipment – swabs, bottle, bags, labels, scissors etc. During removal of clothing the victim should stand on a brown paper sheet, shiny side upwards. Each item should be inspected and described before handing it to the police officer who places the item in a paper bag. All injuries should be described and drawn with relevant measurements on the body chart. For complex injuries it is very important to consider photography. It is mandatory to use a photographer of the same gender for photographs of an intimate or genital origin (Table 26.4, 26.5, 26.6).

ABSENCE OF GENITAL INJURY

Data about the genital injuries sustained by victims of sexual assault are derived only from women who choose to report the incident and so the

Table 26.4.   The forensic examination

Forensic examination	
Time commenced	General appearance and emotional status
Clothing – items	Brown paper and couch paper
Clothing – description	Detailed examination – record on body charts
Details of injuries/lesions	Dimensions – size and shape
Position – using body chart	
Colour	Associated swelling
Degree of healing	Associated tenderness
Inspection	
Secretions/stains	– faeces/foreign material/blood
Discharge	– amount/viscosity/site
Bleeding	– source
Injuries	– scratches/bruises/petechiae/lacerations
	– tears –hymenal/forchette/perineum
	– anal – tear (fissure)/swelling/warts
	– gape/reddening/haemorrhoids
	– degree of healing of lesions
Speculum	– type of speculum used
Protoscopy	– where anal penetration alleged/suspected, injury/blood/discharge

For speculum or proctoscope examination, warm water should be used for lubrication. Occasionally lubricating jelly is necessary. The use of lubricant and site at which it is used to assist the examination must be documented.

Bimanual examination	– indicated if victim has pelvic pain
Victim's reaction to examination (free text)	

results of studies reporting the presence or absence of injury must be interpreted with care due to this self-reporting bias. The absence of genital injuries should not negate an allegation of sexual assault or rape but the presence of genital injury is thought to carry more weight in obtaining a successful conviction. In a retrospective view of case records of women from the Northumbria police area, only 22 out of 83 women had genital injuries (27 per cent), but 68 out of 83 had some form of physical injury (82 per cent) (Bowyer 1997). It was concluded that the absence of genital injury should not be used as pivotal evidence by the police or CPS (Crown Prosecution Service). Moderate or severe genital injury occurs in approximately one per cent of victims. A similar incidence of genital injury was reported in a study of 440 cases of reported sexual assault where 16 per cent of all the victims had visible genital injury (Cartwright 1987).

Table 26.5.   Forensic samples

ALL SWABS ARE TAKEN IN PAIRS

Control swabs	– wet and dry
Buccal swab	
Skin swab	– at site of kissing/sucking/ejaculation/bite (moistened if necessary)
Saliva specimen	– if oral assault
Head hair combings	
Head hair cuttings	
Right and left nail scrapings	– where visible debris or victim remembers scratching assailant
Nail cuttings	– if evidence of broken nail and victim recalls scratching assailant
Nail filings	– to recover blood staining/skin fragments

Table 26.6.   Intimate samples

External intimate samples
Pubic hair cuttings
Pubic hair combings
Vulval swabs

Internal intimate samples

Introitus	
High vaginal swab (minimum two, ideally four)	
Endocervical swabs	– if more than 48 hours since alleged incident
Perineal swabs	
Anal and rectal swabs	– using a proctoscope – where anal penetration is alleged (from beyond the end of protoscope once obturator removed)
Blood – DNA	– special buccal swab will suffice if patient refuses venesection
Blood alcohol	– specifically record time this sample taken
Tampon	
Sanitary towel	
Urine sample	– where drugs are thought to be implicated
Gown	
Time examination completed	

Reasons for absence of genital injury may include:

(1) Verbal threats to victim, intimidation and threats that failure to comply with assailant's demands will result in physical injury/death to herself, another person or her child. Social and interpersonal coercion play a significant role in marital rape;

(2) Insufficient force is used to produce an injury (especially in sexually active parous women);

(3) Bruises may not become apparent for 48 hours;

(4) Delay in reporting assault allowing healing of lesions;

(5) Use of lubricant at time of rape.

PATTERNS OF INJURY IN POST-MENOPAUSAL WOMEN

Some female survivors of sexual assault sustain more physical injuries than others and one of the factors influencing the type of injury is the victim's age. Post-menopausal women represent only a small percentage of those reporting sexual assault. In Dallas County between 1986 and 1991 only 2.2 per cent of women reporting sexual assault were post-menopausal (Ramin 1992). Trauma in general occurred as frequently in the older woman (67 per cent) as in the younger group (under 50 years of age), but genital trauma was more common (43 per cent) in the post-menopausal group compared with younger women (18 per cent). Almost one in five older women had genital lacerations. Other authors have also reported an increased frequency of genital injuries in the older victim of sexual assault (Cartwright 1989). The increased genital trauma rate is presumably due to post-menopausal atrophy causing increased genital tissue susceptibility.

ULTRAVIOLET LIGHT TO EVALUATE SKIN STAINS

Several studies have shown that ultraviolet light induced fluorescence (UVI) may be used as a part of forensic medical examinations (Stoilovic 1991; West 1992; Lynnerup 1995). Disturbance within the skin of the various components of haemoglobin, melanin, fibroproteins, collagen and fatty tissues result in changes in fluorescence so that traumatised skin illuminated with UV light in a dark room fluoresces (Barsley 1990; David 1994). Body fluids such as semen and saliva also fluoresce. UVI can be used to detect stains at crime scenes and on items of clothing or bedding but further studies are required to evaluate whether or not it is a valuable tool in finding faint signs of skin trauma or locating stains, thus enabling retrieval of material for forensic analysis.

COLPOSCOPIC EXAMINATION OF THE GENITALIA

The role of the colposcope has yet to be established in the United Kingdom but descriptive studies from the United States have revealed that 87 per cent

Table 26.7. Post-examination arrangements

Specimen labels signed by doctor

Scientific aids form signed by doctor and police officer

Genito Urinary Medicine Clinic referral	– initial examination at 1–3 days – follow-up at 7–14 days
REACH counsellor referral	– 7–14 days
Re-examination occasionally indicated if:	– Genital injuries not visible – Examination shortly after incident – Tenderness on examination
Emergency contraception	– Hormonal – up to 72 hours after the incident (Schering PC4) – IUCD – up to 7 days after the incident if more than 72 hours have already elapsed or there are contra-indications to hormonal preparations

Statement preparation and submission to officer in charge

Completion of examination claim form

GP letter

Photography – consent should be sought and documented on the victim consent form

---

of women examined within 48 hours of sexual assault had positive findings (Slaughter 1992). It was felt that the technique is so simple, quick and efficacious that it should be included in rape examination protocols. Injuries are predominantly to the posterior fourchette, labia minora, hymen and fossa navicularis and chiefly lacerations, ecchymoses and swelling. A later study compared colposcopic examination undertaken within 24 hours of penile penetration during sexual assault with consensual sexual intercourse and revealed that 89 per cent of the 142 women who experienced non-consensual sex had genital injuries whereas only 11 per cent of 75 women who had voluntary sexual intercourse had a colposcopic finding of genital injury (Slaughter 1997).

PHOTOGRAPHY

The role of photographs of injuries, especially complex skin trauma, should be an adjunct to the description of the findings (Table 26.7). It has been claimed that a carefully observed, well-documented description of any injury or groups of injuries is worth many photographs (Bunting 1996) whilst others claim that a photograph can be worth a thousand words if the assailant is claiming consent and the attorney has pictures of the victim with a black eye or worse (Ledray 1993). A photograph can, on occasions, have a dramatic effect in court. However, the victim should be made aware of the possible

Table 26.8.   Statement

Statutory declaration
Doctor's qualifications, appointment, relevant experience
Victim's details (excluding address)
Time   – Examination commenced
                             – Examination completed

Place of examination
Names of other persons present during examination
Details of   – History of assault
                             – Source of history
                             – Alcohol/drugs consumed by victim

Details of examination
Details of each forensic specimen submitted
Name, rank and number of police officer receiving samples
Post-examination arrangements
                             – Photography
                             – Admission to hospital
                             – Genito-urinary medicine (GUM) referral
                             – Counsellor
                             – Emergency contraception
                             – GP correspondence (if victim agrees)
Opinion

disclosure of the photographic evidence in a crowded courtroom before she consents to this form of evidence being utilised. If possible, the doctor should accompany the victim where photographs of the genital area are required, to chaperone the victim and ensure that the lesions are demonstrated appropriately.

STATEMENT

The statement should have a professional appearance and should be checked for errors before submitting it to the police (Table 26.8). Errors discovered later are 'corrected' by preparing a supplementary statement. In England and Wales the statement must include a statutory declaration with the date and signature at the end of the declaration and at the bottom of each page, accompanied by a witness's signature on each page. It is also good practice to add a signature at the end of the final paragraph on each page if there is any remaining space.

Example of a Police Witness Statement

Northumbria Police Witness Statement Page (1)

Statement of ....

Age if under 21 .... (if over 21 insert over 21)

This statement (consisting of ...... pages each signed by me) is true to the best of my knowledge and belief and I make it knowing that, if it is tendered in evidence I shall be liable for prosecution if I have wilfully stated in it anything which I know to be false or do not believe to be true.

Acknowledgement

I would like to acknowledge the help given by Miss Tracey Cole, REACH Project Manager, in the preparation of this paper.

REFERENCES

Bang, L. (1993) Who consults for rape? *Scand J Prim Health Care* **11**, 8–14

Bang, L. (1993) Rape victims – assaults, injuries and treatment at a medical rape trauma service at Oslo Emergency Hospital. *Scand J Prim Health Care* **11**, 15–20

Barsley, R.E., West, M.H. and Frair, J. (1990) Forensic photography, ultraviolet imaging of wounds on skin. *American Journal for Medicine and Pathology* **11 (4)**, 300–8

Bowyer, L. and Dalton, M.E. (1997) Female victims of rape and genital findings. *Br J Obstet Gynaecol* **104**, 617–20

Bunting, R. (1996) 'Clinical examination in the police context' in W.D.S. McLay (Ed.) *Clinical Forensic Medicine* pp. 59–73. London: Greenwich Medical Media

Cartwright, P.S. and Moore, R.A. (1989) The elderly victim of rape. *S Afr Med J* **82**, 988–9

Cartwright, P.S. and The Sexual Assault Study Group (1987) Factors that correlate with injury sustained by survivors of sexual assault. *Obstet Gynecol* **70**, 44–6

Crane, J. (1996) 'Injury' in W.D.S. McLay (Ed.) *Clinical Forensic Medicine*, pp. 143–62. London: Greenwich Medical Media

Cravin, S.A. (1996) Assessment of alleged rape victims – an unrewarding exercise. *S Afr Med J* **86**, 237–8

David, T.J., Sobel, D.D.S. and Sobel, M.N. (1994) Recapturing a five month old bite mark by means of reflective ultraviolet photography. *Journal for Science* **39**, 1560–7

Davies, A. and Wilson, E. (1974) The persistence of seminal constituents in the human vagina. *Forensic Scientific* **3**, 45–55

Dupré, A.R., Hampton, H.L., Morrison, H. and Meeks, G.R. (1993) Sexual assault. *Obstet Gynecol Surv* **48**, 640–8

Geist, R.F. (1988) Sexually related trauma. *Emerg Med Clin North Am* **6**, 439–66

General Medical Council (1995) 'Confidentiality' from *Duties of a Doctor. Guidance from the General Medical Council.* pp.2–14. London: General Medical Council

Hampton, H.L. (1995) Care of the woman who has been raped. *N Engl J Med* **332**, 234–7

Hockbaum, S.R. (1987) The evaluation and treatment of the sexually assaulted patient. *Emerg Med Clin North Am* **5**, 601–22

Ledray, L. (1993) Sexual assault nurse clinician: An emerging area of nursing experience. *AWHONN's Clinical Issues* **4**, 180–90

Lynnerup, N. and Hjalgrim, H. (1995) Routine use of ultraviolet light in medico-legal examinations to evaluate stains and skin trauma. *Med Sci Law* **35**, 165–8

Marchbanks, P.A, Lui, K.J. and Mercy, J.A. (1990) Risk of injury from resisting rape. *Am J Epidemiol* **132**, 540–9

Ramin, S.M., Satin, A.J., Stone, I.C. and Wendel, G.D. (1992) Sexual assault in post-menopausal women. *Obstet Gynecol* **80**, 860–4

Slaughter, L. and Brown, C.R.V. (1992) Colposcopy to establish physical findings in rape victims. *Am J Obstet Gynecol* **166**, 83–6

Slaughter, L., Brown, C.R.V., Crowley, S. and Peck, P. (1997) Patterns of genital injury in female sexual assault victims. *Am J Obstet Gynecol* **176**, 609–16

Stoilovic, M. (1991) Detection of semen and blood staining using polight as a light source. *Forensic Sci Int* **51**, 289–96

West, M.H., Barsley, R.E., Hall, J.E., Hayne, S. and Cimrancic, M. (1992) The detection and documentation of trace wound patterns by use of an alternative light source. *J Forensic Sci* **37**, 1480–8

Whatley, M.A. (1993) For better or worse: The case of marital rape. *Violence and Victims* **8**, 29–39

Willott, G.M. and Allard, J.E. (1982) Spermatozoa – their persistence after sexual intercourse. *Forensic Sci Int* **19**, 135–54

Willott, G.M. and Crosse, M.M. (1986) The detection of spermatozoa in the mouth. *Journal of Forensic Science Society* **26**, 125–8

Wilson, E.M. (1982) A comparison of the persistence of seminal constituents in the human vagina and cervix. *Police Surgeon* **22**, 44–5

Wright, A.M., Duke, L., Fraser, E. and Sviland, L. (1989) Northumbria women's police doctor scheme: a new approach to examining victims of sexual assault. *BMJ* **298**, 1011–2.

Young, W., Bracken, A., Goddard, M. and Matteson, S. (1992) The New Hampshire Sexual Assault Medical Examination Protocol Project Committee. Sexual assault: Review of a National Model Protocol for Forensic and Medical Evaluation. *Obstet Gynecol* **80**, 879–83

Chapter 27

Sensitive vaginal examination

Patricia Crowley

INTRODUCTION

Vaginal speculum examination and bimanual palpation of the female internal genitalia are among the most intimate and potentially embarrassing examinations carried out in clinical medicine. Most women do not mind being examined vaginally if the examination is performed by a doctor who is skilled, sympathetic and gentle. Many women with gynaecological complaints are reassured by such an examination and many minor gynaecological complaints can be effectively managed by a competent pelvic examination, preceded by an explanation about its purpose and followed by effective communication about the findings. Complaints about sexual impropriety in association with intimate examinations are rare. However, some patients experience considerable distress, anger and confusion following insensitive vaginal examination and may experience long-lasting difficulties as a result.

CHAPERONAGE

Guidelines issued by the General Medical Council's (GMC) Standards Committee suggest that wherever possible, patients undergoing an intimate examination should be offered a chaperone or invited to bring a relative or friend to the consultation (General Medical Council 1996). Currently, practice varies; in some gynaecological outpatient clinics a chaperone is available only to women being examined by male doctors. Some doctors are accompanied by a chaperone when performing gynaecological examinations in hospital clinics but not in private consulting rooms.

In a study of male and female adults and teenagers in a general practice setting in the US, Penn and Bourguet (1992) found that the majority of patients of either sex and all ages did not care if a chaperone was present. However, substantial proportions of adult women (29 per cent) and female teenagers (46 per cent) preferred a chaperone to be present during a breast, pelvic or rectal examination by a male physician. Thirty-six per cent of adult women and 63 per cent of female teenagers wanted a chaperone present during a first examination of these regions. Adults of both sexes felt that a nurse would be the best chaperone, whereas teenagers ranked a parent first and a nurse second. Patients indicated that they felt comfortable asking for a chaperone.

Phillips *et al.* (1981) assessed the attitudes of teenagers of both sexes to chaperonage during intimate examinations. Young males and females strongly preferred to be accompanied, generally by a family member. With increasing age, males preferred to be alone with the physician, whereas females preferred to be accompanied. Regardless of sex and age, virtually none chose the company of peers. The US literature indicates that male paediatricians and specialists in adolescent health are more likely to use a chaperone during pelvic examination of adolescent females but a surprisingly high proportion of male doctors from these specialities do not use chaperones (Buchta 1989). In a survey of general practitioners in the UK, Speelman *et al.* (1993) found that 75 per cent of female and 21 per cent of male GPs never use a chaperone when performing intimate examinations on patients of the opposite sex. None of the female doctors and 16 per cent of the males always offer a chaperone in these circumstances. Only one per cent of respondents did not have a practice nurse.

A chaperone is 'one, especially an older woman, who accompanies a girl for protection, restraint or appearance's sake'. The Association of Police Surgeons define a more sympathetic role for a chaperone in cases of alleged sexual assault as one who 'supports and befriends the victim' (Howitt and Rogers 1996). Many women attending for gynaecological consultations or procedures would also value the presence of one who 'supports and befriends'. The advantages of chaperonage are self-evident. Chaperonage is the ultimate safeguard of the patient against abuse during examination. Great emphasis is given to the role of the chaperone in protecting the patient against sexual abuse but this is probably very rare. A more important role for a chaperone may be the protection of the patient against real or perceived abuse. The presence of a chaperone acts as a safe-guard against a doctor causing unnecessary discomfort, pain, humiliation or intimidation during examination. A chaperone may provide reassurance to an anxious patient. On occasions when the doctor's attention is focused on performing procedures such as colposcopy or hysteroscopy, the nurse-chaperone may maintain communication and eye-contact with the patient. A chaperone may assist an infirm or disabled patient while dressing and undressing. Obviously, the presence of a chaperone protects doctors against false allegations of sexual abuse. Medical indemnity organisations consider the presence of a chaperone helpful to the defence of a doctor against an allegation of sexual misconduct during an intimate examination. However, as such allegations are extremely rare, it is important that this aspect of chaperonage does not receive unnecessary emphasis (Kirby 1997). Such a public perception could reduce the ability of the chaperone to fulfil the roles described above.

There is concern that necessary examinations will be neglected because of the unavailability of a chaperone. The potential disadvantages of a chaperone include the cost of employing a nurse or other individual to fulfil this role. Gynaecological consultations occasionally provide an opportunity for women to confide deeply sensitive information about sexual abuse, previous termination of pregnancy, or domestic violence. The presence of a chaperone may intrude in a confiding doctor-patient relationship and may lower a doctors acuity in detecting non-verbal signs of distress from the patient. This drawback is potentially offset by confining chaperonage to the physical examination and allowing one-to-one communication for the consultation. Some patients' level of embarrassment may increase in proportion to the number of individuals present during an examination.

While some patients may welcome the presence of a family member acting as chaperone, there are potential disadvantages. The presence of a family member may reduce the likelihood of disclosure of sensitive information and delay the development of self-confidence in young women. The presence of a dominant male partner may inhibit communication about past gynaecological or obstetric history, marital or sexual problems or domestic violence. An accompanying female relative may bring to the consultation her own agenda of prejudices and fears about gynaecological examinations.

A chaperone should be provided for all patients undergoing vaginal examinations, irrespective of the gender of the gynaecologist. There is an important difference between a policy of offering a chaperone to women who request one and providing a chaperone to all women with an opt-out choice for those who wish. Under the former policy, less assertive women may be afraid to request a chaperone or may feel they are being difficult if they do so. If the patient prefers to be examined without a chaperone this request should be honoured. Where chaperonage cannot be offered because of medical emergency or staff shortages, the patient should be informed of the unavailability of a chaperone and her consent to proceeding with the examination obtained.

SENSITIVE AND SPECIFIC VAGINAL EXAMINATION

Pelvic examination should not be considered an automatic and inevitable part of every gynaecological examination. Prior to performing pelvic examination, it is essential for the gynaecologist to consider what information will be gained by the examination, and whether the same information is already available, or is going to be obtained from another source such as ultrasound or examination under anaesthesia, regardless of the findings during clinical examination. It is useful to consider whether the planned examination is a 'screening' or a 'diagnostic' test. A skilled and gentle pelvic examination is a necessary and important part of the assessment of many gynaecological symptoms. However, the predictive value of 'routine' bimanual pelvic examination as a screening test in asymptomatic women is very poor. In a study of routine pelvic examination in 2623 healthy, asymptomatic, volunteers ranging between 25 and 92 years of age, Grover and Quinn (1995) found a bulky or fibroid uterus in 12.9 per cent of women and abnormal adnexal findings in 1.5 per cent. The specificity of vaginal examination for malignancy was 99.9 per cent. No ovarian malignancies were identified at initial screening.

The low productivity of pelvic examination in the asymptomatic young woman prior to commencing use of the oral contraceptive pill (Huber and Huber 1975) makes it difficult to justify such an examination which may deter uptake of contraception in vulnerable young women. The British Society for Colposcopy and Cervical Pathology considers that bimanual examination of the pelvis should be performed in a woman attending for colposcopy only if indicated (Luesley 1996).

In symptomatic women, appropriate digital or speculum examination can be very productive, for example, in assessing a patient with uterovaginal prolapse or in evaluating a patient with dyspareunia. The availability of transvaginal ultrasound examination may increase the predictive value of pelvic examination. Some 'one-stop' outpatient clinics are being equipped with this facility. A randomised trial of conventional bimanual examination versus transvaginal ultrasound in combination with conventional bimanual examination would be desirable before this becomes standard practice for all gynaecological clinics.

A practical guide to sensitive vaginal examination

In the course of a gynaecological consultation, it is usually best if the history is taken with only the patient present as this will afford maximum confidentiality and enable the doctor to gain the patient's confidence. Pelvic examinations, however, whether by male or female doctors, nurses or mid-wives, should normally be performed in the presence of a female chaperone, preferably unrelated to the patient.

An explanation about the contribution of the pelvic examination towards a diagnosis in the context of the presenting complaint is an essential part of the preamble to obtaining informed consent for examination. Verbal consent should be obtained prior to all pelvic examinations. Patients should be provided with private, warm changing facilities. After undressing there should be no undue delay prior to examination. The practice in some outpatient clinics of interviewing one patient while another is waiting for examination may save a small amount of time but increases anxiety, conveys the impression of a conveyor belt and may lead to consultations being overheard. Gowns provided for outpatient gynaecology patients should be comfortable and compatible with modesty. Improvements in the design of gowns have been shown to reduce anxiety (Williams et al. 1992). Some patients will welcome a choice between donning a gown or continuing to wear some of their own clothes e.g. a wide skirt with underwear removed. Alternatively, they may welcome the opportunity of bringing their own robe. Muslim women will wish to continue wearing their head-dress. The woman should be given every opportunity to undress herself with assistance from a nurse, chaperone or relative only if this is necessary due to infirmity. No assistance should be given with removing underwear unless absolutely necessary.

Every effort must be made to ensure that intimate examinations take place in a closed room that cannot be entered while the examination is in progress and that the examination is not interrupted by phone calls, bleeps or messages about other patients.

In addition to the explanation given prior to the examination, it may be helpful to give a running commentary on what is being done during the examination. Terms of endearment such as 'pet', 'love' or 'dear' should be avoided during consultations, especially while performing the pelvic examination. No remarks of a personal nature should be made during the examination, even if they may be clinically relevant. For example, advice about the risks of sunbathing prompted by the presence of a deep sun-tan should be given after the examination has concluded. Similarly, no comment or discussion about body weight should take place while the woman is undressed, despite its relevance to gynaecological problems. Poor self-esteem and embarrassment may deter obese women from attending gynaecologists (Adams *et al.* 1993). In the assessment of a woman with dyspareunia, valuable information is obtained by assessing the ability of digital examination to reproduce the dyspareunia. This is the only situation in gynaecological practice where sexual problems should be discussed during the examination, as opposed to before and afterwards.

Throughout the examination the doctor should remain alert to verbal and non-verbal indications of distress from the patient. Doctors who are trained to combine the physical examination with an awareness and acknowledgement of the patient's feelings will learn more about the patient and give rise to fewer complaints.

Position for pelvic examination

Offering a choice of position may help to reduce the sense of vulnerability and powerlessness complained of by some women following unsatisfactory experiences of pelvic examination. Usually the dorsal position is chosen for examination with a Cusco speculum. The Sims or left lateral position is used for Sims speculum examination and the full lithotomy position is rarely used in the UK unless the examination is being performed as part of a colposcopic assessment of the lower genital tract. In a survey of practice in Great Britain, Amias (1987) noted that the choice of position for digital and speculum examination is determined more by habit and geography than by practical clinical considerations. Seymore and colleagues (1986) showed that pelvic examination in the semi-sitting position provoked less anxiety than examination in the supine position. Whatever position is used, the patient must be made comfortable and provided with as much covering as feasible. It may be easier to preserve an appropriate degree of modesty with the patient lying on her side than on her back, but many women find an unseen approach from the rear most alarming, and are less certain where the finger or speculum is going. Some women may have a preference and this should be honoured if at all possible.

During the examination the patient must be told about each manoeuvre prior to it being performed. Many women find the bimanual abdominal/vaginal examination to be the most intimate of examinations. Its use should be restricted to occasions when it is necessary that such an examination be performed. At the conclusion of speculum or bimanual examination the patient should be given some tissue with which to remove any remaining lubricating gel from her introitus and clearly told of the examiner's findings, preferably after she has dressed in privacy and is seated back in the consulting room. Although the patient, particularly if elderly, may appreciate the presence or help of a nurse or chaperone whilst she is re-dressing, it is preferable if the consultation subsequent to examination is conducted with only the doctor and patient present for reasons of confidentiality, unless of course the patient wishes otherwise.

GYNAECOLOGICAL INVESTIGATIONS INVOLVING VAGINAL EXAMINATION

Endovaginal ultrasound

The use of transvaginal ultrasound using a vaginal probe overcomes the need for a full bladder and compensates for the poor resolution experienced with transabdominal ultrasound in obese patients. The deeper parts of the pelvis may be visualised accurately. While this technique is usually well accepted by patients (Timor-Tritsch *et al.* 1988), the fact that it is a much more intimate examination than transabdominal ultrasound must be borne in mind. Women who have never before experienced ultrasound examination or whose previous ultrasound experience consisted of transabdominal ultrasound may be taken aback by the appearance and use of the transvaginal probe and by the condom-like sheaths used to cover the probe. This examination is sometimes performed by a gynaecologist in an outpatient clinic and sometimes by a radiographer or radiologist. The gynaecologist initiating this investigation has a responsibility to explain to the patient what is entailed and to ensure that this investigation is not attempted in women for whom it is obviously inappropriate such as women with an intact hymen, elderly women with a narrow atrophic vagina, women with radiation stenosis or vaginismus. If there is uncertainty as to the suitability of the woman for transvaginal ultrasound, preliminary digital vaginal examination by a gynaecologist is essential. A chaperone should be provided for this procedure as the radiographer or radiologist may be an unfamiliar person and the examination usually takes place in a dimly lit room.

Colposcopy

Referral for colposcopy following abnormal cervical cytology is distressing and can lead to anxiety and psychosexual problems (Campion *et al.* 1988). The need for examination in the lithotomy position, the fear of malignant disease and an awareness of the association between cervical neoplasia and sexually transmitted disease combine to make this potentially one of the most traumatic investigations in gynaecology. The guidelines for good practice laid down by the National Health Service Cervical Screening Programmes in conjunction with the British Society for Colposcopy and Cervical Pathology are a model for the appropriate conduct of all intimate examinations and should be followed (Luesley 1996). Many of these guidelines are applicable to the conduct of analogous clinics such as urogynaecology and outpatient hysteroscopy. They emphasise the need for an appropriate clinical environment with adequate privacy, changing facilities and a suitable couch. Prior to attending for colposcopy, women should be supplied with written or diagrammatic and verbal information about colposcopy and related destructive or ablative procedures performed on the cervix. Informed consent for the colposcopic examination itself and also for any destructive or ablative treatment at the same visit, the 'see and treat' approach, must be sought before the woman has undressed and lies on the colposcopy couch. It would be inappropriate to obtain consent for a procedure while the woman is already on the couch or in lithotomy position.

Hysteroscopy and outpatient endometrial biopsy

Outpatient hysteroscopy and endometrial biopsy are now a routine part of the investigation of menorrhagia, intermenstrual and postmenopausal bleeding. Patients should be appropriately selected and well-prepared for this procedure. The provision of written material prior to clinic attendance and an adequate verbal explanation prior to commencement of the investigation is essential. Facilities and comfort should be of the same standard as for colposcopy. The presence of a fully-trained nurse familiar with the procedure is essential so that chaperonage is always available.

Urodynamic investigations

These investigations are conducted by gynaecologists, urologists or nurse practitioners. The need for the modified lithotomy position, the insertion of rectal and urethral transducers and the requirement to micturate in public make this another embarrassing and undignified procedure. Once again, the provision of adequate written information in advance and the presence of an encouraging nurse-chaperone may reduce some of the indignities.

VAGINAL EXAMINATION IN SPECIFIC CIRCUMSTANCES

Intimate examinations in Asian women

The religious and cultural background of Muslim and Hindu women make intimate examinations particularly difficult. They have been brought up with a strong cultural taboo against being touched by any man other than their husband. Muslim and Hindu women have a clear preference for women doctors when intimate examinations are necessary. In general practices or hospital clinics where this request is difficult to meet, it may be possible to staff a clinic on an occasional or sessional basis. Nudity may be particularly difficult and embarrassing for these women. All sensible measures to reduce the extent and duration of nudity should be taken which do not jeopardise the thoroughness of the examination. For instance, embarrassment may be reduced by undressing only one area at a time.

As with all women, an adequate explanation of the nature and purpose of the examination, given before the woman undresses, reduces anxiety. The presence of a female chaperone is regarded as essential, particularly if an examination has to be performed by a male doctor. A nurse-chaperone is preferred as women would be embarrassed to be examined in the presence of a friend or family member; the presence of a link worker or professional interpreter is preferable to having a family member act as interpreter as the Asian Family Counselling Service is aware of rare cases where a family member has wittingly or unwittingly altered the sense of an interpreted conversation with a health professional.

Both Muslim and Hindu women have particular taboos about menstruation. Hindu women are barred from the temple and the kitchen at this time. A pelvic examination during menstruation is unacceptable except as a medical emergency.

The first vaginal examination and the examination of younger women

The conduct of the first vaginal examination may influence the young woman's confidence in, and uptake of, gynaecological and family planning services for the rest of her life. As with all medical interventions it is worthwhile taking a moment to consider the necessity of the examination, whether it is a screening or diagnostic procedure, and its likely productivity. Digital or speculum examination is almost never indicated in a young woman who has not yet had sexual intercourse. The productivity of 'routine' examination prior to prescribing the oral contraceptive pill for the first time is extremely low (Huber and Huber 1975). It is essential that teenagers are aware that the prescription of the oral contraceptive pill is not predicated on undergoing a pelvic examination. In an asymptomatic young woman, cervical screening need not commence until three years after she has first become sexually active.

Many young women approach the first vaginal examination with pre-conceptions which must be dispelled prior to proceeding with the examination. In a study of a random sample of Danish teenagers Larsen and Kragstrup (1995) found that among those who had not had a pelvic examination, 48 per cent thought the examination would be painful, 29 per cent feared that the doctor would discover abnormal anatomy, 67 per cent felt they would be embarrassed by exposing their genitals and 23 per cent expected to be indisposed for the rest of the examination day. Against this background, it is obvious that the first vaginal examination must be used as an educational opportunity. Extra time must be devoted to an explanation of the purpose and nature of the pelvic examination. Such examinations are ideally carried out in a family planning clinic or adolescent gynaecology clinic by individuals with experience of taking adolescents through the first vaginal examination. Following an explanation of the nature of vaginal examination, the first vaginal examination should begin with inspection of the external genitalia and reassurance about anatomical normality. A mirror can be used to educate the patient about her anatomy. A gentle one finger examination is necessary to establish whether the hymen is present or not. If speculum examination is being performed for the first time, it may be useful to demonstrate the speculum to the patient prior to the examination and to allow her to handle it. A small, warmed, lubricated speculum is used. Some younger women seem prepared to insert the speculum themselves and this technique has been found useful in forensic examination of women who have been raped or sexually abused. In a particularly apprehensive woman, the process of the first pelvic examination may be spread out over a number of consultations, starting with information, working through inspection of external genitalia, handling of specula, to digital and speculum examination with the patient being given the option to halt, defer or proceed with each step. In a symptomatic woman, especially presenting as an emergency, such an approach may not be practical.

Patients who experience difficulty with pelvic examination

A woman experiencing difficulty with vaginal examination may present in a number of ways. During history taking she may reveal a history suggestive of vaginismus, a history of rape, sexual abuse or domestic violence, or a history of a previously traumatic vaginal examination or psychologically or physically traumatic childbirth. Alternatively, there may be no evidence of a problem until vaginal examination is attempted. At examination she may exhibit great anxiety with hyperventilation, tearfulness or a 'frozen' or un-usually detached attitude. Vaginal examination may be made difficult or impossible by inability to relax or abduct the thighs.

How to proceed in these cases will vary, but usually it is best to abandon a 'difficult' examination and invite the patient to dress and then discuss the problem. A key factor is the nature of the presenting complaint. When the gynaecological presentation has been a request for screening or for management of a chronic problem such as infertility, investigation and management of the difficulty with vaginal examination can take priority. If, however, there is a significant or acute gynaecological complaint, then its investigation and management must proceed, compensating for the information lacking because of failure to perform pelvic examination. The presence of a significant or acute gynaecological problem may mandate the use of pelvic (but not transvaginal) ultrasound or laparoscopy. A complaint of abnormal vaginal bleeding in a woman in whom speculum examination is impossible may require examination under anaesthesia. Following investigation and management of the acute problem, appropriate steps should be taken to address the underlying difficulty with vaginal examination.

Women who experience difficulty with vaginal examination should be given every opportunity to facilitate disclosure of any underlying sexual or marital difficulties or traumas. A calmly articulated statement such as 'some women who find internal examinations difficult feel this was caused by something that happened to them in the past' may open up a taboo subject for discussion. None of these discussions should take place until the woman is fully dressed and alone with the doctor. It must not be assumed that all women who experience difficulty with pelvic examination have a background history of sexual abuse, domestic violence or sexual difficulties. It is important that they are not badgered into revealing a problem when none exists.

A multi-disciplinary approach may be necessary, with referral to the appropriate agencies for women traumatised by sexual abuse or domestic violence and for those requiring psychosexual counselling. Rehabilitation of a woman following a previously traumatic pelvic examination requires a detailed discussion of the circumstances of the previously traumatic examination in an attempt to identify which elements of the examination caused distress. Many patients who are unable to have pelvic examination or who are unduly distressed by it can be helped to cope with the process. A modified behaviour therapy approach can be used to overcome anxiety. The woman may make one or more visits to the clinic when no examination takes place. Later she may be able to undress but not to proceed with examination. She should be given the opportunity to progress at her own pace through a hierarchy of increasingly more intrusive components of the pelvic examination. For instance, she may be encouraged to learn how to insert her own finger into the vagina, prior to allowing the doctor to perform a digital examination. Handling the vaginal speculum and inserting it herself may help to reduce anxiety. These cases are rare, time-consuming and potentially rewarding for the professionals involved. Hospital-based gynaecology clinics may not be the ideal setting for this process, which may be handled more successfully in general practice, family planning or community gynaecology clinics. Key factors for success in such cases are patience and continuity of care. The approach to the problem must be individualised and flexible with constant emphasis on the woman's own autonomy and control over the process.

Pelvic examination in the mentally impaired woman

The basic principles of respect, privacy, explanation and consent that apply to the conduct of intimate examinations in general, apply equally to the conduct of intimate examinations in women who are either temporarily or permanently mentally impaired. A familiar individual such as a family member or carer may sometimes be the best chaperone in this situation. Many women whose IQ is in the mild to moderately-handicapped range are competent to consent to gynaecological examination, especially if a common vocabulary can be established between the doctor and patient. While these women may not be able to understand the concepts of cervical screening, a doctor may include these patients in the National Cervical Screening Programme if that is seen to be in the best interests of the patient and she is able to consent to and tolerate speculum examination. Where consent cannot be obtained due to severe mental impairment or unconsciousness, it is good practice to consult with those close to the patient, although legally, nobody can give consent to treatment on behalf of another adult (Sommerville 1993). In the absence of informed consent for any of the procedures listed as intimate examinations, the doctor must act in the patient's best interests, giving careful consideration to whether the proposed examination is screening or diagnostic in intent. Resistance to pelvic examination should be interpreted as refusal. If the procedure has to be abandoned, alternative measures should be taken as necessary for the patient's health.

Intimate examinations in the anaesthetised patient

Obviously, informed consent should be obtained for any intimate examinations that are undertaken under anaesthesia. Consent for examination under anaesthesia by medical students is discussed elsewhere. It is good practice for all personnel in the operating theatre to treat the woman with the same gentleness and respect that they would apply were she awake, avoiding personal comments and protecting the patient's modesty wherever possible. Women who are asked to walk to the operating theatre for surgery should be provided with dressing gowns. Women should be given the option of removing their own underwear prior to anaesthesia. If a woman chooses to wear disposable underwear to theatre this should be removed by a female staff member. Consent, preferably written, should be obtained for the administration of analgesic drugs by rectal suppository while the woman is anaesthetised (Vyvyan *et al.* 1995) or alternatively, the woman should be given the option of inserting the rectal suppository herself, prior to induction of anaesthesia.

Examination of an adult victim of an alleged sexual offence

The examination of a woman following an alleged sexual offence should usually be carried out by a doctor who has received specific training in the appropriate conduct of such an examination and in the collection of forensic evidence. However, circumstances may arise where a gynaecologist may be called upon to fulfil this duty, particularly when the victim is brought to a gynaecology department because of injury or where a request from the victim for examination by a female doctor cannot otherwise be honoured. A detailed account of the appropriate conduct of this examination is available elsewhere in Chapter 27 and a study by Howitt and Rogers (1996).

Calls to such cases should be dealt with speedily, as undue delay may add to the distress of the victim and lead to a loss of potentially valuable forensic evidence. These patients should be handled sympathetically and should never be made to feel that their complaint has been doubted. A specially-trained woman police officer will be made available to befriend and support the victim, chaperone and assist the examining doctor, and ensure that appropriate procedures are followed with respect to the preservation of the chain of evidence.

Consent for the examination and collection of forensic evidence must be obtained by the doctor and must never be assumed. The process of, and reasons for, the whole examination must be explained to the woman, who should be informed that there is no obligation to consent. She must be made aware of the fact that information from the examination will be passed on to the police, courts and thereby possibly to the defendant. Written consent for examination is preferable under these circumstances.

Every effort should be made to establish a rapport with the woman before the examination commences, and to make the examination the first step in a healing process rather than a continuum of the assault. Obviously, the examining doctor should display exceptional gentleness. Equally important are measures aimed at restoring the woman's violated sense of autonomy. The woman should be allowed to control the pace of the examination and be given a choice about examination positions. Most gynaecologists would dispute the necessity for the examination in lithotomy position advised by Howitt and Rogers (1996). The woman should be assured of her right to stop the examination at any time. Respect for the woman's modesty is essential. At no time should she be subjected to total nudity.

VAGINAL EXAMINATION IN PREGNANCY

There is no scientific evidence to support the use of a 'routine' vaginal examination at the first antenatal visit. Clinical pelvimetry is not a valid means of predicting the outcome of labour (Hofmeyr 1989). Speculum examination may be necessary if cervical cytological screening or screening for bacterial vaginosis is indicated. 'Routine' vaginal examination later in pregnancy is practised widely in some European countries. There is no evidence that it reduces the risk of preterm labour or has any effect on pregnancy outcome (Kaufman 1995). Three-quarters of the women interviewed as part of the randomised trial of routine vaginal examination in pregnancy rated the vaginal examinations as the most unpleasant aspect of their pregnancy care.

Digital or speculum examination may be indicated in the evaluation of early pregnancy bleeding, the assessment of possible cervical incompetence or the assessment of the cervix prior to induction of labour. Ultrasound examination may be an alternative in some situations, but may have to be performed transvaginally. There is no evidence to support the use of rectal examination as a means of assessing the cervix in pregnancy or labour, and as women find it more distressing than vaginal examination there can be no place for it (Murphy et al. 1986).

All the courtesies, explanations and need for privacy described for gynaecological examinations apply equally to the pregnant woman. As pregnancy advances, digital or speculum examination may become increasingly uncomfortable due to engagement of the head or the need to reach a posterior cervix. A small proportion of women will find vaginal examination extremely difficult. This may be due to vaginismus relating to a previously traumatic vaginal examination, previous sexual abuse, or for reasons that are not known to either the woman or her doctor. In some cases vaginal examination can be successfully accomplished following discussion and an agreement that it will be abandoned if it becomes intolerable. In cases where it remains impossible, alternatives strategies need to be adopted. If the examination is required with a view to induction of labour, the cogency of the indication for delivery should be reviewed. If there is an incontrovertible indication for delivery, it may be necessary to proceed with epidural analgesia prior to performing a vaginal examination, recognising that this may commit all involved to early delivery. Women who manifest a significant difficulty with vaginal examination during pregnancy should be invited to return for review after delivery to consult a gynaecologist, family planning specialist or general practitioner who has an interest in this problem.

A curtained-off bed in an antenatal ward or shared labour ward affords insufficient privacy for vaginal examination, especially if other patients or their partners are within earshot. A suitable examination room should be provided on all antenatal wards and labour wards and, with the exception of emergencies, women should be transferred to a private area for pelvic examination.

Manual removal of a retained placenta

Women who undergo manual removal of a retained placenta under epidural or spinal anaesthesia occasionally report a sense of personal violation because of the uniquely penetrative nature of the procedure. Adequate explanation, gentleness and support from attending midwives during the procedure will usually prevent this from being a traumatic procedure. However, fully-informed consent may not be possible in the presence of postpartum haemorrhage. The obstetrician performing the procedure should visit the woman prior to her discharge from hospital to ascertain that there is no residual confusion, anger or trauma.

TRAINING UNDERGRADUATE AND POSTGRADUATE STUDENTS

In order to ensure that women presenting with gynaecological problems or requesting screening or contraception have access to the highest standard of care, undergraduate medical students and postgraduate trainees in general practice, family planning and obstetrics and gynaecology must be taught how to perform pelvic examination. This training includes all aspects of good practice already mentioned; explaining to the patient what is going to happen, obtaining consent, performing the examination in a skilled and gentle manner, detecting and interpreting abnormal findings and communicating these findings to the woman afterwards. The first step towards maintaining these standards is teaching by example. However, practical experience is also essential. Teaching pelvic examination is obviously difficult. Women are understandably reluctant to be examined by inexperienced individuals. The embarrassment and inexpertise of many students conveys itself to the patients. Any woman agreeing to be examined by a medical student has to have the examination repeated by the supervising gynaecologist. Women are particularly likely to refuse examination by male students.

A survey of medical students in the UK and US in 1984–5 revealed that 46 per cent of medical students in the UK obtained their first experience of pelvic examination by examining an anaesthetised patient, while 70 per cent of students in the US performed their first pelvic examination on a volunteer (Cohen *et al.* 1988). The use of non-patient volunteers, either paid or unpaid, is commonplace in the US, Australia and the Netherlands. These women may be designated as gynaecological teaching assistants and often work in teams of two with one woman instructing and the second woman undergoing the pelvic examination. They are not highly paid and appear to be motivated by altruistic feminism. We are not aware of non-patient volunteers taking part in any undergraduate teaching programme in the UK or Ireland at present.

The value of examination under anaesthesia as a means of instructing medical students is limited. It occasionally provides an opportunity to examine women with a specific finding such as a pelvic mass or utero-vaginal prolapse but is of no value in teaching the combination of communication and expert examination that characterise sensitive pelvic examination.

Students should be taught how to don gloves and handle a vaginal speculum in a classroom setting and to practise this until fumbling has been eliminated.

A certain expertise can also be obtained by using a mannequin in a clinical skills laboratory. The student can then observe the teaching gynaecologist performing a pelvic examination in an awake patient at an outpatient clinic. Permission for this should be sought by the consultant. Finally, the student should perform pelvic and speculum examination in an awake patient under supervision.

Consent

It is properly accepted that explicit consent of patients is required for medical students to:

(1) 'Sit in' during gynaecological and obstetric consultations;

(2) Be present in operating theatres as observers and assistants;

(3) Perform clinical pelvic examinations of both conscious and anaesthetised patients.

Currently, practice varies between medical schools with respect to how consent is obtained and by whom. There are some educational advantages to medical students seeking and obtaining consent personally. Such a practice may inculcate a lifelong respect for the autonomy of patients. However, an insistence that consent is obtained by a doctor indicates recognition of the importance of such consent. In cases where pelvic examination under anaesthesia is regarded as being of educational value, written consent must be obtained from the woman before she comes to the operating theatre. This consent should preferably be given for a named rather than a generic medical student.

Assessment

Traditionally, all medical undergraduates were called upon to perform a speculum examination as part of the final professional MB examination in obstetrics and gynaecology. Although a small number of academic departments adhere to this practice, it is rapidly disappearing, partly due to the practical difficulties of mounting this exercise, but mainly from an acceptance that such assessments are better made during the course of clinical instruction. The ordeal of the exercise, perhaps mostly for the candidate, certainly for the patient and not least for the assessors, could hardly be justified by the value of such assessments. The presence of at least five individuals, patient, candidate, chaperone and at least two assessors often seemed to turn such 'intimate' examinations into a public performance.

More telling however, is the likelihood that many candidates found such assessments the most daunting prospect of their entire training and would approach it with fear. Once over, there may have been a feeling of relief that they would never have to face such an ordeal again. The negative attitudes which this might sometimes engender towards a crucially important clinical procedure were potentially counter-productive.

Postgraduate training

The ability to perform courteous and competent pelvic examinations is regarded as a prerequisite for Membership of the Royal College of Obstetricians and Gynaecologists. Up to the present, summative assessment of this skill has formed part of the Membership examination. This will cease to be the case from November 1998.

It is essential that this arrangement is replaced by genuine formative assessment during structured training and that appropriate technique, behaviour and expertise are not assumed. Trainees must be observed performing pelvic examination and should be prepared to accept constructive criticism of their technique and communication skills.

THE KEY TO SENSITIVE VAGINAL EXAMINATION IS COMMUNICATION, CONSENT AND CHOICE

Communication

Communication about the purpose of a proposed examination or investigation is essential to obtaining informed consent. Where the patient is about to undergo an unfamiliar procedure or investigation, verbal descriptions may need to be backed up by easily understood written or diagrammatic material. During intimate examinations and investigations communication is a two-way process, with the examining doctor offering reassurance and courtesy while remaining alert to both verbal and non-verbal signs of distress from the patient. Following an examination or investigation the findings must be communicated to the patient. In view of the reported incidence of young women who have anxieties or misunderstandings about the normality of their anatomy, the first vaginal examination should be used as an educational opportunity.

Consent

We have stressed the need for consent for all the procedures discussed. For pelvic or speculum examination *verbal consent* is sufficient as this is backed up by *implied consent* when the woman undresses to prepare for examination. In order to give *informed consent* for more complex procedures and investigations such as colposcopy, patients may require access to written, verbal and diagrammatic material. Consideration should be given to introducing written consent for some procedures where current practice requires verbal consent only.

Many women whose IQ is in the mild to moderately-handicapped range are competent to consent to gynaecological examination, especially if a common vocabulary can be established between the doctor and patient. Where consent cannot be obtained due to severe mental impairment or unconsciousness, it is good practice to consult with those close to the patient, although legally, nobody can give consent to treatment on behalf of another adult (Sommerville 1993). In the absence of informed consent, the doctor must act in the patient's best interests. Resistance to pelvic examination should be interpreted as refusal.

Consent for examination and collection of forensic evidence from a woman who is the victim of an alleged sexual assault must never be assumed and written consent for examination is preferable under these circumstances. Written consent must be obtained for examination under anaesthesia. If this is to be performed by a medical student for training purposes, explicit written consent must be obtained for a named individual.

Choice

For many women, the availability of some choice about the conduct of intimate examinations may reduce their sense of vulnerability and so it is particularly important to offer choice to women who experience difficulty with vaginal examination and to those who have been assaulted. There are a number of areas where it is possible to offer the woman some options. A chaperone should be offered to all women but they should be aware of the option to be examined without one. Women should be able to choose between left lateral dorsal, recumbent and semi-recumbent positions for speculum and bimanual examination. Women who are finding examination distressing should be offered the option of abandoning it.

REFERENCES

Adams, C.H., Smith, N.J., Wilbur, D.C. and Grady, K.E. (1993) The relationship of obesity to the frequency of pelvic examinations: do physician and patient attitudes make a difference? *Women Health* 20, 45–57

Amias, A.G. (1987) Pelvic examination: a survey of British practice. *Br J Obstet Gynaecol* 94, 975–8

Buchta, R.M. (1989) Use of chaperones during pelvic examinations of female adolescents. Results of a survey. *Am J Dis Child* 141, 666–7

Campion, M.J., Brown, J.R., McCance, D.J. *et al.* (1988) Psychosexual trauma of an abnormal cervical smear. *Br J Obstet Gynaecol* 95, 175–81

Cohen, D., Wakeford, R., Kessel, R.W. and McCullough, (1988) Teaching vaginal examination. *Lancet* ii, 1375

General Medical Council (1996) *Guideline on Intimate Examinations.* London: GMC

Grover, S.R. and Quinn, M.A. (1995) Is there any value in bimanual pelvic examination as a screening test? *Med J Aust* 162, 408–10

Hofmeyr, J. (1989) 'Suspected cephalopelvic disproportion' in I. Chalmers, M. Enkin and M.J.N.C. Keirse (Eds) *Effective Care in Pregnancy and Childbirth*, p.495. Oxford: Oxford University Press

Howitt, J. and Rogers, D. (1996) 'Adult sexual offences and related matters' in W.D.S. McLay (Ed.) *Clinical Forensic Medicine* pp.193–218. London: Greenwich Medical Media.

Huber, D.H. and Huber, S.C. (1975) Screening oral contraceptive candidates and consequential pelvic examinations. *Stud Fam Plann* **6**, 49–51

Kaufman, K. (1995) 'Weekly vaginal examinations' in M.W. Enkin, M.J.N.C. Keirse, M. Renfrew and J.P. Neilson (Eds) *Pregnancy and Childbirth Module*. Cochrane Database of Systematic Reviews. London: BMJ Publishing Group

Kirby, A. (1997) A breakdown in communications. *Independent on Sunday. Real Life.* 30th March 1997 p. 5

Larsen, S.B. and Kragstrup, J. (1995) Expectations and knowledge of pelvic examinations in a random sample of Danish teenagers. *J Psychosom Obstet Gynaecol* **16**, 93–9

Luesley, D. (1996). Standards and Quality in Colposcopy. National Health Service Cervical Screening Programme Publication No. 2.

Murphy, K., Grieg, V., Garcia, J. and Grant, A. (1986). Maternal considerations in the use of pelvic examinations in labour. *Midwifery* **2**, 93–7

Penn, M.A. and Bourguet, C.C. (1992) Patients' attitudes regarding chaperones during physical examinations. *J Fam Pract* **35**, 639–43

Phillips, S., Friedman, S.B., Seidenberg, M. and Heald, F.P. (1981) Teenagers' preferences regarding the presence of family members, peers, and chaperones during examination of genitalia. *Pediatrics* **68**, 665–9

Seymore, C., DuRant, R.H., Jay, M.S. *et al.* (1986) Influence of position during examination, and sex of examiner on patient anxiety during pelvic examination. *J Pediatr* **108**, 312–17

Sommerville, A. (1993) 'Consent and refusal' in *Medical Ethics Today*, pp. 1–35. London: BMJ Publishing Group

Speelman, A., Savage, J. and Verburgh, M. (1993) Use of chaperones by general practitioners *BMJ* **307**, 986–7

Timor-Tritsch, I. E., Bar-Yam, Y., Elgali, S. and Rotlem, S. (1988) The technique of transvaginal sonography with the use of a 65MHz probe. *Am J Obstet Gynecol* **158**, 1019–24

Vyvyan, H.A. and Hanafiah, Z. (1995) Patients' attitudes to rectal drug administration. *Anaesthesia* **50**, 983–4

Williams, J.G., Park, L.I. and Kline, J. (1992) Reducing distress associated with pelvic examinations: a stimulus control intervention. *Women Health* **18**, 41–53

Chapter 28

Models of specialist and gynaecological practice

Discussion

Edwards: Thank you for three stunning presentations. I would like to make two additional points on Helen Cameron's work on rape. You probably know that the Sexual Offences Protected Material Act will shortly be introduced, and it will be a significant step forward where the defendant wishes to defend himself in rape cases. You were talking about disclosure and consent. Where is this material going? That material can now only be accessed in the presence of a solicitor and clear guidelines are set down for the regulation of where that material goes.

There was a recent domestic violence case in London where injuries were inflicted on a woman's genitals. In fact, they were burned with lighter fuel, and there were other injuries. The defendant wished to defend himself. He then had access to all the material, including the photographs, and took that material down to the local pub. The end result was that she was so deeply traumatised by the experience that she dropped the charge and the Crown Prosecution Service, even in the presence of overwhelming corroborative evidence, did not proceed with the case.

Secondly, there is a legal point which is a matter of concern, and comes back to consent. If the Law Commission had its way in changing current rape legislation, it would ensure that consent would only be a defence where there was the presence of violence, and you flagged that up as still a key issue. In many cases of rape there is no physical violence, and specifically you mentioned the genitalia. The Law Commission is of the view that consent would not be a defence unless there were immediate threats of physical violence. The current position from the Court of Appeal, although it has never been implemented, is that submission is not the same as consent. However, although we have one decision from the Court of Appeal in the case of Olive Boja, in reality that particular case would never get past the police or the Crown Prosecution Service.

I am carrying out some research on pleas. On the rape front it is absolutely staggering. This has not been looked at across the board before because we have not had statistics from the Home Office which have broken it down into 'guilty' and 'not guilty' pleas. We find in rape cases, that in 80 per cent of cases which went to court in the first half of 1995 the plea was one of 'not guilty'. That is staggering if you look at other offences

Those are good and bad areas. If the Law Commission had its way, then for women who do not have physical injury it would not be regarded as rape. That is the reality in prosecution terms. It would either not be prosecuted, or there would be a finding of acquittal.

In respect of the gynaecological examination, that goes back to ideologies and the very damaging way in which pre-menstrual syndrome has been used. I did a little work on this. If we look to some of the prescriptions that were issued shortly after this became the craze and the phase, Valium went down as Duphaston went up. It seemed to be the 'mother's little helper' or the palliative of the seventies. From a medico-legal point of view, this has been an area of great concern. Some of us tend to assume that pre-menstrual tension is really the answer, when the question you should really be asking is about domestic violence.

Jones: There are some special issues regarding orthodox Jewish women and examination. Patricia Crowley mentioned Asian women, but there is a further issue that if you cause some bleeding at the time of the examination, that will cause a problem for her.

S. Bewley: I have a comment about the insertion of the speculum by the woman herself. Faye Hutchison, who was on Patricia Crowley's working party, inspired me years ago when talking about the first examination of young women in the Brook clinic. She said 'Well, just get women to put it in themselves'. I found that rather shocking and queried whether women can just put it in, and she said that women did tend to know where their vaginas are. She pointed out that gynaecologists find it very difficult to give up the power of the speculum. I thought that was very intriguing. It can be very healing for a woman that she herself is penetrating herself, choosing the speed, time and so forth. The tension women have just goes as they put the speculum in. It is quite extraordinary and I can highly recommend it. I do not use it as a routine, but for anyone who is the slightest bit nervous I would invite them to do it. It is a marvellous technique.

Spence: I was quite shocked by that presentation as I had never thought of students learning how to examine anaesthetised patients. I feel actually quite nervous about that.

Is there anything to stop them doing the examinations on each other? I do not mean that in an oppressive way towards female medical students. There must be examinations that female students can do on male students? I do not know.

Crowley: That was done in medical schools in the US for a while, but it did not work.

Spence: My suggestion comes from the extreme disquiet and nervousness I feel about anaesthetised patients.

Crowley: You can take it already, and more so after the publication of the College's report on intimate examinations, that we are stating that this is not a good way for students to learn. Even in cases where it is thought to be of value for students to examine somebody who is anaesthetised, that has to be with the signed consent of the woman, and not for generic students but for a specific named individual student she has actually met, as opposed to students in general.

O'Brien: It would be hard to identify a medical school in this country now where specific consent is not obtained prior to an examination taking place under anaesthesia. It was certainly something that was instituted in the University of London ten years ago and should now be in all medical schools. I am not saying it is absolute, but I would challenge you to find a medical school where it does not occur.

S. Bewley: Technically, examination by a student without consent is legally an assault, and medical students need to be well aware of that, because they will be the ones who are under the charge of assault. That is partly why it has stopped. The problem, which still exists, is that there is absolutely no system of monitoring. When we have asked them about it, not one single medical school has been monitoring consent, or monitoring what has been going on in their District General Hospitals. However, I think you can be quite confident that the medical students themselves and the professors know, and the schools have the procedures, but there is a mopping up operation still to be completed.

C. Bewley: Siobhan Lloyd said something about another way of doing vaginal examinations. I often suggest to student midwives that they examine themselves. That experience will only give them the experience of one vagina and cervix, but they are amazed to think that such a thing can be done, and that it might be useful.

Wilson: Of course Susan Bewley is right. Technically, it is an assault to examine, without good medical reason, a woman who is under anaesthetic. However, just on the point of consent, this is a purely practical issue but you must be careful that you do not, as doctors are fond of saying, 'consent the patient'. I recently refused consent, mainly because I was being examined in a hospital where I teach, and was not particularly keen on having students present who I would later stand in front of. I was met with, 'Well, don't you understand that it is really important for the learning process? Why don't you want students there? You are being very obstructive!' So, get consent, but please give women the opportunity to refuse consent, and don't question when they do.

Jones: Back to the difficult vaginal examination again. It is very important for all women to know that they can just say 'no' to the examination. There are very few occasions when it is absolutely essential.

Another point is not only allowing the woman to insert the speculum herself but to have her hand on your hand when you are carrying out the examination, with the implied or verbalised understanding that if she tells you to stop then you will do so immediately. Doctors know that with patients who are very ticklish, if you have your hand on their abdomen then they will giggle. But, if their hand is on yours during the abdominal examination, they never laugh: the tickle response is gone. It is the same with a vaginal examination, if her hand is on yours when your hand is in her vagina, for most women it is a control issue and they understand that you will stop instantly. It changes the dynamic of the entire examination.

Hepburn: Richard Jones was saying that there are very few occasions when it is absolutely essential to carry out a vaginal examination. Even when we think it is absolutely essential, however, the woman can still say no. We should not impose our perceptions of what is appropriate or necessary on the woman. Even if it is a matter of life or death, they always have the right to say no. It is often worth telling women when you first see them that you will not carry out any kind of examination unless they are happy and agree to it, and that they always have the right to say no. You should always preface what you are doing with that kind of comment, so that you emphasise their rights from the very beginning.

Edwards: Yes, it would be good if you started out like that. However, there are many women here and we could draw on our own experiences. If you are sick and ill, and need help, even if you are the Queen, then God becomes the healthcare professional. If you think, or may think, that by refusing consent to vaginal examination you may not receive the full treatment or you may not have the complaint investigated as it might or should be, then the question of consent is uniquely different. You will go along with things because you put your faith in God, and God is the professional. You are so vulnerable when you are sick. You rely totally and implicitly on that professional.

If professionals start out by explaining that something is not absolutely necessary how, as the patient, do you know how necessary? My worry is that many women will consent to all kinds of things which may be unnecessary unless it is made absolutely clear that 'this is vital and absolutely necessary and we would like your consent', or, 'this is not necessary'. If the physician is making those judgements all the time, you do not know where you stand, so you consent, assent and submit to things in all kinds of circumstances that you are very unhappy about, but you never question because you are in a loop of powerlessness. You feel concerned that if you question it, and it goes down on your record, it may affect the kind of treatment you receive from the next person along the line.

Hepburn: I could not agree more. It is not really a question for individual consultations. We need to change the whole perception people have of their relationship with healthcare professions. That goes right back to involving communication skills and training of staff. It involves the work we do with non-professional groups. It has huge ramifications. I understand the point you make, but sometimes, if we explain to people why we are doing something and its purpose, you can make it clear to people that they have the right to opt out at any point. We should change people's perception of us as a profession so that we do not need to do it quite like that each time.

Lewis: I welcome Patricia Crowley's guidelines, and wish to make a recommendation that College Council consider sending them to other bodies such as the Royal College of General Practitioners. I know they do not cover all GPs, but when I was a GP I sometimes now shudder to think what I did. I *think* I did my vaginal examinations pretty sympathetically but I know that my male partners did not. GPs, practice nurses and midwives could all usefully use these guidelines. Could we have a wider dissemination, please?

Yearnshire: Bearing in mind that the last session was on rape examination, I agree that this must be dealt with sensitively, but if a woman does not agree to a medical examination, there will be no rape case. There is not really an option if you are looking for a criminal outcome here.

Jones: But that is still a matter of consent, as long as the woman understands that is the issue.

I have a comment about the reproductive healthcare system in Glasgow. You commented that there were some negative feelings about what you are doing, or that there is a stigma attached to your group and the standards were not consistent throughout the hospital. In our hospital in Connecticut we have made it part of the beginnings of employment for every employee, including the mop man and the person who brings the food around. Everyone has to have domestic violence sensitivity training. Everybody undergoes this as a condition of employment, in the entire hospital. There is no stigma attached to it being asked by a particular service.

Hepburn: There are always difficulties in balancing the need to provide appropriate care for special needs, whatever these special needs may be, and the risk of causing stigmatisation. Sometimes, the very fact that you are providing specialist services may make people feel stigmatised, and again, that is affected by the way we sell it. However sensitive we are, that balancing can always cause problems.

SECTION 8

OBLIGATIONS AND CONSTRAINTS

Chapter 29

Abuse in the medical workplace

Richard F. Jones III

The health professions are increasingly aware and alert to the presence of battering in their patients. As reflected in the medical literature and by this conference, a collaborative effort is building in which medicine and the community are intervening for battered women. Yet, paradoxically, the medical community itself permits, if not fosters, abuse in the workplace.

Every person who has gone through formal training in the health profession has experienced this. This is demonstrated by anecdotes that people such as myself, who are administrators and in practice, deal with on a daily basis. It is also demonstrated in published data that examine the unpleasant side of the educational experience of students and residents (Alder 1980; McCue 1982).

We often hear physicians reflect on the rigours and stress of their training years: the long hours, the exhaustion, the time away from home and family. Those times are usually viewed as a rite of passage, as if they must be endured in order to join the guild.

Yet as is often the case when we look back we tend to idealise reality. It is hard to reconcile these recollections of the past with the evidence of personal turmoil in the lives of students and residents. Loneliness, depressive reactions, disrupted marriages, drug abuse, cognitive impairment and suicidal thoughts and actions occur in as many as one-third of this group (McCue 1985).

The personal turmoil of the medical workplace is known to all who work there. Each of us can fill in our own blanks in the equation. Examples are:

(1) Communication problems between physicians; such as between the surgeon and the anaesthetist;

(2) Interactions between the physician and the nurse or between the surgeon and the operating room technician;

(3) Communication between the attending physician and the house officers or students;

(4) Communication between house officers and students.

Most of the time this is verbal, emotional or psychological abuse. Sometimes it is physical abuse and a dark and terrible secret is that too often it is sexual abuse.

Uhari and colleagues (1994) evaluated the physical and psychological mistreatment of medical students at two medical schools in Finland. Three out of every four students reported experiencing some kind of mistreatment during their medical education. Sexual and psychological mistreatment, physical threats and verbal abuse were common.

The American Medical Association asked senior students at ten medical schools in the United States how often, if ever, they perceived themselves being mistreated or harassed during the course of their medical education (Baldwin *et al.* 1992). Results show that perceived mistreatment most often took the form of public humiliation (86.7 per cent), though someone else taking credit for one's work (53.5 per cent), being threatened with unfair grades (34.8 per cent) and threatened with physical harm (26.4 per cent) were also reported. Students also reported high rates of sexual harassment (55 per cent) and pervasive negative comments about entering a career in medicine (91 per cent).

Residents and attending physicians were cited most frequently as sources of this mistreatment. With the exception of more reports of sexual harassment from women students, perceived mistreatment did not differ significantly across variables such as age, sex, religion, marital status or having a physician parent. Scores from the ten schools also did not vary significantly, although the presence of a larger percentage of women in the class appeared to increase overall reports of mistreatment from both sexes.

The author felt that mistreatment and harassment in medical schools was a widespread and common phenomena. Nearly all medical students (96.5 per cent) reported some negative experience of this kind. Residents and attending physicians were most frequently cited as the perpetrators. The study raised questions about why students do not complain and why older physicians deny the existence of the problem. Further, if child abuse is an appropriate analogy, is there the potential for a 'transgenerational legacy', where the observation or actual experience of abuse is the most frequent antecedent of becoming either a perpetrator or victim of abuse? In a hierarchical system the power or control rests in the hands of those above you. The misuse and abuse of this authority is an ever-present danger. Medical training is such a system.

This problem also exists at the residency training level. Komaromy and co-workers (1993) at the University of California in San Francisco mailed questionnaires to 133 internal medicine residents inquiring about sexual harassment. Of female residents, 73 per cent had been sexually harassed during their training. Questionnaire studies are always subject to bias and interpretation and the sample size is small. Further, the 62 per cent response rate raises the issue of whether those who responded are more likely to have been harassed than those who didn't. Nevertheless, a problem exists since, even if none of the non-respondents had been harassed, the incidence would still exceed 50 per cent.

Cook and colleagues (1996) reporting in the Canadian Medical Association Journal found that 93 per cent of respondents (171/184) reported one or more episodes of sexual harassment during their residency programme. Further, they asked with whom the residents confided, if at all, and what reasons were given for not confiding in anyone. Most confided in another resident or friend, some with a physician supervisor but none with a sexual harassment officer. Of interest, the most common reason for not reporting the incident (45 per cent) was that the resident did not think the behaviour was a problem! As expected, however, others felt that some form of retribution might occur.

Abusive behaviour in the workplace is unacceptable. That most of us have experienced it personally or have observed it in our institutions as part of our rite of passage does not sanction its continued existence. What solutions might there be?

The whole subject of domestic violence, workplace violence and sexual harassment is receiving increasing public attention and the law is starting to look at definitions from the victim's perspective. It is not unlike what has happened with informed consent theory. Not long ago the standard in informed consent was 'what should a reasonable physician tell his or her patient?' Now in the US the standard is 'what does a reasonable patient need to know?' (as defined by patients)!

In 1991, an appellate court in the US ruled that sexual harassment must be judged from the perspective of a reasonable woman since 'conduct that many men consider unobjectionable may offend many women' (*Ellison v Brady* 1991). No longer will harassment be defined by the perpetrator. Hence, there are legal methods that can be used but, although various penalties may provide a deterrent effect, prevention, as in all crimes, is ultimately more satisfactory.

The essence of prevention must be education and training. Each institution should have periodic lectures on sexual harassment with an opportunity for open discussion. This should be coupled with an institutional commitment to ending this problem. Department leadership and visibility are crucial to the success of such a programme. A reporting and investigating policy should be established. Confidentiality must be maintained to assure privacy for all. Conflict resolution training is known to be helpful and should be implemented. Protocols can be formulated to facilitate anonymous investigation of real and alleged infractions. Sanctions must be put in place for perpetrators. At each step of our very hierarchical professional ladder junior people look to their senior mentors for guidance. How we conduct ourselves in our offices, clinics and operating rooms is noticed by those who follow us. We need to clean our house.

REFERENCES

Alder, R., Werner, E.R. and Kosch, B. (1980) Systematic study of four years of internship. *Pediatrics* **66**, 1000–8

Baldwin, D.C. Jr, Dougherty, S.R. and Eckenfels, E.J. (1992) Student perceptions of mistreatment and harassment during medical school. A survey of ten United States schools. *West J Med* **155**, 140–5

Cook, J.D., Liutkus, J.F., Risdon, C.L., Griffith, L.E., Guyatt, G.H. and Walter, S.D. (1996) Residents' experiences of abuse, discrimination and sexual harassment during residency training. *Can Med Assoc J* **154**, 1657–65

Ellison v Brady (1991) 9th Cir 924F 2d 872

Komaromy, M., Bindman, A.B., Haber, R.J. and Sande, M.A. (1993) Sexual harassment in medical training. *N Eng J Med* **328**, 322–6

McCue, J.D. (1982) The effects of stress on physicians and their medical practice. *N Eng J Med* **306**, 458–63

McCue, J.D. (1985) The distress of internship. Causes and prevention. *N Eng J Med* **312**, 449–52

Uhari, M., Kokkonen, J., Nuutinen, M. *et al.* (1994) Medical student abuse: an international phenomenon. *JAMA* **271**, 1049–51

Chapter 30

Careless talk costs: the limits of confidentiality in histories of violence

Petra Wilson

INTRODUCTION

When the medical profession is expected to deal with violent behaviour amongst people, whether as acts by or against patients or against practitioners, it will be necessary to balance a number of competing interests and rights. Perhaps one of the most difficult interests to balance against other competing interests is that of patient confidentiality. In respecting confidentiality, the practitioner must try to weigh the relative costs and benefits of one individual's safety against respecting another's right to privacy. In this complex procedure only one thing is certain; whatever information is shared must not be shared carelessly.

This chapter will outline the ethical and legal duties which are pertinent to the subject of patient confidentiality. It will then consider the extent to which those duties may affect the decision-making process in which the health care practitioner will have to decide how to treat information concerning violence which has been discovered.

The duty of confidentiality

The principle of medical confidentiality may be defined as a means of reinforcing two fundamental ethical principles: respect for autonomy and the duty of beneficence (British Medical Association 1992; Bok 1983; Beauchamp and Childress 1994). In order to respect the patient as an autonomous person in control of her own destiny, the doctor must respect that the patient retains control over her information, even after she has shared it with her doctor. Yet in order to treat patients to the best of their ability, practitioners must also be in possession of all relevant information concerning their patients' health and must be empowered to act upon that information for the benefit of patients. The correct balance of the two duties lies in understanding when the duty of respect for the autonomy of one patient is outweighed by the duty of beneficence such that information must be shared, even if to do so will amount to a paternalistic act which overrides the autonomy of one or more patients.

How the health care practitioner should strike that balance and should treat information is described, and to some extent regulated, in the ethical codes and legal duties which the practitioner must accept if practice is to be deemed in accordance with professional standards.

The ethical codes

If one accepts the Hippocratic Oath as the cornerstone of medical ethics and the foundation of good clinical practice, then patient confidentiality must surely be a key principle of good medical practice for it states:

> [W]hatever in connection with my professional practice, or not in connection with it, I see or hear in the life of men, which ought not to be spoken of abroad, I will not divulge as reckoning that all should be kept secret.

More modern statements of the principle can be found in the Declaration of Geneva and the International Code of Medical Ethics which state:

> I will respect the secrets which are confided in me even after the patient has died. (Declaration of Geneva)

and

> A doctor owes to his patient complete loyalty. A doctor shall preserve absolute secrecy on all he knows about his patient because of the confidence entrusted in him. (International Code of Medical Ethics)

Taken together, the three statements would seem to suggest that the medical profession continues to regard the principle of confidentiality as important, but not absolute: the words 'ought not to be spread abroad' and 'respect' in the more recent codes are not words which denote an absolute standard.

However, it may be argued that the codes are little more than formulaic shorthand for a commonly espoused, but widely ignored, principle. The extent to which the principle is compromised by routine practice was discussed famously by Siegler (1982) who, on being asked to guarantee the confidentiality of a hospital patient's record, investigated the number of professionals who had had access to the record in question. He found that in a typical American teaching hospital at least 25 and up to 100 health care workers, including administrative staff, routinely had access to patient records. On discovering this Siegler returned to his patient who retorted 'I always believed medical confidentiality was part of a doctor's code of ethics. Perhaps you should tell me just what exactly you people mean by confidentiality'.

The experience reported by Siegler demonstrates that on a daily basis medical practitioners are making the decision to share information and breach confidentiality. In many cases the breach will be minor, or possibly non-existent, since the patient may have accepted that her information would be shared in this way. It is not surprising, therefore, that the bland statements of the ethical codes have remained unchanged for so long and have not evolved into a more sophisticated range of duties which can take account of the varying degrees of respect for patient privacy between which the practitioner must choose and which will now be considered in the context of violence.

The legal duties

If the ethical guidelines are vague and open to much interpretation one might hope that the legal duties of confidentiality imposed on health care professionals would be clearer. However, here again practitioners are left largely to their own devices.

It is important to note that there is no general right to privacy in English law, and that a duty of confidentiality must have arisen in each given situation in order for an individual to be able to claim that a breach of confidentiality has occurred. The most recent legal exposition of situations in which such a duty will be deemed to exist arose as a result of the publication of *Spycatcher*. In the House of Lords case which followed the publication Lord Goff made clear the duty of confidentiality by stating that:

> [A] duty of confidentiality arises when confidential information comes to the knowledge of a person (the confidant) in circumstances where he has notice, or is held to have agreed, that the information is confidential, with the effect that it would be just in all circumstances that he should be precluded from disclosing the information to others. (*Attorney General v Guardian Newspapers Ltd (no 2)* 1988, p. 658)

Notwithstanding the duty as outlined above, Lord Goff went on to add a general limiting factor:

> [A]lthough the basis of the law's protection of confidences is that there is a public interest that confidences should be preserved and protected by law, nevertheless, the public interest may be outweighed by some countervailing public interest which favours disclosure. (*Attorney General v Guardian Newspapers Ltd (no 2)* 1988, p. 659)

It is interesting to note here that although Lord Goff reiterates the principle that confidences should be respected, he does so on the basis that such respect is in the public interest. In contrast to the North American treatment of this issue there is no mention of an individual's interest in her own privacy. Montgomery has noted that this general construction may be used to frame confidentiality in such a way that it may, in certain circumstances, be impossible for an individual to make a personal claim for the privacy of her medical record (Montgomery 1990).

The principle of confidentiality is further defined by three pre-requisites, all approved in *Spycatcher*:

(1) The information must have the necessary quality of confidence about it;

(2) The information must be imparted in circumstances importing an obligation of confidence;

(3) There must be unauthorised use of the information to the detriment of the party or parties concerned.

In *Spycatcher* their Lordships did not agree as to the extent to which detriment must be shown,[1] although they did accept that in cases of medical confidence the principle is, in itself, so important that a breach of confidence is detrimental, even if no immediate damage results.

Thus it is established in law and medical ethics that there is a principle of confidentiality which ought normally to be protected, even if generally the duty is not absolute. Some occasions may arise, however, in which an ethical or even legal duty to breach confidentiality may arise, as in cases where a crime has taken place.

Confidentiality in crime

When a health care practitioner learns in the course of examining a patient that an act of violence has been perpetrated against or by the patient, a criminal act may often be discovered. The possession of such knowledge does not, however, usually impose any duty.

The general position in English law is that there is no duty to reveal information about crimes to the police. Section 5(5) of the Criminal Law Act 1967 translated into statutory law the decision in *Rice v Conolly* (1966) that 'though every citizen has a moral or, if you like, a social duty to assist the police there is no legal duty to that effect' (per Parker L.J. p.414). Furthermore, the police will only be able to seize confidential medical records where an order to do so has been made by a circuit judge. A magistrate may not make such an order (section 9 of the Police and Criminal Evidence Act 1984).

However, while a health care professional may thus claim there is no duty to report a crime, there is not an absolute freedom to withhold information from the police. A health care practitioner cannot claim legal privilege for confidential medical information. The medical record must be revealed if ordered by a court. Failure to allow the court access to medical records may make the health care practitioner guilty of a contempt of court and liable to a fine or imprisonment (*D v NSPCC* 1977).

---

[1] In the House of Lords, Lord Griffiths considered that the element had to be established, Lord Keith thought otherwise, and Lord Goff left the question open, pp. 640, 650, 659.

The lack of legal privilege does not mean, however, that health care practitioners should always give access to a medical record in litigation. The guidance of the General Medical Council (GMC) (1991) states:

> Where litigation is in prospect, unless the patient has consented to disclosure, or a court order has been made, information should not be disclosed by a doctor merely in response to demands made from other people such as a third party's solicitor or an official of the court.

Certain other situations exist in which the doctor is required to divulge information learnt in the course of practice. In *Hunter v Mann* (1974) for example, when a doctor treated a man and woman who said they had been involved in a car accident, but who had failed to report the incident to the police, the police were able to rely on section 168(3) of the Road Traffic Act 1972 in asking the doctor to reveal the identity of the two patients:

> Where the driver of a vehicle is alleged to be guilty of an offence to which this subsection applies .... (b) any other person shall if required as aforesaid give any information which is in his power to give and which may lead to the identification of the driver.

Thus, where a health care professional discovers that an act of violence has occurred there is a legal obligation to give that information to the police only in very limited circumstances. Ethically, however, it may be considered right to report such information. Such an occasion may arise where the violence learnt of in an interaction with a patient gives rise to concerns for the health and safety of other individuals.

CONFIDENTIALITY IN THE FACE OF RISK TO THE HEALTH OR SAFETY OF A PERSON

When doctors are required by law to breach the confidentiality of the doctor/ patient relationship they will not have to attempt to balance the competing ethical duties described above. In the majority of cases, however, no such legal duty will arise and evidence of violence to a woman will bring with it a competing set of interests. Fears about the future health of the woman or other people will, in particular, demand careful ethical reasoning. In some cases the risks will be so great that the balance will be struck easily, in others it will be much more difficult. Below, a series of scenarios is used to depict the shades of grey between the doctor's duty to respect autonomy on the one hand, and to act beneficently on the other.

Case 1

Alison seeks the advice of her doctor following an act by an unknown assailant during which she was bitten. Tests reveal that viral hepatitis was transmitted to Alison.

Where the doctor makes a diagnosis of a disease classified as a notifiable disease under the Public Health (Control of Diseases) Act 1984, there is a legal requirement to report the diagnosis to the relevant authorities. Since viral hepatitis is such a disease, the diagnosis will have to be reported. The attack itself need not be reported, although the name of the assailant (if known) could be given to the authorities so that they may advise treatment.

Where a non-notifiable venereal disease is transmitted, the identity of the patient should be protected, but the name of the assailant may be given as the source of infection for the appropriate contact tracing to take place according to the NHS (Venereal Diseases) Regulations 1974.

Case 2

Bryony seeks the advice of her doctor after a violent attack by her partner. In the course of the examination it becomes evident that Bryony, her daughter Celia and her partner's former wife Denise, are all at serious risk of further attacks.

In the course of the examination Bryony will give a certain amount of information to her doctor and other health care workers both orally and simply as a result of her presentation.

The first task of the practitioner faced with the potential risk to Bryony, Celia and Denise, will be to explain the need to pass on information about the attack to other professionals who may help all three parties at risk. Thus the health care practitioner might:

(1) Counsel Bryony to inform the police so that they may apprehend the partner;

(2) Inform Celia's school so that they may prevent the partner from gaining access; and

(3) Inform Denise personally.

If Bryony will not share such information herself she may, of course, consent to her doctor passing on the information to the relevant parties. Such sharing of information as is necessary may be passed on without any question of a breach of confidence, although doctors should be careful that they have good reason to believe that the accused perpetrator committed the crime before involving outside agencies.

Furthermore, although it is highly logical to accept that if a patient waives her right of confidentiality, information may be shared, a doctor should accept that the concept of consent is not uncomplicated. Consent in medicine will always beg questions of capacity, power structure in the relationship, and informed consent. As when a practitioner seeks to rely on the consent of a patient, in adherence to the Sidaway principle,[2] the practitioner must ensure that the patient understands what she is consenting to and also must ensure that the consent to breach of confidentiality is not a result of duress by any other party.

If, however, Bryony withholds consent to the sharing of information, then the doctor will have to very carefully balance Bryony's interest in confidentiality with the risks to Celia, Denise and Bryony herself.

Celia's potential risk is perhaps intuitively the easiest to deal with since she is still a child and is arguably the most vulnerable. However there is no easy solution to the problem as, contrary to popular belief, there is no special legal exception to the general duty of confidentiality for the protection of children at risk of violence. However, the guidance of the Joint Working Party on Child Protection (1993) advises that where a child is at risk, the child's interests must always be regarded as paramount and will usually require disclosure to the relevant authority.

Thus, although Celia's case might be slightly easier to decide, with respect to both Celia and Denise the doctor must ask if their risk outweighs Bryony's right of confidentiality. The question is therefore 'is there a public interest in breaching confidentiality?'

Both the legal and ethical starting points are that disclosure in the public interest may be justified only rarely (General Medical Council 1995). If a doctor wants to override Bryony's wishes, she should assure herself as much as possible that Celia and Denise are at risk and that disclosure will help protect them from such risk. In making this decision three decided legal cases may help.

The first decision was in the American case of *Tarasoff v Regents of the University of California* (1976) which involved a man, Poddar, who expressed fantasies of killing Tarasoff during therapy at the University Hospital. The psychiatrist was very concerned about Poddar's propensity to violence and attempted to have him detained in hospital, but was unsuccessful. Some two months later Poddar killed Tarasoff. Tarasoff's parents successfully sued the University for failing to warn her of the risk.

---

[2] *Sidaway v Bethlem Royal Hospital Governors* (1984) This case concerned a woman who underwent surgery to relieve pain in her neck and shoulders. The doctor told her of the possibility of disturbing a nerve and the possible consequences of this. She claimed he did not tell her of the risk of damage to the spinal cord and its consequences. Such damage arose and the woman was partially paralysed and sued the doctor for negligent failure to inform her of the risks of the operation. The law as it stands now is that the doctor must give the patient as much warning of possible consequences of treatment as a reasonable doctor would.

The key question for current purposes is whether a similar decision would be reached by the English courts and therefore whether a duty to warn parties at risk exists. Applying the decided English cases and the opinion of scholars (Jones 1990; Mackay 1990), it would seem that the same facts would not give rise to a duty in English law, because there was a lack of proximity between the psychiatrist and the party at risk. Therefore, in order for a *Tarasoff*-type duty to inform to exist in the current scenario, it must be shown that the doctor owes a duty of care to Celia and Denise and that the risk is sufficiently great.

On the first issue it could be argued that Bryony's doctor would owe a duty of care to Celia, since she is the child of a patient. Similarly, if Denise is registered with the same doctor then a duty could be owed to her also. On the second issue the decision in *Hill v Chief Constable of West Yorkshire* (1988) is of some assistance. In that case the mother of a victim of Peter Sutcliffe (the Yorkshire ripper) attempted to sue the Chief Constable of the enquiry for failing to exercise reasonable care and thus putting her daughter at risk. The Court held, however, that the police owed no specific duty to the victim who could not have been known to them. By analogy the doctor would have to anticipate a high degree of risk that Byrony's partner would injure Denise, for any duty to arise. If, furthermore, the doctor to whom Bryony had disclosed the attack believed that not only Celia and Denise, but also other people to whom she owed no duty of care were at risk, she might argue that a relevant authority should be notified notwithstanding Bryony's refusal. In such a situation the decision in *W v Egdell* (1989) might be helpful.

W v Egdell concerned a patient who was serving a sentence in a hospital for the manslaughter of five neighbours. He was diagnosed as suffering from paranoid schizophrenia. After ten years he applied for appeal to the Mental Health Tribunal with a view to transfer to another secure unit and ultimate conditional release. His solicitors instructed Dr Egdell to make a psychiatric report on W. After examination Egdell wrote a report which suggested that W might have paranoid psychosis rather than schizophrenia and that therefore the drug treatment was less likely to work. On the basis of the report the solicitors withdrew the application to the tribunal. Dr Egdell, however, sent a copy of the report to the hospital and urged them to send a copy to the Home Secretary. The Home Secretary referred W's case to a mental health tribunal and sent a copy of the report to the hospital where he was held. W sought an injunction to stop the board using the information as well as damages against the hospital and Home Secretary for sending the report. It was held at first instance that Egdell's duty was not to W alone. Given the nature of the patient and his condition, the doctor had a duty to the public to inform the relevant authorities about his condition. The Court of Appeal agreed that the judge at first instance had struck the correct balance between the two duties.

W v Egdell may be used, therefore, to argue that the common good of the general public might justify breach of confidentiality. Accordingly the attack on Bryony could, in certain circumstances, justifiably be reported notwithstanding Bryony's refusal of consent. However, the same concept of public good might also be used to issue an injunction against the breach of a confidence. *X v Y and Others* (1988) is a case of a health authority against a newspaper. One or more of the employees of the health authority had supplied the newspaper with information concerning two doctors being treated in a hospital in the health authority area. The information identified the doctors by name and stated that they were continuing to practise despite receiving treatment for AIDS. In reaching their decision that the newspaper could not publish the names of the doctors, the court held that confidentiality must be preserved in the interests of the public protection, not in the interests of the individuals involved.

The cases discussed above will also be of relevance in deciding if the doctor may override Bryony's refusal of consent to share information, in order to protect Bryony herself. This may even be the case if Bryony were to argue that she had consented to the acts of violence (*R v Brown* 1993). However, if Bryony's capacity to withhold her consent is not questionable, it would be very hard to justify such a disclosure for her safety, since the autonomy of the patient is accepted to extend to situations where she makes decisions which are potentially harmful to herself:

> [E]very adult has the right and capacity to decide whether or not he will accept medical treatment, even if a refusal may risk permanent injury to his health or even lead to premature death ... it matters not whether the reasons for the refusal were rational or irrational, unknown or even non-existent'. Lord Donaldson in *Re T (Adult: Refusal of Treatment)* 1992, p. 799.

Case 3

Ellie, after a sexual assault by an unknown assailant is diagnosed HIV positive by a GUM clinic. Ellie does not wish her HIV status to be included on her medical notes to be sent to her GP.

The issues to be considered in this situation have to a certain extent already been considered with respect to *X v Y* discussed above, in which the general public interest in confidentiality in HIV and AIDS cases was shown. In this case, however, two further issues arise:

(1) Can the GP care adequately for Ellie without knowing all the facts? and

(2) Is the GP at any personal risk if ignorant of Ellie's HIV status?

The GMC Guidelines on HIV and AIDS (1995) argue that with adequate counselling a patient like Ellie might be persuaded to allow transfer of the information. Where this cannot be achieved, the GMC argue that where risk to the health of the treating health care team can be identified they must be informed of such risk. Similarly, where a patient cannot be persuaded to protect her sexual partner from risk, he too should be informed if a real risk can be identified. On this point it should be noted, however, that while such warning of sexual partners may protect the partners, it has been shown in one American study to put the HIV-positive woman at a significant risk of domestic violence (Rothenberg and Paskey 1995).

CONCLUSION

The discussion above has shown that a wide range of ethical and legal duties will have to be balanced when violence is revealed in the course of a consultation. Focusing on the balance between the principles of autonomy and beneficence, it has been shown that the decision is largely left to the clinical ethical judgement of the practitioner rather than absolute legal duties.

The discussion has not considered the problems of confidentiality which can arise when the violence in question happens within the health care setting: when patients injure patients or staff, or when acts of violence are perpetrated by staff against colleagues or patients. These issues have not been considered because they are primarily questions of common law duties of care and health and safety legislation. Health care practitioners are required to ensure that they are offering their services in a safe manner and are providing a safe place of work for employees. Confidentiality may be an issue where the act of violence prompts one health care worker to want to report another to the appropriate authorities. In such cases of whistleblowing it may be necessary to use patients' confidential information to substantiate a claim and accordingly the duties outlined above will have to be considered (McHale 1993).

Whatever the situation which gave rise to the violence, it is vital that the conduct of the practitioners in dealing with its consequences do not add to the injuries by careless talk amongst themselves. The finding of Weiss's study (1982) of 177 patients and 109 hospital doctors showed that while 18 per cent patients believed a doctor would discuss patients at parties, 80 per cent medical staff reported doing so. This must not be replicated.

REFERENCES

Attorney General v Guardian Newspapers Ltd (no 2) [1988] 3 All ER 545
Beauchamp, T.L. and J. F. Childress (1994) *Principles of Biomedical Ethics.* London: Oxford University Press
Bok, S. (1983) 'The Limits of Confidentiality' *The Hastings Centre Report.* February 24–31
British Medical Association (1992) *Rights and Responsibilities of Doctors.* London: BMJ
D v NSPCC (1977) 1 All ER 589
General Medical Council (1991) *Duties of a Doctor; Guidance from the GMC.* London: General Medical Council
General Medical Council (1995) *Duties of a Doctor; Guidance from the GMC.* London: General Medical Council

Hill v Chief Constable of West Yorkshire [1989] AC 53

Hunter v Mann [1974] QB 767

Joint Working Party of the Department of Health, British Medical Association and Conference of Medical Royal Colleges (1993) *Child Protection: Medical Responsibilities* London: BMA

Jones, M. (1990) Medical confidentiality in the public interest. *Professional Negligence* **6**, 16–24

Mackay, G. (1990) Dangerous patients: walking the Tarasoff tightrope. *Med Sci Law* **30**, 52–6

McHale, J. (1993) Whistleblowing in the NHS. *Journal of Social Welfare and Family Law* **6**, 52–7

Montgomery, J. (1990) Victims of threats – the framing of HIV. *Liverpool Law Review* **12**, 25–53

R v Brown (1993) 2 All ER 75

Re T (Adult: Refusal of Treatment) [1992] 3 WLR 782 at 799

Rice v Conolly [1966] 2 QB 414

Rothenberg, K. and Paskey, S. (1995) The risk of domestic violence and women with HIV: implications of partner notification. *Am J Public Health* **85**, 1569–76

Sidaway v Bethlem Royal Hospital Governors [1984] 1 All ER 643.

Siegler, M. (1982) Confidentiality in medicine –a decrepit concept. *New Eng J Med* **307**, 1518–21

Tarasoff v Regents of the University of California [1976] 131 CR 14

W v Egdell [1990] 1 All ER 385

Weiss, B. (1982) Confidentiality expectations of patients, physicians and medical students. *JAMA* **247**, 2695–7

X v Y and Others [1988] 2 All ER 648

SECTION 9

FUTURE DIRECTION

Chapter 31

Training the specialist

Richard F. Jones III

Although domestic violence has existed for centuries, the medical community has not viewed it as a public health issue until recently. The American College of Obstetricians and Gynecologists' (ACOG) involvement began in 1985 when a portion of the annual clinical meeting (ACM) was devoted to it. Later that year the ACOG President, Luella Klein, participated in the Surgeon General's workshop on domestic violence. Since then, the ACOG has devoted enormous time, energy and resources into the education of its physician members and their patients.

Following is a chronology of our programme on family violence:

1985

Scientific Session on Violence in Women's Lives at ACM;

ACOG Past President Luella Klein, meets with Surgeon General Koop and HHS staff to explore the depth of the domestic violence problem and to consider ACOG involvement in a national campaign against domestic violence;

Luella Klein participates in the Surgeon General's Workshop on Violence and Public Health.

1987

Technical Bulletin (101) entitled 'Sexual Assault' released;

ACOG collaborates with the National Coalition Against Domestic Violence to publicise national awareness month;

ACOG Committees view March of Dimes (MOD) video on 'Battering During Pregnancy'; ACOG staff reviews MOD health professionals training resources;

ACOG newsletter article publicises the issue, gives a hotline phone number and offers a bibliography compiled by the Public Health Service;

ACOG participates in the Shelter Aid program: a reception, press conference, and screening of a television programme on domestic violence;

ACOG Government Relations Department co-sponsors a national legislative briefing on Capitol Hill.

1988

ACM includes a Scientific Session on domestic violence which is reported in the ACOG newsletter;

At an awards ceremony in Washington, DC, the ACOG is recognised by Shelter Aid for contributions in publicising domestic violence issues;

ACOG Government Relations Department prepares a legislative briefing for the National Conference of State Legislatures, later repeated at several district meetings;

Interview with Fellow in American Medical Association (AMA) News regarding ACOG's efforts to address domestic violence issues.

1989

ACOG publishes a Technical Bulletin entitled 'The Battered Woman', and distributes it to all Fellows;

ACOG publishes Patient Education pamphlet 'The Abused Woman' and distributes it to all Fellows;

Rolodex card with 24-hour toll-free hotline number mailed to all Fellows;

Resources on domestic violence published in the ACOG newsletter;

Press conference with Dr Koop, Surgeon General, and Luella Klein;

Washington Post editorial commends ACOG for its involvement and for bringing the issue of domestic violence to the attention of Fellows.

1990

ACOG Guidelines on crisis intervention for domestic violence included in PRÉCIS IV (1990).

1991

Committee on Adolescent Health Care prepares a committee opinion on violence in adolescent dating;

Dr Richard Jones III, President Elect, convenes a focus session to brainstorm on the topic of the Presidential Initiative;

ACOG co-sponsors (with National Women's Health Resource Center) a one-day conference on violence against women, Washington, DC.

1992–1993

ACOG President Dr Richard Jones III, identifies domestic violence as priority for his tenure and delivers a keynote address charging Fellows to educate themselves and to become involved;

Short- and long-term goals set for ACOG activities against domestic violence;

ACOG continues to highlight the issue in publications and continues to distribute resources upon request;

Council on Resident Education in Obstetrics and Gynecology (CREOG) incorporates domestic violence into its curricula.

1993

ACM features President's Program dedicated to domestic violence issues. Topics cover legal, social, and health aspects of violence in women's lives;

ACOG produces continuing medical education video on domestic violence which is distributed to Fellows by Searle and featured at the ACM;

Public information packet is compiled for distribution;

Dr Richard Jones III completes media tours with reporters in over 20 cities and 65 members of the ACOG tape radio interviews to air across the country in October. The interviews focus on the prevention of family violence and the role of the obstetrician-gynaecologist. ACOG issues a 'Woman's Health' column for publication in 1,400 newspapers;

ACOG produces 'You Are Not Alone' campaign with posters, tent cards, and patient education materials distributed to all Fellows.

1994

ACOG co-sponsors with AMA and the National Institute on Justice a national conference on domestic violence;

ACOG newsletter highlights upcoming National Domestic Violence Awareness Month.

1995

Family Violence Work Group established;

Pocket cards with safety plans printed and distributed during ACM; plans developed to mail to all Fellows and other interested individuals and institutions;

ACOG requests a pharmaceutical company to donate money from its 'Women's Health Walk' to a local shelter and advocacy organisations at the ACM;

ACOG updates the technical bulletin and distributes it to all ACOG Fellows;

ACOG Family Violence Work Group develops a medical education slide lecture and distributes it to all obstetric and gynaecology Residency Program Directors and Department Chairs.

1996

ACOG reprints pocket cards with a new national hotline number and begins development of Spanish language pocket card with hotline numbers;

ACOG receives an educational grant to conduct a day-long workshop on domestic violence for more than 200 obstetric and gynaecology residents. The workshop was held in conjunction with the ACM;

ACOG receives an educational grant to send a Family Violence Work Group member to present a slide lecture at each District Annual Meeting;

ACOG Past President Dr Richard Jones III is invited to present the Plenary Session on violence against women at the 1997 FIGO World Congress in Copenhagen, Denmark;

Dr Richard Jones III is invited to submit an article on violence against women to the International Journal of Gynecology and Obstetrics;

Family Violence Work Group co-chair Ronald Chez is invited to present ACOG slide lecture at the annual CREOG directors' retreat;

ACOG distributes a survey on domestic violence screening practices to 1400 randomly selected members;

ACOG newsletter features an article about the new national hotline.

1997

ACOG invited and agrees to serve as sponsor for major national conference on domestic violence to be held in autumn, 1997. Other sponsors include: the American College of Nurse Midwives, Maternity Centers of America, and the March of Dimes;

ACOG releases a Spanish language pocket card with toll-free national hotline numbers;

ACOG releases Spanish language posters and tent cards;

ACOG receives an educational grant to conduct an educational workshop on domestic violence for more than 200 obstetric and gynaecology residents. The workshop is conducted in conjunction with the ACM;

ACOG develops and distributes rolodex cards with toll-free hotline numbers to all members. The cards provide additional guidance and direction on screening;

Plenary session on violence against women presented at FIGO. Past President Dr Richard Jones III serves as co-chair of the panel.

The ACOG felt that the understanding of domestic violence was an educational imperative that was fundamentally no different from an understanding about the evils of cigarette smoking from a public health perspective. Educators have understood that behaviour is strongly influenced by the interaction between knowledge, values and skills. These can be taught didactically and by example. From a didactic point of view, classroom teaching must cover definitions, statistics, dynamics, ethics and a historical perspective. Further, students must be taught how to incorporate their knowledge into the standard history and physical exam. Finally, they must learn about triage skills (acute versus chronic problems) and management options. Community resources, telephone numbers and the like are all part of classroom teaching. Yet it is well known that our students are very perceptive, therefore teachers must practise what they preach. Grand rounds and case presentations provide an opportunity to experience real-life tragedies in a clinical setting and at the same time these presentations send a strong message to the students that the clinical department has accepted this issue as a legitimate concern and responsibility of the practitioner. A departmental facilitator can be helpful in keeping this issue always in mind.

Obstetrics and gynaecology clinics, the delivery room and the emergency room must be safe places for victims. This must be insisted upon by physician leaders. In addition, the abuse of patients, nurses, students and residents must not be tolerated in our medical schools and hospitals. This is not just the right thing to do, it also is the right model for our students to come to expect. Finally, our various educational bodies have provided further motivation for students to learn. The learning objectives of CREOG and the oversight of the RRC (Residency Review Committee) mandate that there will be education on domestic violence in our training programmes. Further, our Board exams, written, oral and recertification all have questions on this topic. Failure to become Board-certified has significant professional and financial implications for the practitioner. This provides further motivation to learn the basic clinical skills which are required to manage patients who are victims of domestic violence.

Note: Educational materials are available through the resource centre at the American College of Obstetricians and Gynecologists, 409 12th Street, South West Washington DC, 20024/2188, USA.

REFERENCES

The American College of Obstetricians and Gynecologists (1990) *PRÉCIS IV: an update in obstetrics and gynecology.* Washington, DC: The American College of Obstetricians and Gynecologists

Chapter 32

Future direction

Discussion

Mezey: My first point is about sexual harassment. I have been involved in a number of cases, giving psychiatric evidence. Sexual harassment is, legally, a form of sex discrimination. We are talking about behaviour which is gender-based and which creates a hostile environment for the individual based on their gender.

It is not enough to have a psychopathic doctor who chucks nursing staff across the room. One has to demonstrate that he would throw only a female nurse across the room, rather than throwing anybody who comes in his way. That is the problem with some people who behave badly in the workplace, because they are prima donnas or psychopaths or whatever, and who behave badly with everyone, regardless of gender. Therefore, sexual harassment is not the issue for those individuals. You might go for actual bodily harm, but you cannot go for sexual harassment.

The second point is that it is the employer's responsibility to provide a forum where women who feel harassed in the workplace can report their experiences. It is the employer's responsibility to ensure that those experiences are heard and conveyed, and that they act on those reports. There are a number of cases in which I have been involved where organisations have not heeded reports by women of sexual harassment, and have been taken to the cleaners in terms of having to pay up. It may not be very long before health authorities realise that, if you treat women in a disrespectful way which is offensive to them because of their gender, then it will actually cost money. It is also unwise because of all sorts of other personal problems such as days lost because of going off sick, and time costs for the organisation for re-training.

We should not simply look at sexual harassment in terms of physical violence. There are many subtle forms of sexual harassment, the putting down of women, the glass ceiling, and language that is used. I have seen many patients where the doctor refers to 29-year-old women as 'girls'. There is the fact that there are so few senior women in the professions. What is going on? It is not just violence we need to look at, but we should look at all kinds of discrimination against women in the workplace.

Finally, when we talk about abuse of women as professionals, we must not forget that a good deal of genuine abuse of patients takes place by professionals and by doctors. Patients *are* abused by professionals. It is not just between colleagues that this sort of behaviour goes on.

Hepburn: These are observations for Petra Wilson, but I would welcome her comments. One of the areas we end up discussing frequently on the question of confidentiality is subjectivity. We have already touched on that today when we were talking about consent to examinations. We could be reasonably objective when we list why we want to do an examination, or why we might want to breach confidentiality, but the necessity to do these things becomes very subjective. So our idea of what is essential might not be the same as somebody else's.

We find this with situations where people want to breach confidentiality. You might tell someone why you think it is important to pass on information, but they might not agree with you about the importance. We also find that within different professional groups there are different interpretations. The obstetricians, midwives, health visitors, GPs, social workers, drugs workers and the police all have different interpretations of what is required by confidentiality.

Some people perceive that the General Medical Council (GMC) guidelines, specifically with regard to HIV diagnosis, tell us that we should never breach confidentiality, except in overwhelming situations, whereas others see the fact that it tells you you can do it in overwhelming situations as a sanction to let people do it (General Medical Council 1995). The subjectivity in deciding how significant the circumstances are is an issue we never quite manage to resolve.

Wilson: In making the balance, you have competing duties. When you are breaching confidentiality, it is about balancing competing duties. Much as I would like to be able to tell you that there is a clear law which tells you how to make that balance, there is not. The only way you can make that balance is through workshops, learning and discussing cases as much as possible. Of course, discussing cases confidentially!

There are particular issues. HIV led me into this area of work. It was through doing work in HIV that I did an increasing amount of work on confidentiality, and how I eventually ended up at the European Commission. Confidentiality in HIV is probably the best teaching example we have, because it becomes an issue of balancing risks and looking carefully at the sort of information that we still have to be extra careful about.

One issue you alluded to, which arose in Richard Jones's discussion, is what to do where there is abuse in the workplace. In order to blow the whistle on your colleague, you may have to use patients' confidential in-formation. That will be really difficult. Reporting an abusive colleague might be one situation. Another situation might be protecting a colleague against some other risk, perhaps HIV, that they might be under. I know that opens another can of worms.

Making the decision and deciding how you will blow the whistle on a colleague, or how you will warn a colleague about a risk they have, calls you to examine very carefully exactly why you are passing that information on. You need to work out the cost/benefit analysis, that balance, very carefully. I cannot stress enough how important it is to make that balance in each case, and it is most unfortunate that there is no good guideline anywhere.

Hepburn: On the question of different professional groups interpreting it differently, we usually end up saying that there are no legal differences in how we are all constrained. There are more ethical, moral or professional obligations. How do you deal with the question of different professions' obligations?

Wilson: There is one interesting legal difference. The United Kingdom Central Council for Nursing Health Visiting and Midwifery regulates how nurses and midwives can pass on information slightly differently. They have one very useful clause which states that you cannot pass on information for managerial ease. That is another point which needs to be taken on board. It is the only professional code I know of which says that you cannot pass on information just because it makes it easier to manage the patient, or to manage financial affairs.

There are possibly subtle differences between the ways in which different professions handle information. It particularly becomes an issue when you are dealing with a profession which concentrates on child welfare, because a whole new dynamic is brought into play.

Hepburn: One of the specific problems is that the health visitors we work with often feel that they are legally obliged to report when they think a child is at risk, whereas the doctors and midwives do not. Various others do not seem to be sure whether they should report or not.

Wilson: There is a great deal of misinformation about exactly when a legal duty to report exists, which makes it clear how much education is needed in this area.

Jones: When you are trying to balance beneficence, autonomy and maleficence, the institutional ethics committee can sometimes give you a little objectivity. That is what we resort to at home. We take these sorts of conundrums to the ethics committee. There is a lawyer there, and an ethicist and other physicians, and it is somewhat helpful.

Kerr-Wilson: One problem is that we do not all have institutional ethics committees. All hospitals have research ethics committees, but they do not all deal with such problems as this. Most of the Colleges and national organisations have such committees. There are an increasing number of institutional ethics committees, but not invariably.

S. Bewley: Some of us are very suspicious of them anyway, if it is just washing the hands of the health professional's duty.

Yearnshire: In our region, the teachers and the health workers view for child abuse, and then they will report back to their seniors who will have a multi-disciplinary group meeting on that child. Whether that is a local arrangement or not, it seems to work very well.

Everything Petra Wilson said is spot on, but, when the wheel comes off, the person who has made the wrong decision is absolutely crucified. That is when you start getting guidelines. It is a minefield.

Edwards: I wanted to pick up on the spirit of Gillian Mezey's comments in part response to Richard Jones's paper. This afternoon we will again consider recommendations, and this must always be underscored with creating a cultural climate.

Back to the whole issue of sexual harassment. We could have as much policy and as much law as possible. I accept that it will cost local authorities a great deal of money. But women are still very silent and will remain silent. We certainly know that we only have to turn to the North and we can think about what happens to assistant chief constables, and what happens to female obstetricians, without naming anybody in particular. It is not just talking about sexual harassment if they challenge their organisations. We can lay down what policy we like. From policing experience, with a great deal of police policy on domestic violence and on wider issues, we have found that it does not necessarily change attitudes. It does in time, but we should not think that making recommendations or setting and laying down policy will be some wonderful magic wand which will change everything overnight. It is the cultural climate, the culture and the attitudes which have to be confronted and changed.

In a way, it is adding to the wonderful strides Richard Jones has made, but also being inspired by his eloquent overview of the issues relating to sexual harassment amongst professionals in this country, and the great difficulties.

Spence: There is an additional issue alongside what Gill Mezey has said, about what happens to some female medical students during their training. In my work as head of the counselling service at the university where I am based, I am sometimes very shocked, not by the level of harassment, because I would not put it as boldly as that, but by the degree of bullying of female medical students by male medical students.

It is a very difficult place to be in relation to confidentiality because, as a counsellor, I cannot do anything unless the student decides to take it somewhere. We have developed a friendly set of professors and senior members of staff with whom the students can discuss these issues. It is not satisfactory, but, as stated earlier, the definition and the response has to be the woman's, or the man's, and has to start from where they are.

It poses all sorts of institutional problems, particularly when we see this played out right at the beginning of people's medical careers, and then possibly the whole way through the system.

Harwin: Picking up on the limits to confidentiality, I do not know how medical guidelines and codes work. If confidentiality is breached, is it made clear to women, particularly in situations of domestic violence, that it will be? Are they informed that it is going to be breached before it is? For us, that is a key issue. Our confidentiality in refuges, certainly our good practice model, says quite clearly that there will be times, particularly in relation to child protection issues, when it is not possible to continue to protect a child by supporting the non-abusing parent, who is usually the mother, and that referrals will have to be made. In some areas, we have joint agreements with social services departments. The confidentiality policy states quite clearly that women are told in advance that:

(1) If this information is disclosed, then it may have to be passed on; and

(2) If it is felt necessary to pass it on, then they are told before it is passed on.

Is there a similar principle?

Yearnshire: I have a similar comment on Siobhan Lloyd's point. Certainly in respect of sexual harassment, the harassment is as perceived by the person themselves. We have made a duty on our supervision that if they observe it, they are to do something about it. Sometimes the victim does not know what to do, does not want to do it, and does not bring attention to themselves, but that does not let the supervisors off the hook not to deal with it.

Crowley: Let me back you 100 per cent on that. Things happened to me when I was a trainee in the specialty which I tolerated at the time but, looking back, years later, sitting exactly at this spot, I can recall what I was asked in my oral examination for my membership examination. I now see it for what it was, which was sexual harassment. At the time, I was intent on passing the exam, and whatever question I had to answer, I was going to answer it and pass my exam.

Similarly now, I observe female residents who are undoubtedly being sexually harassed, and they think it is all good fun and part of getting on with their careers. I see it as harassment, and they do not.

Wilson: Nicola Harwin asked whether, in a medical setting, patients know when their information is going to be used and their confidentiality breached.

I do now know the answer in a hospital. In general practice the guidelines say that doctors are supposed to make patients aware of how information is handled within that practice.

I recently finished a study involving 1493 patients and 306 GPs. Ninety per cent of the GPs said that they discuss confidentiality with their patients at the first interview, when the patient registers and that they displayed posters and/or had leaflets about confidentiality. Of the patients who responded, only nine per cent had any notion of what the duty of confidentiality was, or could ever recall having seen posters, which *were* there in the surgeries. I went to the surgeries and I saw that the posters were there, but the patients were not taking it in. It is very important that patients are educated about what confidentiality is in a medical setting and what its limits are, otherwise we cannot talk about consenting to sharing information.

C. Bewley: Siobhan Lloyd made a point about educating male and female students together. It is very well documented that in situations where there are mixed groups, then attention is more often given to what the male students have to say, than to what the female students have to say. It is very common for women to be sitting next to a male student, to tell him something of interest, and then for that man to voice it as his own. In fact, in midwifery, where we have very few male students, it presents quite a challenge when, in a mixed group, the male student frequently will speak more than the female students. Attention is given to him, and it is difficult to maintain that man's integrity and dignity while at the same time ensuring that everyone has an equal share of education opportunities.

Mezey: In relation to Nicola Harwin's question, I deal with perpetrators, and have always told them if I was going to breach a confidentiality. That usually means that, if somebody makes a threat in my hearing that they intend to attack somebody or want to kill somebody, I will then inform them that I will contact that individual in person. I will do that while they are in the office, if that is what they want, and I will inform them of what has just been said. That is slightly different, but I would have thought the same principles would apply with seeing individuals who report violence. You should always inform them that that is what you are going to do, and why you intend to do it. That is probably the courageous and right way to proceed.

I have a quick comment on Stephanie Yearnshire's remarks. I do not think the onus is on the observer to report sexual harassment. Very often in working environments which are hostile and where there is a great deal of sexual harassment, the observer is very much a part of the oppressed and powerless group that has no voice. Talking to women who have been in that sort of environment, there is often a sense that 'There but for the grace of God go I. It is happening to that woman, but I had better not speak out. I will not put my head above the parapet because bad things will happen to me.'

It is rather like the situation of victims of domestic violence and victims of abuse in families. It is often very difficult for them to speak out. It should not be their sole responsibility, but the organisation should create an environment where that kind of behaviour is simply not tolerated, and, when it is detected, it is acted upon effectively. The perpetrator should be punished or removed from the cnvironment, not the woman who is generally in a much lower status position.

Yearnshire: I meant supervisor. If I said observer, I apologise. I meant it was the supervisor's job, the sergeant or the inspector.

Stevens: You used both words, but the classic example is that a couple of weeks ago I was at a surgical rotation interview committee at which there was an ageing gent to my right, who was usually conspicuous by his absence. I had never met him in a year and a half working at the hospital because he was always doing private practice. We had seven female candidates, which was nice, and he laid into all of them about whether they were serious about this career path and whether they realised how difficult it was going to be. After he had done this about twice, to my disbelief, I laid into him. If you do not do something, you do not stop it. I hope I will not see him again until he retires. I am not his favourite person, but you have to tackle it, and sometimes it is only the seniors who can do that.

Hepburn: Going back to confidentiality, we find that it is one of the challenges, but it is not an insurmountable problem in multi-disciplinary working. At least if we all know amongst the different groups who work together how we interpret confidentiality, then we can tell women in advance that we will share information in a different way because of different people's perceptions. We can offer women advice in advance about how we would pass on information, and then you can avoid the crisis if they have been warned in advance about the limits.

We find it is a problem, however, that women will come to us and tell us about people who have breached confidentiality. They may have told them that they are going to breach it, but they do not tell the women until after they have given the information. That is much more difficult, because the women cannot take the information back.

Cameron: On disclosure, according to the GMC on confidentiality (1995):

Disclosure in the patient's medical interest: If you are convinced that it is essential in the patient's medical interest, you may disclose relevant information to an appropriate person or authority. You must tell the person before disclosing any information. If you believe a patient to be a victim of neglect or physical or sexual abuse, and unable to give or withhold consent to disclosure, you should usually give information to an appropriate responsible person or statutory agency in order to prevent further harm to the patient. In these, and similar circumstances, you may release information without the patient's consent.

S. Bewley: Also in the GMC guidelines (1995) there is the catch-all, saying that whenever you do it, be prepared to defend yourself. A complaint can go to the GMC, although not many do. At all times, your judgement may be questioned. So that keeps a barrier on us.

Richardson: The British Medical Association has fairly recently produced a book on ethics which I have found much more helpful than the GMC guidance (British Medical Association 1993). It gives many more practical examples, but it does emphasise that if you are going to release information without the patient's consent, you really must tell them.

I have found it difficult training male health professionals in, for example, sensitive examinations, in how to deal with domestic violence. If you routinely offer the woman a choice as to who she sees, and she opts to see a woman health professional rather than a man, how do you deal with that? I have found that a particular problem for myself, trying to organise training for male GP registrars.

Thirdly, on the subject of training materials, I have a question to the College about how they are planning to put together their curricula. There appears to be a great deal of terrific stuff which has come out of the American College of Obstetricians and Gynecologists, and I hope we do not feel that we have to re-invent the wheel when it comes to training materials and educational programmes.

Jones: It is there for the taking, so filch away! With regard to confidentiality, we are now entering the era of the electronic record, and confidentiality of the electronic record has all sorts of very complicated implications, even though people have to have access codes.

Recently in our city a very famous international skater, a young Russian girl aged 17 or 18, was in an automobile accident when she was drunk. No one knew she was drunk. She went to the hospital and her alcohol level was checked. She was admitted to the hospital, fortunately, not my hospital, and there were 24 enquiries of her electronic record. Of course, when you make an enquiry of a medical record, you identify yourself, so some of these people were not very clever. Nevertheless 24 people in the hospital, all unauthorised, found out about what had happened to her, and that this girl was drunk. Someone leaked it to the Associated Press. That person no longer works at that hospital. The electronic record is a big problem in medicine.

Wilson: With regard to the electronic patient record (EPR), my job is supposed to be to ensure that all the electronic patient record systems that are developed for use in the European Union can be properly confidential. We have a great deal of problems with that. People should rest assured that we are not going to have an EPR system in this country which is unsafe.

For that reason, it will take us much longer to get there than the National Health Service (NHS) Executive would like. It will take longer than it probably needs to take, but everyone involved is very much aware of the need to get this right. This means getting some resolution with the US about encryption systems.

Friend: I am determined, if nothing else comes out of this, that the College should take on board the idea of training. We need to get together within the College to agree how this can be implemented. I have already plundered and I am pleased to hear that I can plagiarise the American system. I have even used their questions in talking to my patients, but I have changed the spellings slightly.

It struck a note with me when Richard Jones talked about the beds in his hospital which have been funded by charity and are tucked away in a secure, pleasant, sensitive area. I have no doubt that all the doctors around here have admitted, under the NHS from time to time, patients who, although they did not recognise it at the time, were also escaping from a situation at home.

The organisational issue in relation to this is that our hospitals in this country are almost exclusively now what we call 'Trust' hospitals. These Trust hospitals are governed financially by the money they can acquire from the commissioning health authorities, which comes down from the central Department of Health. My point about this is that, when we set up this study group, I thought we should contact NAHAT (National Association of Health Authorities and Trusts), which is an organisation which takes into account both the Trusts and the health authorities. It has now changed its name, but still serves the same function. I made a few contacts to find out whether anyone would like to join us here, but no one appropriate was available.

Should we, as a group, make movements towards this organisation, in terms of helping us to put forward any recommendations? In the American context, have the managerial and administrative side been very helpful in relation to this or not?

Jones: The short answer is yes. They are very helpful. If they think they can get someone else to pay for anything, they are very helpful. The administrators, certainly at our hospital, were very happy to help us contact various agencies which had money to give for this sort of thing. They helped us, and it was very successful.

You do not have these systems here, but the auxiliary (the volunteers at the hospital who raise money for all sorts of charities within the hospital) took this on as an issue. They organised a big dance and a Runathon and a clothes sale – lots of ways to raise money. We used them all. We will do almost anything to make money for this issue.

Mezey: In terms of inclusion on the training programme, we need to have something specifically on gender awareness in training for all health professionals. That is a much broader subject than simply domestic violence, or violence against women.

Spence: We do not need to go across the pond. We have Women's Aid who have been doing training in this arena for the last 20 years and have some excellent training materials.

S. Bewley: Jo Richardson mentioned offering women choices to do with gender awareness. We have heard that, particularly in the rape examinations, and for some cultural preferences, patients prefer women. This is quite a serious problem for women in the obstetric and gynaecological consultation. I am concerned that we are being too generous when saying, 'Yes, of course you must have a woman doctor because she is more sensitive, or you have more needs.' It does sound as though we are saying that we have not trained the men very well, or that we cannot get them up to the same standard. That is just unacceptable. Poor performance by our specialists in the past is not good enough. I am not saying that we must not offer a choice, because we must, but when we cannot, it actually places a tremendous burden on women. It also reinforces notions, and we cannot let our male colleagues down, that they are not capable of the sensitive vaginal examination that Patricia Crowley talked about.

Certainly, in my clinic, we have articulate white middle class women and also some Muslims and so on, asking for only a woman doctor. I have a different concept of medical need, and I want to see the sickle cell patient who has had four miscarriages and not just the articulate woman who knows how to say, 'I want to see Dr Bewley with no medical student'. There is a tension there again. I am not saying that I should determine it, but we should not give everything to the patient, because the demand actually comes out in a slightly biased way.

Jones: I practise in a group of eight obstetricians and gynaecologists, four men and four women and three advanced practice nurses. Somebody has to stand up for the poor battered male here. It is very unfortunate to perpetuate in any way the notion that if you are a male you are not sensitive and if you are female you are. In fact, two of my female partners are just deaf on pre-menstrual syndrome (PMS)! This is not rocket science, but women can be damaging to other women. We need to promote gender neutrality in this issue, and not fall into the trap of saying, 'I understand why you would want a female, because, after all, she is more soft and fuzzy and understands these issues, and those poor stupid brutes don't get it.' Some of that goes on. To a certain extent, it is abusive when female physicians buy into the issue that women have it and men do not. It is delicate, but I would not want to be a 35-year-old male specialising in obstetrics and gynaecology and getting into the system now. They are going to have a hard time. That is rather unfair.

Stevens: Purely logistically, in my service we are not always in a position to offer a female doctor if required. Similarly, there are times when we are entirely staffed by women and we do not have a male to offer. We offer the same courtesy to gentlemen if it concerns part of their anatomy which they may not want examined by the next passing female doctor. We offer choices in both directions, but we cannot always fulfil them. There are times when we have to say we cannot. That may not be satisfactory, but it reinforces your point that we have to train both genders to be able to deal with the embarrassments or worries of the other.

Cameron: That is absolutely right in general obstetrics and gynaecology practice. I always ask the patients if I can have a medical student. I do not have any regard to their gender or ethnic origin at all. I just ask if they mind if my medical student comes in, and almost forget what their gender is.

How far should we take choice in terms of rape examination? I am not asking questions about domestic violence or sensitive vaginal examination, but specifically about rape examination with respect to the all female rota as we have in the North East for on-call duties. What are the feelings from the floor about that?

Yearnshire: Certainly, research has indicated that the victims of rape, and I am not talking about a general examination here, both male and female, have intimated that they would prefer to be examined by a woman. We are concerned about care in dealing with victims. They have a number of rather nasty systems to face anyway. It would be difficult to say, 'Yes, you might want a woman, but it is a male GP who is on call so you can have him.' It is written into the whole system. I would be willing to be persuaded but it would be hard to go back for any other reason than care, and ask to have men in there as well.

Mezey: With rape victims, many women have said it was incredibly helpful to be seen by a trustworthy, decent, gentle man, after having been raped. Actually, in itself, it was quite a therapeutic experience. From my understanding of the literature, it is much more to do with the attitudes, skills, experience and sensitivity of the individual the woman encounters, rather than necessarily their gender. There may be an initial disquiet or discomfort if they hear that they are going to see a man, but that can be overcome.

Obviously one should not foist any old bloke on these women, particularly after that kind of traumatic experience. However, coming back to what Susan Bewley said, men have to be trained in this. There are many men who would like to be trained, and who do not want to be excluded from this area of work. It is important to give women the choice and to accept that some will want to be seen by a man, and may feel that to be very positive. They actually want to believe that not all men are like the man who just raped them.

Jones: There are women who would prefer to be seen by a man. Often this is an older woman, who grew up in a different system and who cannot believe that some young woman could really be her doctor, because that is not her paradigm. My mother is 93, and she cannot imagine going to a female doctor. I think she is foolish, but that is how she views it.

In my practice, not infrequently one of my female partners will see a patient with a huge fibroid and the patient will ask my female partner if perhaps Dr Jones could do the surgery. I am sure that this has happened to other women physicians where the patient wants an experienced man at the table doing the surgery. This is quite infuriating to the female physicians and I understand it, but of course they have just hammered me the day before about how they are better at seeing PMS. There is a certain amount of inter-office rivalry on a sexual basis!

REFERENCES

British Medical Association (1993) *Medical Ethics Today: Practice and Philosophy.* London: BMA
General Medical Council (1995) 'Confidentiality' from *Duties of a Doctor. Guidance from the General Medical Council.* pp.2–14. London: General Medical Council

SECTION 10

RECOMMENDATIONS

Chapter 33

Conclusions

---

1. The relationship between violence against women and the effects on women's health brings this issue within the remit of obstetricians and gynaecologists.

2. Violence against women encompasses physical, sexual, emotional and psychological abuse. It is rarely an isolated event and usually escalates in frequency and severity. The Study Group largely concentrated on domestic violence whilst recognising that there is a spectrum of violence against women. Certain specific manifestations such as stranger violence, elder abuse, female genital mutilation, physical or sexual abuse of children, and violence against men were not considered.

3. There is a wide diversity of manifestations and effects of domestic violence. Presentations in obstetrics and gynaecology include various non-specific symptoms (e.g. pelvic pain) and signs, and more specific presentations due to acts of violence against women's reproductive organs (e.g. pregnant uterus, genitalia and breasts).

4. There is a lack of robust data on the prevalence of violence and its effects on women's health but research suggests a lifetime prevalence of domestic violence against women of around 25 per cent in the United Kingdom. Approximately 30 per cent of women seek help soon after the first or subsequent attack. Depression, drug and alcohol abuse and other mental health problems are associated with, and may be exacerbated by, domestic violence.

5. Women often remain in abusive relationships as there are risks in leaving. When a woman decides to leave a violent partner, violence often escalates (many domestic homicides occur at this time). It takes time and courage for women to be able to leave violent situations, although approximately 50 per cent of women leave their violent partners within two-and-a-half years.

6. Domestic violence affects all socio-economic groups, although poverty may make it more difficult for women to leave the relationship. Disability, sexuality and ethnicity may affect the perception of violence and escape options, so awareness of the specific issues for these groups is important. The incidence, presentation and willingness of women to disclose abuse may differ according to ethnic group. This emphasises health professionals' duties and responsibilities to give appropriate and culturally sensitive help and support.

7. Although domestic violence is a common feature of family relationships this does not make it acceptable. Health professionals should appreciate that many assaults are also defined as criminal acts. Perpetrators of violence against women have an obvious interest in keeping their behaviour private, which is important in identifying those at risk.

8. Most violence is perpetrated by men whose characteristics overlap with those of non-perpetrators. It is likely that multi-agency work stands most chance of influencing this group. Interventions with perpetrators are only likely to be effective within a legal framework.

9. Doctors should be suspicious of the validity of consent by victims to violent acts which are life threatening, painful or degrading. Consent in 'intimate relationships' must be treated with caution as victim 'consent' may indicate assent or submission rather than being valid and freely given.

10. Disclosures of violence require privacy, confidentiality and sensitive questioning by non-judgmental staff. Women may not disclose violence unless asked directly.

11. Obstacles to obstetricians and gynaecologists recognising and acting upon violence against patients include disbelief, reluctance to 'open the can of worms', wasting precious time, fear of being offensive, perceived inadequacies in management, perceived personal risk or risk to others, ignorance about the availability of appropriate local services and frustration about failure to influence outcome. However, these concerns are largely exaggerated and remediable. Not recognising violence also leads to a waste of time, energy and money, unnecessary investigations and treatment, continuing suffering and, in extreme cases, homicide. It fails our patients.

12. Obstetricians and gynaecologists need to be active in developing medical awareness of violence against women. Routine and sympathetic enquiry is important and appropriate for relevant health professionals. In managing violence against women it is important to develop effective multi-agency approaches.

Chapter 34

Recommendations arising from the Study Group on Violence Against Women

1. The Study Group strongly recommends that the RCOG makes a policy statement about violence against women.

2. The Study Group considers that violence against women is common and serious. It is a public health issue and the RCOG should be committed to its eradication. The RCOG could take a national and international role in raising consciousness amongst obstetricians and gynaecologists about domestic violence, and developing appropriate research strategies and training packages.

3. The management of violence against women requires a multi-agency approach with the following criteria:
   (a) Priority for women and children's safety;
   (b) Emphasis of women's empowerment and choices;
   (c) The delivery of specific and appropriate integrated services;
   (d) The offer of effective legal protection within the civil and criminal law;
   (e) The development of strategies for dealing with perpetrators;
   (f) Raising community awareness of the issue.

Clinical practice

Clinical practice recommendations have been graded from 'A' to 'C' according to the strength of evidence on which each is based.

1. The Study Group recommends the development of practical guidelines for prevention, detection and management of violence in the clinical situation.

   A *Grade B* recommendation based on experimental data

2. Guidelines should be developed in conjunction with other professional groups including the Royal College of General Practitioners, Royal College of Psychiatrists, Faculty of Accident and Emergency Medicine,

Royal College of Midwives, Royal College of Nursing and other relevant community groups. Note should be taken of the effective management strategies already carried out within the community, e.g. by the police and local authorities.

A *Grade C* recommendation based on the consensus view of the Study Group.

3. All health professionals should adopt a non-judgemental and supportive response to women who have experienced physical, psychological or sexual abuse and be able to give basic information to women about where to get help.

A *Grade B* recommendation based on experimental data.

4. Enquiry about a history of violence should be included routinely in any social history. Obstetricians and gynaecologists should consider introducing questions about violence during the course of all obstetric and gynaecological consultations. In general practice, enquiry could be made at the new patient registration, and in midwifery, at the booking interview.

A *Grade B* recommendation based on experimental data.

5. Routine screening has been found to be acceptable to, and indeed welcomed by, many patients. Screening by interview, not questionnaire, appears more effective. The employment of structured screening questionnaires and repeated enquiry increased detection rates.

A *Grade B* recommendation based on experimental data.

Screening tools need to be developed which are appropriate to the health service facility using them with reference to the constraints of time, personnel and educational level.

A *Grade C* recommendation based on the consensus view of the Study Group.

6. The introduction of routine enquiry and referral systems should be accompanied by an educational programme for professionals, in consultation with local groups, and preferably delivered by those already working in this area.

A *Grade C* recommendation based on the consensus view of the Study Group.

7. Obstetricians and gynaecologists should identify ways in which they may contribute to the development of voluntary sector services, must maintain up-to-date knowledge of their local voluntary and statutory services in their area, and make information available to women.

A *Grade C* recommendation based on the consensus view of the Study Group.

8. Obstetric and gynaecological departments should display and disseminate information and telephone numbers of local refuges, social services, men's groups, police, rape crisis and victim support services so that it is accessible to patients and staff.

   The RCOG should develop patient education material on violence against women.

   Grade C recommendations based on the consensus view of the Study Group.

9. When language translation is required, hospital-recognised interpreters and not family members should be used.

   A *Grade C* recommendation based on the consensus view of the Study Group.

10. In order to facilitate disclosure of sensitive information, all pregnant women should have one consultation with the lead professional involved in her pregnancy care which is not attended by the partner or by any family member. Women attending for gynaecological consultation should have the opportunity of being interviewed alone where possible. Family members are not appropriate chaperones.

    A *Grade C* recommendation based on the consensus view of the Study Group.

11. All maternity systems should have a set of notes for confidential information that is kept separate from the 'hand-held' notes.

    A *Grade C* recommendation based on the consensus view of the Study Group.

12. Accurate and complete documentation of histories, injuries and outcomes must be meticulous and confidential. If a civil action or criminal case is pursued (even sometime in the future) this may be important evidence.

    A *Grade C* recommendation based on the consensus view of the Study Group.

13. There is a prima facie ethical and legal duty of confidentiality. Healthcare professionals should give patients the opportunity to report experiences of violence wherever possible and should assure patients that information will be treated sensitively. They should seek patients' consent to sharing information about acts of violence with other (non-clinically involved) professionals wherever possible. Information about violence should only be shared without such consent:

    (a) Where it is wholly inappropriate to seek consent or the patient has not been successfully persuaded to give consent; and

    (b) Where the professional is convinced that there is a real risk to the health or safety of an identifiable party (General Medical Council 1995).

Clear documentation about the nature of disclosure without consent, and to whom, must be made.

A *Grade C* recommendation based on the consensus view of the Study Group.

14. With respect to consent to the medical examination and disclosure in immediate connection with judicial proceedings, medical practitioners must be conversant with the General Medical Council principles of confidentiality (General Medical Council 1995). The details of consent must include reference to medical examination, the collection of forensic evidence and the disclosure of details of medical records to the police or Crown Prosecution Services.

A *Grade C* recommendation based on the consensus view of the Study Group

Education and training

1. All obstetricians and gynaecologists should be taught basic information about violence against women. All obstetricians and gynaecologists should be trained to ask questions sensitively.

2. Training packages should include knowledge of violence and its presentations in obstetrics and gynaecology, gender awareness, communication skills to detect violence and knowledge of appropriate management responses. Trainees and specialists must be aware of the confidential status of related information.

3. There should be evaluation of all the above both in structured training and the MRCOG examination.

4. Training should begin at undergraduate level and become an integral part of the programme of specialist training extending into continuing medical education.

5. A co-ordinated multi-disciplinary approach should be made regarding the theoretical and practical training issues for specialist registrars in rape examination. Educational programmes need to be provided at deanery level to encompass the theoretical component of the main log book module on 'rape' before observing clinical practice and subsequent supervised assessments of a rape victim.

Research

1. Robust research data are lacking in the British Isles. There is an urgent need for research into prevalence and models of intervention, especially for planning services. Research funding into violence against women should be a priority of national research funding agencies.

2. Particular research needs include:
   (a) The prevalence of violence in various obstetric and gynaecological presentations (e.g. pelvic pain, dyspareunia, abdominal pain in pregnancy, antepartum haemorrhage, premature labour, pregnancy loss and recurrent miscarriage, postnatal depression and pre-menstrual syndrome);
   (b) The benefits and costs (medical, psychological and financial) of routinely asking all women about their experiences of violence;
   (c) The influence of a partner's presence during consultation and examination, particularly on the patient's ability to report incidents of violence;
   (d) The impact of violence against women on their longer-term health;
   (e) The generation of reliable auditable outcomes to evaluate screening and intervention;
   (f) The effectiveness of interventions with perpetrators;
   (g) Experience of violence and harassment against women doctors and medical students during training.

3. Notification arrangements should be set up within the Confidential Enquiry into Maternal Deaths (CEMD) and the Confidential Enquiry into Stillbirths and Deaths in Infancy (CESDI) so that the contribution of violence to these deaths can be monitored.

National, health and social policies

1. Good medical practice depends on the provision of social and legal services which support women and children experiencing violence. The Study Group recommends an urgent review of these services.

2. Women's Aid and other agencies in the voluntary sector have played a key role in putting violence against women on the public agenda, and in the provision of initial support services. The Study Group recommends that all health professionals should support and liaise with these key agencies as part of a multi-agency approach to tackling violence against women.

3. The Study Group recommends that the government should have a broad based strategy to help victims of violence. It should support the building of effective interfaces with other agencies and voluntary organisations including social services, housing and the criminal justice system. In particular, more resources may be required as reporting and detection increase.

4. Violence against women is a public health problem. We support the government's efforts to raise awareness of violence against women. In particular we support liaison between the various initiatives underway so

that professional bodies and other interested parties can learn from each other.

5. The Study Group supports the implementation of a number of measures to improve strategic responses to violence against women:

(a) Twenty-four-hour local access to women's specialist advocacy and support services through a national strategy for the funding and expansion of refuge and outreach services, developed in conjunction with the Women's Aid Federation;

(b) A national public awareness programme using television and other media which is co-ordinated to ensure effective strategic responses by a wide range of statutory and voluntary agencies;

(c) A national freephone 24-hour helpline (or the continuation and expansion of the Women's Aid National Helpline) for women to provide:
(i) Information about local refuge numbers,
(ii) Information about local services,
(iii) Counselling;

(d) An increased provision of resources for places in refuges and shelters and for counsellors;

(e) Improved access to long-term safe housing through the provision of affordable housing;

(f) Improved legal protection under civil and criminal law. Training for professionals and the judiciary would be helpful in order to improve sensitivity and understanding of the dynamics and effects of gender-based violence;

(g) Integrated responses within both civil and criminal law systems to ensure that violence against women, and their children, is effectively tackled. In particular a review is required of current social policy in relation to child access arrangements under the Children's Act 1989 which continue to undermine effective violence-reduction strategies and may place women at risk.

6. The Study Group also recognises the need for a strategic and co-ordinated approach for improving the National Health Service response to violence against women. The Study Group recommends the development of a Department of Health strategic policy framework within which there is multi-agency approach to training, service planning and service delivery.

7. We support efforts by the police to collect good corroborative evidence and to consider the prosecution of domestic violence offenders, even in the absence of the victim, in appropriate cases.

8. The Study Group is concerned about a recent revision of civil law and the Family Law Act 1996 which excluded women not co-habiting with male partners from protection.

The study group participants unanimously believe that the implementation of these recommendations would begin to address the problem of violence against female patients which most sectors of the community, including health care workers, have neglected for too long.

REFERENCES

General Medical Council (1995) 'Confidentiality' from *Duties of a Doctor. Guidance from the General Medical Council*, pp.2–14. London: General Medical Council

Domestic violence recognition and management in accident and emergency

These guidelines focus on violence directed against women. This is because the incidence of victimisation and the resulting mortality, morbidity and socio-economic difficulties presently affect women very much more than men. It is recognised, however, that the number of male victims is increasing, and much of the following guidance is applicable to both sexes.

THE SIZE OF THE PROBLEM

- Twenty-five per cent of women surveyed attending US emergency departments presented a clinical picture consistent with abuse, but only three per cent of women attending were identified as victims of domestic violence.

- Twenty-five per cent of women questioned in UK studies reported being the victim of domestic violence at some time.

- Twenty-five per cent of all assaults reported to the police are the result of domestic violence.

- Fifty per cent of murdered women are killed by their partner or ex-partner.

THE LEGAL POSITION

Domestic violence is a crime like all other violent crimes and should be prosecuted once reported in the same way as all other such crimes. The victim can be subpoenaed as a witness. Where the patient does not wish to report her assault to the police, this should be respected. Admission may buy time for discussion and reflection where the clinician feels that the risk of homicide or serious injury is great but the patient refuses police involvement. Where the patient is incapable of consent, the consultant in charge must be consulted whether to release information when a 'serious arrestable offence' has occurred. The victim may also take action through the civil law, e.g. exclusion and non-molestation orders.

PRESENTATION

Domestic violence affects women of all classes, races and creed.
Maintain a high level of suspicion.
It may commence at times of acute stress, e.g. unemployment.
There is an association between the beginning of violence and first pregnancy.

Presenting complaints	Pattern of attendance
Injury, often multiple	Patient attends late
Rape	Partner answers for patient
Suicide/parasuicide	Over-vehement denial of abuse
Psychiatric illness/substance abuse	May be frequent attender
Pelvic pain	On multiple prescribed drugs
Multiple somatic complaints	Patient may be pregnant

EXAMINATION

The presenting complaint is only part of the picture; enquire about, and
with the patient's consent, look for other symptoms and signs of abuse.
Document meticulously. Photograph injuries with patient's written consent.
Sign and date all notes and photographs, and attach firmly to patient's
medical record.

Indicators of abuse	Characteristic injuries	Document
Patient	Facial injury	Time, date, place of abuse
Evasive/embarrassed/ apologetic	Perforated eardrums	Witness to incident
Anxious/depressed	Detached retina	Injury:
Passive	Neck injury esp. marks	Size
	Breast injury	Pattern
Injuries	Abdominal injury when	Age
Affect areas normally clothed	pregnant	Location of abuse
Inconsistent with mechanism stated	Genital injury	Signs of sexual abuse
	Burns/scalds/bruises	Non-bodily evidence, e.g. torn clothing
At multiple sites	Bizarre injuries	
Symmetrically distributed		Patient's explanation
Of differing ages		Your opinion re causation

APPROACH TO THE PATIENT

Exclude partner, interview in privacy, stress confidentiality.

- Ask direct questions gently, stating that domestic violence is common and it is routine to enquire about home circumstances where there is a possibility of abuse on clinical grounds.

- Be non-judgemental, do not directly condemn partner, do not criticise patient for staying with him.

- Emphasise the appropriateness of the patient's attendance.

- Focus on informing the patient: Stress that violence in the home is illegal, that expert help is available and legal intervention is possible. Supply contact details for support organisations, e.g. Women's Aid.

- Discuss safety: How much at risk does the patient feel – of homicide? – of suicide? Are there weapons in the house? What has she tried before? What sources of support does she have? What possible safe havens? Are there children? Are they safe? Help her examine her options.

- Move at the patient's own pace. Nurture the patient's right to make her own decisions.

TREATMENT

Treat the physical illness or injury.
Seek psychiatric help where depression is prominent or for parasuicide.
Hospitalise if there is no other safe option, or the patient is too emotionally exhausted to make her own decisions.

WHAT HAPPENS NEXT?

If the patient is returning to her partner: give her contact numbers and written information (on legal options, help available etc.), offer referral, help her plan an escape route for emergency, advise her to keep money and important financial and legal documents hidden in a safe place. If the children are at risk, consider referral to social services, preferably with patient's consent.

If the patient does not wish to return and needs a place of safety: consider friends or relatives, try emergency housing (contact duty social worker), contact local refuge, police may offer protected accommodation, hospitalise if all fails.

Refer to:

> Women's Aid (National Helpline: 01272 633542)
> GP
> Police, if so requested by patient
> Social work (re-housing needs as well as counselling support) and,
> if indicated: Ethnic link workers
> Rape Crisis (National Helpline: 0171–837 1600)
> Victim Support (National Office: 0171–735 9166)
> Citizens' Advice Bureau (for legal advice)
> Alcohol or drug abuse support organisations
> Family planning clinic

LOCAL FIRST-LINE RESOURCES

Police Domestic Violence Unit
Station .... Telephone ....

Women's Aid
Contact hours available .... Telephone ....
Contact duty social worker for help with emergency housing, child care, etc.

Appendix II

Useful contacts

WOMEN'S SUPPORT, REFUGES, ADVOCACY AND INFORMATION

Women's Aid

Women's Aid Federation of England (refuge, legal advice and emotional support)
PO Box 391, Bristol BS99 7WS
0117 944 4411 (office)
0345 023468 (24 hour national helpline)

London Women's Aid
0171 392 2092 (24 hours)
Northern Ireland Women's Aid Federation
129 University Street, Belfast BT7 1HP
01232 249 041 or 01232 249 358

Scottish Women's Aid
13/9 North Bank Street, Edinburgh EH1 2LP
0131 221 0401

Welsh Women's Aid
01222 390 874 (Cardiff)
01970 612748 (Aberystwyth)
01745 334767 (Rhyl)

Victim Support

National Association of Victim Support Schemes (National office)
Cranmer House, 39 Brixton Road, London SW9 6DZ
0171 587 1162 (referrals)
0171 735 9166 (enquiries)

Victim Support Northern Ireland
Annsgate House, 70/74 Ann Street, Belfast BT1 4EH
01232 244039

Victim Support Republic of Ireland
29/30 Dame Street, Dublin 2
00 353 1 6798673

Victim Support Scotland
14 Frederick Street, Edinburgh EH2 2HB
0131 225 7779

Other groups

Gingerbread (self-help groups for single parents)
16–17 Clerkenwell Close, London EC1R 0AA
0171 336 8183

Miscarriage Association
C/o Clayton Hospital, Northgate, Wakefield, W Yorks WF1 3JS
01924 200799

Rape Crisis (support/counselling)
PO Box 69, London WC1X 9NJ
0171 837 1600 (24 hour helpline)

Refuge
2–8 Maltravers Street, London WC2R 3EE
0171 395 7700 (office)
0990 995443 (24 hour crisis line)

Rights of Women (ROW) (advice and referral)
52–54 Featherstone Street, London EC1Y 8RT
0171 251 6575 (office)
0171 251 6577 (advice)

Samaritans
0345 909090

Shelter National Campaign for the Homeless
0800 446 441 (freephone)

Still-birth and Neonatal Death Society
28 Portland Place, London W1N 5DE
0171 436 7940 (office)
0171 436 5881 (national helpline)

Specific Groups

ASHA Asian Women's Resource Centre
0171 274 8854

Asian Women's Resource Centre
0181 961 6549 (National organisation)

Chinese Women's Refuge Group
209–215 Kings Cross Road, London WC1X 9DB
0171 837 7297 (answer phone outside office hours)

Latin American Women's Rights Service
0171 831 4145

London Irish Women's Centre
59 Stoke Newington Church Street, London N16
0171 249 7318

Southall Black Sisters (advice, advocacy and referral)
52 Norwood Road, Southall, Middlesex UB2 4DW
0181 571 9595

CHILDREN

Childline (for children)
Freepost 1111, London N1 0BR
0171 239 1000 (office)
0800 1111 (freephone)

NSPCC (National Society for the Prevention of Cruelty to Children)
0800 800500 (national helpline)

Parents Anonymous (for parents who feel they may abuse their children)
6–9 Manor Gardens, London N7 6LA
0171 263 8918 (24 hour service)

MEN

Domestic Violence Intervention Project (court mandated programmes)
0181 563 7983

Domestic Violence Probation Project (court mandated)
1 Parliament Square, Edinburgh EG1 1RF
0131 469 3408

Everyman Project (Support services for men wishing to stop behaving violently/abusively)
142 Landor Road, London SW9 9JA
0171 737 6747

ALCOHOL AND DRUG ABUSE

Alcoholics Anonymous (welcome individual patients' calls)
0171 352 3001 (national helpline)

Alcohol Concern (National umbrella organisation, support services)
Waterbridge House, 32–36 Loman Street, London SE1 0EE
0171 928 7377 (not for individual patient use)

TRAINING CONTACTS

Andrea Tara-Chand
Leeds Interagency Project: Women and Violence (offers training nationally)
Unit A3, CHEL, 26 Roundhay Road, Leeds LS7 1AB
0113 234 9090

Debbie Seaborn
Room 42, Community Safety Unit (safety, raising awareness etc.)
Hammersmith and Fulham Council, Town Hall, King Street, London W6 9JU
0181 576 5660

Liz Kelly
Child and Woman Abuse Studies Unit (research, training and consultancy)
University of North London, Ladbroke House, 62–66 Highbury Grove, London N5 2AD
0171 607 2789 ext. 5014

Women's Support Project (training, information and library)
Granite House, 31 Stockwell Street, Glasgow G1 4RZ
0141 552 2221

PROVISION OF LOCAL INFORMATION SHOULD INCLUDE ACCESS TO THE FOLLOWING:

Police station (domestic violence unit)
Organisations giving legal advice and list of solicitors
Branches of national organisations giving refuge, help and advice
Access to emergency housing, e.g. District Housing Officer
Citizens advice bureaux
Dept of Social Security and employment office
Organisation willing to help children
Community Health Councils
Accident and emergency departments
Support/counselling groups
Alcohol groups
Organisations for specific community groups
Organisation for men willing to receive help for their violent behaviour

Index